RELIABILITY ENGINEERING
BIBLE

RELIABILITY
ENGINEERING
Bible

◆ ◆ ◆

Bryan Dodson & Dennis Nolan

Quality Publishing
Tucson, Arizona

Quality Publishing, Inc.
2405 N Avenida Sorgo, Tucson, Arizona 85749-9305
1-800-628-0432

Published 1995
Printed in the United States of America

04 03 02 01 00 99 98 97 96 95   5   4   3   2   1

Dodson, Bryan
    Reliability engineering bible / Nolan, Dennis. — 1st ed.
    Includes bibliographical references and index
    1. Quality control.   2. Reliability (Engineering).
  I. Nolan, Dennis.   II. Title.

Library of Congress Catalog Card Number: 94-065481

ISBN (Cloth): 0-930011-14-7

To Mirian, Lois and Matthew.
B.D.

To my loving daughters and granddaughter, Christina, Andrea, and Karissa.
D.N.

Contents

♦♦♦

Preface

The primary purpose of this text is to present the entire body of knowledge for reliability engineering as defined by the American Society for Quality Control (ASQC) in their Certified Reliability Engineer (CRE) examination booklet. The outline provided by ASQC was followed closely with each section forming a chapter, with the exception of *Reliability Design Review* and *Management Control* which were combined to form Chapter 9. The order of the material provided by ASQC was also changed to provide more logical flow. ASQC's outline listed probability distributions in the last section. This makes little sense, as probability distributions form the foundation of many reliability models. The size of the chapters varies greatly. In following ASQC's outline, some topics warranted more extensive coverage than others. Chapter 3, *Distributions,* and Chapter 4, *Prediction, Estimation, and Apportionment Models,* are the two longest chapters. These chapters provide the foundation of reliability engineering from a mathematical standpoint.

The material is presented with the practitioner in mind; thus, proofs and derivations have been omitted, and numerous examples have been included. For those desiring proofs and derivations, references are provided at the end of each chapter. It is the authors' goal that individuals with a basic knowledge of statistics will be able to pass the ASQC CRE exam after reading this text and working the exercises at the end of each chapter.

Practitioners will find this text valuable as a comprehensive reference book. As stated earlier, the entire reliability engineering body of knowledge is covered in detail, and it is not necessary to wade through pages of proofs and derivations to find answers. It is recommended that this text be used as a two-semester sequence in reliability for college courses or as an 80-hour seminar for practicing engineers. Students should have a familiarity with basic probability and statistics before attempting this material.

The text consists of three basic parts. Chapters 1 and 2 provide an introduction, Chapters 3–6 cover reliability mathematics, and Chapters 7–11 describe the non-quantitative aspects of reliability. Those preparing for the CRE exam should concentrate on Chapters 3–6 and be familiar with the remaining chapters. The majority of the material on past CRE exams is contained in Chapters 3 and 4. Also, be aware that some material contained in Chapters 3–5 is beyond the scope of the CRE exam. For example, the CRE exam may have questions related to using maximum likelihood estimators to estimate the parameters of the Weibull distribution, but due to time constraints, the examinee will probably not be asked to estimate the parameters of the Weibull distribution using maximum likelihood estimators. Other advanced material that is unlikely to appear on the CRE exam is transformation of random variables, Markov analysis, and reliability allocation.

♦ ♦ ♦

Acknowledgments

The authors are grateful to many individuals for helping prepare this book. Most notable are the reviewers. Several reviewers were anonymous, but you know who are, and we thank you for your comments. A special thanks goes to John Miller, James McLinn, Tom Pyzdek, and Peter Worden whose many comments greatly improved the manuscript.

Also, I would like to thank Gerald Knighton, Mike Mehay, Pam McNeally, and Lori Hupy. These individuals are all former supervisors during my tenure at Alcoa, and it was their influence and guidance that allowed me to gain an understanding of reliability engineering. (B.D.)

RELIABILITY ENGINEERING
BIBLE

1

Introduction

The need for reliability engineering became apparent during World War II. The availability of Naval electronic equipment was approximately 70%; the availability of Army equipment was less than 40%; over 60% of airborne equipment shipped to the far east arrived damaged; the mean time to fail for bomber electronics was less than 20 hours; the cost of repair and maintenance was over ten times the original purchase price, and so on.

A portion of the problems was due to the increased complexity of the equipment. The fields of communications and transportation experienced rapid increases in complexity, and manufacturers capitalized on advances in electronics and control systems. The Department of Defense (DOD) recognized the problem, realizing that equipment would continue to become more complex. In 1950, the DOD created the Advisory Group on the Reliability of Electronic Equipment (AGREE). The DOD has continued to be a leader in reliability engineering. Much of reliability engineering theory has been developed directly by the DOD, or through research sponsored by the DOD. This is evidenced by the large number of DOD documents on the subject of reliability. A listing of some of these documents is given in Appendix K.

1.1 Life cycle costs

As a result of the problems encountered in World War II, the concept of **life cycle cost** was developed.

The original purchase price of equipment is only a fraction of the total cost of the equipment over its useful life. The total cost of operating a piece of equipment over its lifetime also includes the following post purchase costs:

- start-up
- planned maintenance
- repairs
- downtime
- spare parts
- fuel or energy

Life cycle costs are displayed graphically in Figure 1.1.

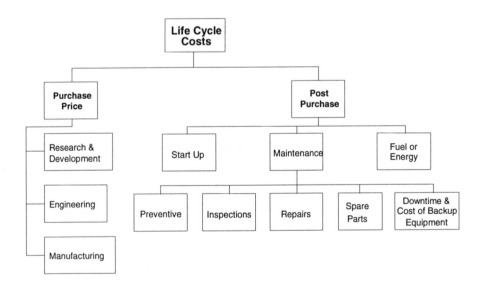

Figure 1.1. Life cycle costs.

By expending more expense on research, engineering, and manufacturing, the purchase price of an item is increased, but the post purchase expenses are decreased because of increased reliability, maintainability and availability. There exists an optimum level of reliability; this is shown in Figure 1.2.

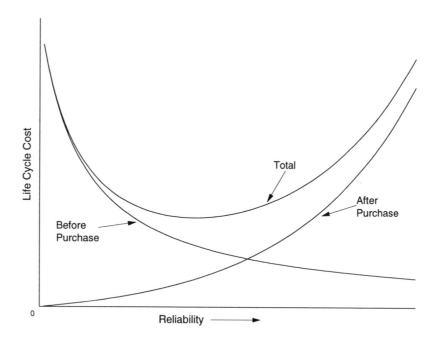

Figure 1.2. The optimum level of reliability.

The optimum level of reliability may not be the same for both the seller and the buyer. The life cycle costs discussed above are from the buyer's point of view. The post purchase costs of the seller include warranty costs and goodwill costs, such as loss of market share.

1.2 The Certified Reliability Engineer Exam

There is a need for individuals with a knowledge of reliability methods. Many employers rely on standardized tests to verify that an applicant has gained knowledge in a subject area. The Certified Public Accountant's Exam and the BAR Exam are examples. There are many others. The American Society for Quality Control (ASQC) established the Certified Reliability Engineer Exam for this purpose. Certification by ASQC as a Reliability Engineer is valuable. It is widely respected throughout industry, and many employers require certification as a condition for employment. The annual salary survey published in Quality Progress points out the value of Certification as a Reliability Engineer. Individuals who are Certified as Reliability Engineers consistently report salaries higher than non-certified individuals. In some cases, the difference exceeds 40%!

1.2.1 Exam-taking strategy

Points are awarded on the CRE Exam for correct answers with no penalty for incorrect answers. Thus, all questions should be answered. There will be approximately two minutes allowed for each question. If you begin to fall behind schedule, answer only the questions you are familiar with and allow 15 minutes at the end of the exam to guess at the question you did not have time to answer. All questions may not carry equal weight. On some occasions, there is a "problems" section at the end of the exam. Each problem is worth 5 points, so be sure to check for the "problems" section. All "questions" on the exam carry equal weight, so you may want to answer lengthy problems at the end of the exam if time allows. Time can be saved by placing markers in your reference books to help you quickly locate key information.

It may be a good idea to be familiar with the exam site. Consider visiting the exam site before the exam to determine where parking is available and to find the location of the building and room where the exam is to be given. On the day of the exam, arrive 30 minutes early to find a seat in the aisle. This will allow quick exits to the rest room or vending machine. Arriving early will also allow time to organize your exam table. The CRE is a five-hour exam and a lunch break may not be given; eat a good breakfast.

1.2.2 What to bring to the exam

The most important items to bring to the exam are your reference books. The application booklet for the CRE Exam contains a list of approved reference books. However, just because a book does not appear in the approved reference list does not mean it is not allowed in the exam. The general rule for allowable reference material is that the material must be copyrighted and must not contain questions and answers to previous CRE Exams. Notice that this does not allow personal notes to be used during the exam. Become very familiar with one or two books so time is not wasted paging through references looking for material. This text, the accompanying solutions manual, and the accompanying condensed formulas booklet will provide a sound basis for the exam. Be aware that ASQC does not allow any books that contain questions and answers to previous CRE Exams.

Some other items that may be of value during the exam are listed below.

Calculator—ASQC requires that the memory be cleared from calculators before starting the exam. Thus, access to any self written programs is not allowed. However, ASQC does allow the use of calculators that have built in statistical routines. With today's technology, these routines can save valuable time during the exam. Bring a battery powered calculator; electrical outlets may not be available. ASQC allows only silent calculators. Calculators with printers may not be allowed.

Snacks—The exam is 5 hours long, and breaks may not be given. Bring a sufficient amount of food to provide energy for the duration of the exam. A thermos with coffee or a small cooler for juice or soft drinks will be valuable if no vending machines are available.

Scratch paper

#2 pencils—Number 2 pencils are required for machine grading of the exam.

Erasers—Plastic erasers provide better erasures than rubber. Using a plastic may prevent a grading error.

Seat assignment and identification—ASQC will not allow you to take the exam if you do not have your seat assignment and proper identification.

Aspirin

Watch

Probability paper

Straight edge

Dictionary of scientific terms

1.2.3 Obtaining examination information

Application packets can be obtained from the American Society for Quality Control, (800) 248-1946.

The ASQC packet will provide:

- Application requirements (knowledge, experience)
- Exam dates (usually twice per year)
- Application deadlines (usually 3 months prior to exam)
- Listing of approved references (may be taken into exam)
- Listing of subjects covered
- Sample questions
- Fees
- Application forms

1.3 Exercises

1. Explain how reliability affects the cost of owning and operating an item over its useful life.

2. Explain the relationship between quality control and reliability.

3. Item A costs $15,000 and has expected maintenance costs of $4,000 per year. Item B costs $22,000 and has expected maintenance costs of $1,500 per year. Using a cost of money (interest rate) of 10%, which item has the lowest life cycle cost assuming a useful life of 8 years with no residual value?

4. Item A costs $25,000. To obtain the required availability on item A, two mechanics at a cost of $21,000 per year each, supplies at a cost of $8,000 and $7,000 worth of spare parts must be maintained. Item B costs $55,000. To obtain the required availability on item B, one mechanic at a cost of $29,000 per year, supplies at a cost of $16,000 and $4,000 worth of spare parts must be maintained. Which item has the lowest life cycle cost assuming a useful life of 12 years with no residual value, and a 10% cost of money (interest rate)?

5. Which automobile has the lowest life cycle cost assuming a 10% cost of money (interest rate)?

	TYPE 1	TYPE 2
Purchase price	$21,000	$23,000
Maintenance cost, year 1	$0	$0
Maintenance cost, year 2	$0	$0
Maintenance cost, year 3	$0	$0
Maintenance cost, year 4	$500	$0
Maintenance cost, year 5	$1,000	$0
Maintenance cost, year 6	$2,000	$500
Trade in value	$11,000	$11,500

1.4 References

Dhillon, B. S. 1985. *Quality Control, Reliability, and Engineering Design*. New York: Marcel Dekker.

Dodson, B. L., and M. D. Mulcahy. 1992. *Certified Reliability Engineer Examination Study Guide*. Tucson, AZ: Quality Publishing.

Dovich, R. A. 1990. *Reliability Statistics*. Milwaukee, WI: ASQC–Quality Press.

Ireson, G. W., and C. F. Coombs. 1988. *Handbook of Reliability Engineering and Management*. New York: McGraw-Hill.

Kapur, K. C., and L. R. Lamberson. 1977. *Reliability in Engineering Design*. New York: John Wiley & Sons.

Kececioglu, D. 1991. *Reliability Engineering Handbook, Volume 1*. Englewood Cliffs, NJ: Prentice Hall.

Lewis, E. E. 1987. *Introduction To Reliability Engineering*. New York: John Wiley & Sons.

Shooman, M. L. 1990. *Probabilistic Reliability: An Engineering Approach*. Malabar, FL: Robert E. Krieger.

♦♦♦
CHAPTER

2

Data Collection, Analysis, and Reporting

Data should be collected and analyzed prior to making decisions that affect the quality of a product, process or operation. Data provides the foundation for forming and testing hypotheses. The outcome of decisions derived from collected data is positively correlated to the quality of data on which the decision is made. Therefore, it is essential to develop a system for retaining and retrieving accurate information in order to maintain or improve product reliability.

Before starting a good data collecting program the objectives for collecting data should be understood. The basic objectives are to:

1. Identify the problem
2. Report the problem
3. Verify the problem
4. Analyze the problem
5. Correct the problem

According to Ireson (1988) the benefits of any good data collecting, analysis, and reporting system are:

1. Reduction of research or redundant test time
2. Assurance that proven parts are specified
3. Assistance for quality assurance and purchasing in obtaining parts
4. Assurance that products are capable of meeting specifications

5. Reduction in time and expense of testing
6. Improvement of capability to estimate reliability

Other important considerations are the accuracy needed, methods to use and who will do the collecting. Before formulating questions and attempting to answer these questions it is important to distinguish between the basic types of data; continuous and discrete. Anything that can be measured; weight, height, length, time, etc., are all examples of **continuous** data. Anything that can be counted; number of accidents, number of failures, or defects are examples of **discrete** data. For more information on continuous and discrete data refer to Chapter 3.

According to MIL-STD-785, the purpose of a failure reporting, analysis, and corrective-action system (FRACAS) is to determine the root cause of the problem, document the problem, and record the corrective-action taken. Considerations for establishing such an information gathering program are outlined in this chapter. Suggested reading for further study is, *"A Reliability Guide to Failure Reporting, Analysis, and Corrective-action Systems."*

2.1 Recording, reporting, and processing

Before a quality analysis can be made a closed loop system that collects and records failures that occur at specified levels must be in place. A "closed loop" system is a feedback loop that determines what failed, how it failed, why it failed, and tracks corrective-action. A program should be developed first to initiate the recording, reporting, and processing of all failures into the design, test and manufacturing processes. The first thing to consider in the recording process is the recording form. It should be clear, simple, and easy to understand by the user. As a minimum the form should include the following information:

- Equipment identification
- Failed part identification
- Type or category of failure
- Time of failure
- Who reported the failure
- Possible causes
- Action taken

- Who initiated action if any

Training should be provided for the more complex forms as necessary. Always provide valid reasons for collecting data. If the data collectors understand why they are taking data they will ultimately understand the need for accuracy when filling in the forms.

A Failure Review Board (FRB) should be established to monitor failure trends, significant failures and corrective-actions. The mission of the FRB is to review functional failure-data from appropriate inspections and testing including qualification, reliability, and acceptance test failures. All failure occurrence information should be made available to the FRB, including a description of conditions at the time of failure, symptoms of failure, failure isolation procedures, and known or suspected causes of the failure. Reports should include data on successes as well as failures. Details of any action taken must also be reported to enable the review board to make exceptions for items that may have been wrongfully replaced during test or service. Open items should then be followed up by the FRB until failure mechanisms have been satisfactorily identified and corrective-action initiated. FRB members should include appropriate representatives from design, reliability, safety, maintainability, manufacturing, and quality assurance. The leader of this group is usually a reliability engineer.

It is important that the term "failure" be defined. For example, ask what a failure means to the organization or process? Failure is defined by MIL-STD-721 as, "The event, or inoperable state, in which any item or part of an item does not, or would not, perform as previously specified."

Failures should also be defined and sorted into categories; relevant, nonrelevant, chargeable, nonchargeable, and alternate failures (refer to Sections 2.1.2 and 2.1.3). All failures occurring during reliability qualification and production reliability acceptance tests should be classified as relevant or nonrelevant. Relevant failures should be further classified as chargeable or nonchargeable. Rules for classification of failures should be in agreement with approved failure definitions or other criteria. Flow diagrams or other modeling techniques depicting failed hardware and data flow should be utilized where possible. Figure 2.1 is a flow diagram for failure categories.

Costs should be included in the recording process, where management approval is needed. Dollars and cents are sometimes the most important factors in management decisions. For example, the costs of redesigning or replacing a certain item could be compared to the cost of not replacing the item. The cost of not replacing the item, thus allowing a failure, should include warranty, liability, customer satisfaction, etc. These costs are usually only qualified estimates since they are difficult or impossible to quantify precisely. In any case include as many cost comparisons as possible for the decision making process.

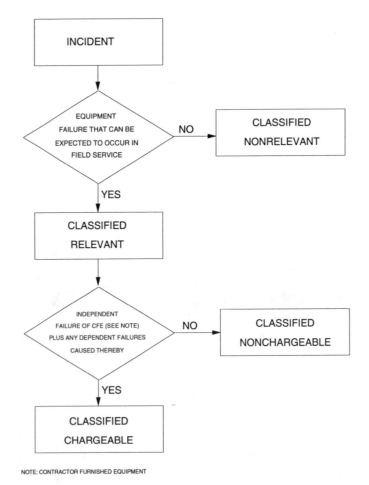

NOTE: CONTRACTOR FURNISHED EQUIPMENT

Figure 2.1. Flow diagram of failure categories (MIL-STD-721).

2.1.1 Failure terms and definitions

Catastrophic failure—A failure that can cause item loss.

Critical failure—A failure, or combination of failures, that prevents an item from performing a specified mission.

Dependent failure—Failure caused by the failure of an associated item(s).

Independent failure—Failure that occurs without being caused by the failure of any other item.

Equipment design failure—Any failure that can be traced directly to the design of the equipment; that is, the design of the equipment caused the part in question to degrade or fail, resulting in an equipment failure.

Equipment manufacturing failure—A failure caused by poor workmanship or inadequate manufacturing process control during equipment construction, testing, or repair prior to the start of testing. For example, the failure due to cold solder joints.

Intermittent failure—Failure for a limited period of time, followed by the item's recovery or its ability to perform within limits without any remedial action.

Mechanism failure—The physical, chemical, electrical, thermal or other process that results in failure.

Multiple failures—The simultaneous occurrence of two or more independent failures. When two or more failed parts are found during troubleshooting and failures cannot be shown to be dependent, multiple failures are presumed to have occurred.

Pattern failures—The occurrence of two or more failures of the same part in identical or equivalent applications when the failures are caused by the same basic failure mechanism and the failures occur at a rate that is inconsistent with the part's predicted failure rate.

Part design failure—Failures that can be traced directly to inadequate design.

Part manufacturing failure—These failures are the result of poor workmanship or inadequate manufacturing process control during part assembly, inadequate inspection, or improper testing.

Primary failure—This type of failure is the result of a component deficiency. These failures result while operating within design limits.

Secondary failure—This type of failure produces operating conditions outside of design limits thereby causing primary failures. The primary failure would not have occurred if the secondary failure had not caused stress outside the design limits.

Software error failure—A failure caused by an error in the computer program.

Unverified failure—The opposite of a verified failure. Lack of failure verification, by itself, is not sufficient rationale to conclude the absence of a failure.

Verified failure—A failure that is determined either by repeating the failure mode on the reported item or by physical or electrical evidence of failure.

2.1.2 Failure categories

Relevant failures—Relevant failures are specified in 1 through 4:

1. Intermittent failures
2. Unverified failures (failures that cannot be duplicated, which are still under investigation, or for which no cause could be determined)
3. Verified failures not otherwise excluded under approved failure categories
4. Pattern failures

Nonrelevant failures—Nonrelevant failures are specified in 1 through 7:

1. Installation damage
2. Accident or mishandling
3. Failures of the test facility or test-peculiar instrumentation
4. Equipment failures caused by an externally applied overstress condition in excess of the approved test requirements
5. Normal operating adjustments (nonfailures) specified in the approved equipment operating instructions
6. Secondary failures within the equipment, which are directly caused by nonrelevant or relevant primary failures (the secondary failures must be proved to be dependent on the primary failure)

7. Failures caused by human errors

Chargeable failures—A relevant, independent failure of equipment under test and any dependent failures caused thereby which are classified as one failure and used to determine contractual compliance with acceptance and rejection criteria. Chargeable failures are specified in 1 through 4:

1. Intermittent failures
2. Unverified or verified failures
3. Independent failures
   a. Equipment design
   b. Equipment manufacturing
   c. Part design
   d. Part manufacturing
   e. Software errors identified, corrected, and verified during the pretest, the system verification, and the test, should not be chargeable as equipment failures
   f. Contractor-furnished equipment (CFE)
4. Relevant failures

Nonchargeable failures—Nonchargeable failures are specified in 1–3:

1. Nonrelevant failures
2. Failures induced by operating, maintenance, or repair procedures
3. Failures of items having a specified life expectancy and operated beyond the specified replacement time of the item

Alternate failure categories—The alternate failure categories specified in 1 through 3 can be used to categorize both hardware and software failures for systems.

1. *Critical failure* is a failure which prevents the system from performing its mission.
2. *Major failures* are specified in a through f:
   a. Any failure that reduces performance of on-line hardware or software so that the system mission capability is degraded but not eliminated
   b. Any failure that prevents built-in test equipment (BITE) from detecting major failures in on-line hardware or software

     c. Any failure which causes BITE to continuously indicate a major failure in on-line hardware or software when such a failure does not exist

     d. Any failure that prevents BITE from isolating and localizing on-line hardware or software major failures to the lowest group

     e. Any failure that causes BITE to continuously isolate and localize a major failure in on-line hardware or software when such failure does not exist

     f. Any failure that causes BITE false alarm rate to exceed the specified level

3. *Minor failures* are as specified in a and b:

     a. Any failure that impairs on-line hardware or software performance, but permits the system to fully perform its objective

     b. Any failure that impairs BITE performance (creates false alarms) but permits BITE, when recycled, to isolate and localize to the required level, except when false alarm rate exceeds specified levels

2.1.3 Determining what information to collect

Deciding what data to collect will depend on the phase of the project—the conceptual, design, production, or maintenance phase. In any case, data should include failures due to equipment failure and human error. The conceptual phase will require the use of data from similar products. The design phase will require research or actual test data for the specific product. The production phase requires the use of a more historical type data derived sometimes from the design stages. The maintenance phase requires the use of actual failure data that may have been acquired with various failure analysis techniques. In short, all failures must be included from development to acceptance.

Five basic steps are outlined below that will help determine what data to collect:

1. Find out what happened. Be as specific as possible. At what level in the overall system, product or process was the event discovered?

2. Method of detection. Internally? Externally?

3. Find out when the event happened. During testing? During production run?

4. Find out if there is a similar event in historical records. If the answer is "yes," it could save time by eliminating some data collection.

5. Find out if there have been any recent changes. Check vendor materials, test conditions, etc.

2.1.4 How will data be collected and reported

Data may be collected by either a manual or automatic means. Most test results or observations are recorded manually on forms customized to collect specific information then input into a computer database. An example of a typical manual data collecting form is shown in Figure 2.2. Data is sometimes taken automatically through the use of electronic devices that send information directly to a database.

The automatic data information gathering technique is usually desirable where continuous monitoring is necessary.

There are no standards for how to record or store data. When data is input into a computer, manually or automatically, both retrieval and use become obviously enhanced. There are many software packages on the market that can be readily tailored to fit specific needs.

2.1.5 Who will collect the information

Deciding who will collect the information will depend on who will use the data, accuracy needed, time and cost constraints. Keep in mind that the person who collects data is not necessarily the one who will use it.

1. Report No.:	2. Report Date:	3. Time of Failure:	4. Equip Type:	5. Equip S/N:
7. Failed Part Description:		8. Failed Part ID:	9. Failed Part S/N:	10. Failed Part Mod No.:

ITEM USAGE:	11. Hrs:	12. Mins:	13. Secs:	14. Cycle Time.	15. Cal. Time:	16. Miles:

17. Failure Occurred During:	18. Action Taken:	19. Replacement:	20. Critical Cause:	21. Date of Failure:
❑ 1. Inspection ❑ 2. Production ❑ 3. Maintenance ❑ 4. Shipping ❑ 5. Field Use	❑ 1. Adjustment ❑ 2. Replaced ❑ 3. Repaired ❑ 4. Retested ❑ 5. Other	❑ 1. Complete ❑ 2. Partial ❑ 3. Tested ❑ 4. Not Tested ❑ 5. None	❑ 1. Priority 1 Name: _____ ❑ 2. Priority 2 Name:	_____ 22. Time of Failure: _____

REASON FOR REPORT (check one) ➡	23. Removal or Maintenance Action Required as a Result of:
	❑ 1. Suspected failure or malfunction ❑ 2. Due to improper maintenance ❑ 3. Damaged accidentally

24. Symptom(s):		25. Condition(s):		
❑ A. Excessive vibration ❑ B. High fuel consumption ❑ C. High oil consumption ❑ D. Inoperative ❑ E. Interference ❑ F. Leakage	❑ G. Noisy ❑ H. Out of balance ❑ I. Overheating ❑ J. Out of limits ❑ K. Unstable op	❑ 110. Arced ❑ 990. Bent ❑ 880. Cracked ❑ 440. Galled ❑ 505. Chafed ❑ 606. Peeled ❑ 707. Eroded	❑ 009. Frayed ❑ 008. Loose ❑ 005. Open ❑ 555. Plugged ❑ 444. Ruptured ❑ 333. Split ❑ 222. Sheared	❑ 120. Shorted ❑ 130. Stripped ❑ 140. Worn ❑ 150. Corroded ❑ 160. Dented ❑ 170. Chipped ❑ 101. Burned ❑ 202. Other

26. Cause of Trouble:			
❑ A. Design deficiency ❑ B. Faulty maintenance ❑ C. Faulty manufacturing ❑ C. Faulty overhaul	❑ D. Faulty packaging ❑ E. Foreign object ❑ F. Fluid contamination ❑ G. Faulty installation	❑ H. Faulty replacement ❑ I. Operator adjustment ❑ J. Undetermined ❑ K. Weather conditions	❑ M. Wrong part used ❑ N. Unknown contaminates ❑ O. Other (amplify)

27. Disposition or Corrective-action (select appropriate code(s) from list below and check boxes at left to indicate action taken in respect to failed item): REASON FOR: NO ACTION ❑ Hold for 90 days ❑ Lack of facilities ❑ Lack of repair parts ❑ Lack of personnel ❑ Other (explain below): _____ ACTION ❑ Adjusted ❑ Removed and replaced ❑ Repaired and reinstalled ❑ Retest and hold ❑ Other (explain below): _____	28. Maintainability Information: HOURS MINUTES Time to locate trouble ____ ____ Time to repair/replace ____ ____ Total time non-operable ____ ____ 29. Component/Subcomponent Replaced With: Description: _____ Part no.: _____ Serial no.: _____

30. Remarks (Furnish additional information concerning failure or corrective-action not covered above—do not repeat information checked above.):

Location:	Department:	Signature:	Date:

Figure 2.2. Failure report form.

2.1.6 What level of accuracy is needed

Accuracy will depend on the product and its intended use. For example, a cook may only need to take time and temperature data at ± minutes and degrees, while a race car designer may want time and temperature in ± tenths of seconds and degrees. For another example, if someone is asked their age 10 days before their 40th birthday, they may reply 39 or 40. Which is more accurate? Which is accurate enough? It could be important enough to require an answer like: 39 years, 355 days, 12 hours, and 15 minutes. Of course, asking a person's age usually will not require that much detail but when asking how long a verified equipment problem has persisted, details do become important.

The program outlined below will help assure that accurate and complete data is collected which meets the objectives for data collecting—identifying, reporting, verifying, analyzing, and correcting problems.

1. **Identify and control failed items.**

    A tag should be affixed to the failed item immediately upon the detection of any failure or suspected failure. The failure tag should provide space for the failure report serial number and for other pertinent entries from the item failure record. All failed parts should be marked conspicuously and controlled to ensure disposal in accordance with all laws, rules or regulations. Failed parts should not be handled in any manner that may obliterate facts which might be pertinent to the analysis and stored pending disposition of the failure analysis agent.

2. **Reporting of problems or failures.**

    A failure report should be initiated at the occurrence of each problem or failure of hardware, software or equipment. The report should contain the information required to permit determination of the origin and correction of failures. The following information should be included in the report:

    a. Descriptions of failure symptoms, conditions surrounding the failure, failed hardware identification, and operating time (or cycles) at time of failure

    b. Information on each independent and dependent failure and the extent of confirmation of the failure symptoms, the identification of failure modes, and a description of all repair action taken to return the item to operational readiness

c. Information describing the results of the investigation, the analysis of all part failures, an analysis of the item design, and the corrective-action taken to prevent failure recurrence (if no corrective-action is taken, the rationale for this decision should be recorded)

3. **Verify failures.**

Reported failures should be verified as actual failures or an acceptable explanation provided for lack of failure verification. Failure verification is determined either by repeating the failure mode on the reported item or by physical or electrical evidence of failure (leakage residue, damaged hardware, etc.) Lack of failure verification, by itself, is not sufficient rationale to conclude the absence of a failure.

4. **Investigation and analysis of problems or failures.**

An investigation and analysis of each reported failure should be performed. Investigation and analysis should be conducted to the level of hardware or software necessary to identify causes, mechanisms, and potential effects of the failure. Any applicable method (test, microscopic analysis, applications study, dissection, x-ray analysis, spectrographic analysis, etc.) of investigation and analysis that may be needed to determine failure cause shall be used. When the removed item is not defective or the cause of failure is external to the item, the analysis should be extended to include the circuit, higher hardware assembly, test procedures, and subsystem if necessary. Investigation and analysis of supplier failures should be limited to verifying that the supplier failure was not the result of the supplier's hardware, software, or procedures. This determination should be documented for notification of the procuring activities.

5. **Corrective-action and follow-up.**

When the cause of a failure has been determined, a corrective-action shall be developed to eliminate or reduce the recurrence of the failure. The procuring activity should review the corrective-actions at scheduled status reviews prior to implementation. In all cases, the failure analysis and the resulting corrective-actions should be documented. The effectiveness of the corrective-action should be demonstrated by restarting the test at the beginning of the cycle in which the original failure occurred.

2.1.7 Who will use the information

Deciding who will use the data is probably of less concern than what data to use. Usually everyone involved in the project will use some portion of the information. Assuring that collected information is available to all as needed, and making it easily accessible is the key.

2.2 Corrective-action and follow-up

The purpose of a corrective-action plan is to eliminate or reduce failures. Prior to implementation, the corrective-action plan should be submitted to management for approval. The system for such action should include provisions to assure that effective corrective-actions are taken on a timely basis by a follow-up audit that reviews and reports all open failure delinquencies to management. The failure cause and classification for each failure must be clearly stated. It is not necessary to include the cost of failure in the corrective-action status report if it was included in the initial report to management for corrective-action approval. This also describes the duties of the FRB (refer to Section 2.1).

The purpose for corrective-action status or follow-up should be obvious—to determine the effectiveness of the corrective-action taken. There are four questions that must be answered during the follow-up phase:

1. Was the failure or problem completely eliminated?
2. Was the failure or problem partially eliminated?
3. Did the corrective-action cause an insignificant change or no change?
4. Did the corrective-action cause a worse condition?

In essence, effective follow-up closes the loop in the "closed loop" system. Each failure must be monitored by continued reporting and analysis until effective results are obtained.

2.3 Summary

Data should be collected, reported, and investigated on all failures. It is important that all failures be categorized as relevant or nonrelevant while at the same time resisting the temptation to classify a failure as nonrelevant due to cost or time constraints.

As changes are made to correct a failure, follow-up is essential to assure the effectiveness of the corrective-action. For example, the corrective-action taken may cause over-stressing of another item that would cause a secondary failure, etc. The effectiveness of any corrective-action should never be assumed without 100% confidence that the decision or change will prevent a like failure. Always keep in mind that the outcome of decisions derived from collected data is positively correlated to the quality of data on which the decision is made.

2.4 EXERCISES

1. Before a failure is reported it must first be:
   a. Identified
   b. Verified
   c. Defined
   d. Recorded

2. The ultimate purpose behind failure data collecting is to:
   a. Identify the failure
   b. Verify that a failure has occurred
   c. Analyze the failure
   d. Prevent recurrence of the failure

3. The basic element of a failure reporting, analysis, and corrective-action system that is most likely to prevent the recurrence of a failure is the:
   a. Corrective-action system
   b. Analysis system
   c. Reporting system
   d. Follow-up system

4. A minor failure may be defined as:
   a. Any failure that causes built-in test equipment to continuously isolate a major failure in on-line hardware when such failure does not exist
   b. Any failure that causes built-in test equipment false alarm rates to exceed the specified levels
   c. Any failure that impairs built-in test equipment performance (creates false alarms), but permits equipment, when recycled, to isolate and localize to the required level, except when false alarm rate exceeds specified levels
   d. Any failure that causes built-in test equipment to continuously indicate a major failure in on-line hardware or software when such a failure does not exist

5. Nonrelevant failures are:
   a. Intermittent failures
   b. Unverified failures that cannot be duplicated
   c. Verified failures not otherwise excluded under approved failure categories
   d. Failures caused by human errors
6. Describe the mission of a failure review board.
7. Failure costs should be included on the:
   a. Corrective-action status report
   b. Initial recording form
   c. The FRB's initial reporting form
   d. The failure analysis report
8. Successes should be reported as well as failures.
   a. True
   b. False
9. The effectiveness of corrective-action is best demonstrated by:
   a. Restarting the test at the beginning of the cycle in which the original failure occurred
   b. Follow-up to see if costs have been reduced
   c. follow-up to see if customers are better satisfied.
   d. Follow-up to see if the problem was completely eliminated
   e. A and d above
10. Describe the best way to verify a failure.
11. State the five objectives for data collecting?
12. A chargeable failure may be:
   a. A intermittent failure
   b. An independent failure
   c. Relevant failure
   d. Unverified failure
   e. All of the above

2.5 References

ASQC Reliability Division. 1977. *A Reliability Guide to Failure Reporting, Analysis, and Corrective-action Systems.* Milwaukee, WI: ASQC–Quality Press.

Ireson, G. W., and C. F. Coombs. 1988. *Handbook of Reliability Engineering and Management.* New York: McGraw-Hill.

US Department of Defense. *MIL-STD-721: Definition of Terms for Reliability and Maintainability.* Philadelphia: Naval Publications and Forms Center.

US Department of Defense. *MIL-STD-785: Reliability Program for Systems and Equipment Development and Production.* Philadelphia: Naval Publications and Forms Center.

♦ ♦ ♦
CHAPTER

3

Distributions

A basic step in many reliability studies is choosing a probability density function. This first part of this chapter defines several popular density functions along with their reliability and hazard functions. The relationships among the probability density function, the reliability function and the hazard function are shown, as well as methods for determining the mean and variance of distributions.

The second part of this chapter covers the techniques of parameter estimation, Bayesian analysis, transformation of random variables, hypothesis testing and confidence intervals.

3.1 Distribution characteristics

Probability density functions (also known as density functions) are grouped into two categories, discrete and continuous. The values a **discrete** density function can take on are limited to integers. For example, in five flips of a coin, the number of heads is limited to 1, 2, 3, 4, or 5; the value 3.7 is nonsense. **Continuous** density functions can take on all values in a specific range. For example, the time to fail may be 1 hour, 1.01 hours, 1.001 hours, 1.0001 hours, etc.

To qualify as a density function two criteria must be met:

1) $f(x) \geq 0$

for all values of x, and

2) $\int_{-\infty}^{\infty} f(x)dx = 1$

for continuous distributions, or for discrete distributions,

$$\sum_n f(x_n) = 1,$$

where the sum is taken over all possible values of n.

The cumulative distribution function (CDF) is the area under the probability density function to the left of the specified value, and represents the probability of x being less than a specific value, $P(X < x)$. For continuous distributions, the cumulative distribution function is defined as

$$F(x) = \int_{-\infty}^{x} f(\tau)d\tau \qquad (3.1)$$

The probability of x falling between two specified values, a and b, is the area under the probability density function from a to b, which is

$$P(a < X < b) = \int_a^b f(x)dx,$$

which is also equal to $F(b) - F(a)$. This is represented graphically in Figure 3.1.

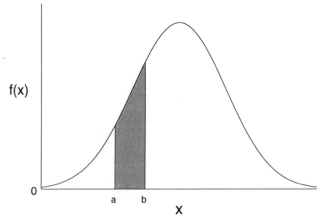

Figure 3.1. Probability of x falling between two specific values.

Note that for continuous distributions the probability of x being exactly equal to any specific value, for example a, is zero. As seen in Figure 3.1, as b moves closer to a, the area (which is equal to the probability) decreases. When b is equal to a, the area is zero.

For discrete distributions the probability of x being exactly equal to a specific value must be greater than zero for some values. For example, in four flips of a coin, where x represents the number of heads obtained, the probability of obtaining exactly 0 heads is 0.0625, the probability of obtaining exactly 1 head is 0.25, etc. This is the probability density function, and is shown in Figure 3.2.

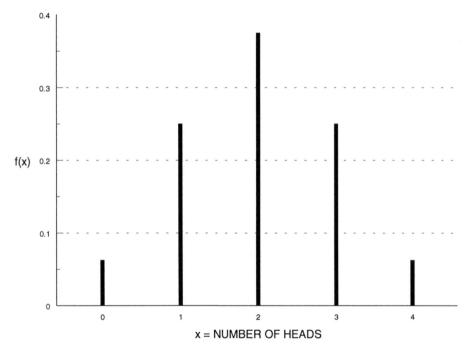

Figure 3.2. A discrete probability density function.

The cumulative distribution function for discrete distributions is

$$F(x) = \sum_{\tau \leq x} f(\tau) \tag{3.2}$$

The cumulative distribution function for the coin-flipping example is given in Figure 3.3.

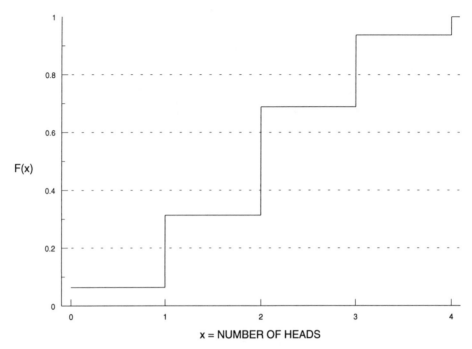

Figure 3.3. A discrete cumulative distribution function.

The reliability function is the complement of the cumulative distribution function, $F(x)$, and is obtained from the probability density function using the relationship

$$R(x) = 1 - F(x) = 1 - \int_{-\infty}^{x} f(\tau)d\tau = \int_{x}^{\infty} f(\tau)d\tau \tag{3.3}$$

The relationship between a reliability function and the cumulative distribution function is shown in Figure 3.4.

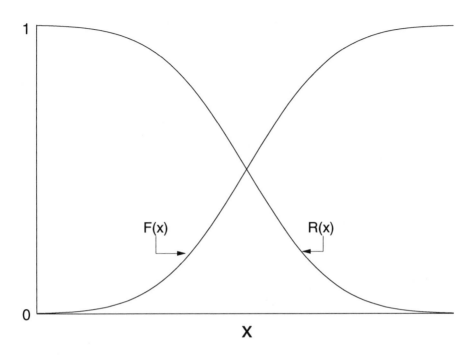

Figure 3.4. The relationship between the reliability function and the cumulative distribution function.

The hazard function is the instantaneous failure rate, and is a measure of proneness to fail. The hazard function is defined as

$$h(x) = \frac{f(x)}{R(x)} \tag{3.4}$$

The reliability function and the probability density function can be obtained from the hazard function using the expressions

$$R(t) = e^{-\int_{-\infty}^{x} h(\tau)d\tau} \tag{3.5}$$

and

$$f(x) = h(x)e^{-\int_{-\infty}^{x} h(\tau)d\tau} \tag{3.6}$$

The expected value, of a distribution can be determined from the expressions

$$E(x) = \int_{-\infty}^{\infty} xf(x)dx = \mu \tag{3.7}$$

or

$$E(x) = \int_{0}^{\infty} R(x)dx = \mu \tag{3.8}$$

The variance of a distribution can be found from the expression

$$V(x) = E(x^2) - \mu^2 \tag{3.9}$$

where μ is the distribution mean, and

$$E(x^2) = \int_{-\infty}^{\infty} x^2 f(x)dx \tag{3.10}$$

Example 3.1

Given the density function

$$f(x) = ax,\, 0 \le x \le 10$$

(a) Determine the value of a that makes $f(x)$ a valid density function, (b) determine the mean and variance of the distribution, and (c) derive expressions for the reliability and hazard functions.

Solution

For the density function to be valid, the area under the curve must equal one. Thus,

$$\int_{0}^{10}(ax)dx = 1 \Rightarrow \frac{a}{2}(x^2)\Big|_{0}^{10} = 1 \Rightarrow \frac{a}{2}(10^2 - 0^2) = 1 \Rightarrow a = \frac{1}{50}$$

From Equation 3.7, the mean of this distribution is

$$E(x) = \int_{0}^{10} x\frac{x}{50} dx = \int_{0}^{10}\frac{x^2}{50}dx = \frac{1}{150}(10)^3 = 6.667$$

From Equation 3.9, the variance of this distribution is

$$V(x) = \int_{0}^{10}\frac{1}{50}x^3 dx - (6.667)^2 = \frac{1}{200}(10)^4 - 44.449 = 5.55$$

The reliability function is

$$R(x) = \int_x^{10} \frac{1}{50} \tau d\tau = 1 - \frac{x^2}{100} \ , \ 0 \le x \le 10$$

The hazard function is

$$h(x) = \frac{f(x)}{R(x)} = \frac{\dfrac{1}{50} x}{1 - \dfrac{x^2}{100}} = \frac{2x}{100 - x^2} \ , \ 0 \le x \le 10$$

Example 3.2

Given the hazard function

$$h(x) = c \ , \ x \ge 0$$

Determine the reliability function and the probability density function.

Solution

The reliability function can be obtained from Equation 3.5.

$$R(x) = e^{-\int_0^x c d\tau} = e^{-cx} \ , \ x \ge 0$$

The probability density function is

$$f(x) = h(x)R(x) = ce^{-cx} \ , \ x \ge 0$$

This is the well known exponential probability density function, and will be discussed later.

Distribution characteristics are often obtained from moment-generating functions. If x is a continuous random variable, the nth moment about the origin is

$$E(x^n) = \int_{-\infty}^{\infty} x^n f(x) dx \tag{3.11}$$

If x is a discrete random variable, the nth moment about the origin is

$$E(x^n) = \sum_x x^n f(x) \tag{3.12}$$

The first moment about the **origin** is the distribution mean; recall that this is equivalent to Equation 3.7. The second moment about the **mean** is the variance; recall that this is equivalent to Equation 3.9. The third moment about the **mean** is the skewness of the distribution. If a single peaked distribution has a long tail to the right, it is said to be skewed right. The fourth moment about the **mean** is a measure of kurtosis, which is a measure of the peakedness of a distribution.

3.2 Normal and lognormal distributions

The normal distribution is a continuous distribution, and is also known as the Gaussian distribution. It is one of the easiest probability density functions to work with. Two useful properties of the normal distribution are additivity of variances and the tendency of sums of random variables, regardless of individual density functions, to be normal when added together (this is known as the central limit theorem or the theory of large numbers). These two properties make the normal distribution very useful when modeling a buildup of tolerances.

The lognormal distribution is also continuous, and is one of the most widely used life distributions. It is highly skewed and lends itself to situations when effects are multiplicative. The lognormal distribution has been used to model the cycles to failure for metals, the life of transistors, the life of bearings, as well as many other phenomenon.

3.2.1 The normal distribution

The normal probability density function is defined as

$$f(x) = \frac{1}{\sigma\sqrt{2\pi}} \exp\left[-\frac{1}{2}\left(\frac{x-\mu}{\sigma}\right)^2\right], \quad -\infty < x < \infty \qquad (3.13)$$

where: μ = the distribution mean (population mean), which is a measure of central tendency or location, and

σ = the distribution standard deviation (population standard deviation), which is a measure of dispersion.

The distribution mean is estimated from the sample mean

$$\hat{\mu} = \bar{x} = \frac{\sum_{i=1}^{n} x_i}{n} \tag{3.14}$$

where n is the sample size.

The distribution standard deviation is estimated from the sample standard deviation

$$\hat{\sigma} = s = \sqrt{\frac{n\sum_{i=1}^{n} x_i^2 - \left(\sum_{i=1}^{n} x_i\right)^2}{n(n-1)}} \tag{3.15}$$

Another commonly used expression for the sample standard deviation is

$$\hat{\sigma} = s = \sqrt{\frac{\sum_{i=1}^{n} (x_i - \bar{x})^2}{(n-1)}} \tag{3.16}$$

Equation 3.15 is more accurate for numerical calculations than Equation 3.16 because of the small values obtained when subtracting individual values form the sample mean.

The normal distribution is not skewed, and the mean, median and mode are all equal. Figure 3.5 graphically represents the normal probability density function.

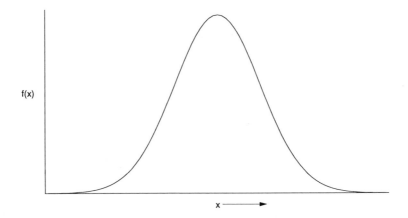

f(x)

x

Figure 3.5. The normal probability density function.

The normal probability density function cannot be integrated implicitly. Thus, the reliability and cumulative distribution functions are often expressed as a function of the standard normal distribution. Transformation to the standard normal is achieved with the expression

$$z = \frac{x - \mu}{\sigma} \qquad (3.17)$$

The standard normal random deviate, z, has a mean of 0 and a standard deviation of 1.0. The standard normal cumulative distribution function, $\Phi(z)$, is tabled in Appendix A and in virtually all statistical texts. However, these tables are becoming unnecessary, as electronic spreadsheets, such as Lotus™ 123 and Microsoft™ Excel have built-in statistical functions.

The normal reliability function is

$$R(x) = \int_x^\infty \frac{1}{\sigma\sqrt{2\pi}} \exp\left[-\frac{1}{2}\left(\frac{\tau - \mu}{\sigma}\right)^2\right] d\tau = 1 - \Phi(z),$$

$$-\infty < x < \infty \qquad (3.18)$$

where: $\Phi(z)$ = the standard normal cumulative distribution function (tabulated in Appendix A).

The standard normal reliability function along with the standard normal cumulative distribution function are shown in Figure 3.6.

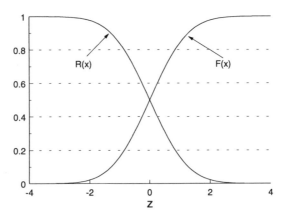

Figure 3.6. The standard normal reliability and cumulative distribution functions.

Example 3.3

A manufacturer produces metal beams with a mean strength of 40 units and a variance of 36. If the strength follows a normal distribution, what is the probability of a particular beam having a strength (a) greater than 52 units, and (b) less than 43 units?

Solution

Part a—the solution is the area under the normal probability density function to the right of $x = 52$.

$$P(x>52) = R(52) = \int_{52}^{\infty} \frac{1}{\sqrt{36}\sqrt{2\pi}} \exp\left[-\frac{1}{2}\left(\frac{x-40}{\sqrt{36}}\right)^2\right]dx$$

Transforming to standard normal gives

$$z = \frac{x-\mu}{\sigma} = \frac{52-40}{\sqrt{36}} = 2$$

From Appendix A, the area under the standard normal curve from $z = -\infty$ to $z = 2$ is $\Phi(2) = 0.9772$. If using Lotus™ 123, this value is found with the function @Normal(2,0,1,0). The first 0 indicates the mean of the distribution is zero, and the 1 indicates the standard deviation of the distribution is one, and the second 0 signifies the cumulative distribution is desired. Thus, if using Lotus™ 123, transformation to standard normal is not required; simply enter the actual mean and standard deviation in the function. In Microsoft™ Excel, this function is =NORMDIST(2,0,1,true). Like 123, the 0 and 1 are the mean and the standard deviation of the distribution. The true indicates the cumulative distribution function is desired. If false is entered, the probability density function is returned.

R(52) = 1–0.9772 = 0.0228.

Part b—the solution is the area under the normal probability density function to the left of $x = 43$.

$$P(x<43) = 1-R(43) = \int_{43}^{\infty} \frac{1}{\sqrt{36}\sqrt{2\pi}} \exp\left[-\frac{1}{2}\left(\frac{x-40}{\sqrt{36}}\right)^2\right]dx$$

> Transforming to standard normal gives
>
> $$z = \frac{43 - 40}{\sqrt{36}} = 0.5$$
>
> From Appendix A, the area under the standard normal curve from $z = -\infty$ to $z = 0.5$ is $\Phi(0.5) = 0.6915$.

The normal hazard function is monotonically increasing, and is defined as

$$h(x) = \frac{f(x)}{R(x)} = \frac{\phi(z)}{\sigma[1 - \Phi(z)]} , \quad -\infty < x < \infty \qquad (3.19)$$

where: $\phi(z)$ is the standard normal probability density function.

The standard deviation appears in the denominator of Equation 3.19 because $\phi(z)$ represents the standard normal probability density function and has a standard deviation of 1. Figure 3.7 shows the standard normal hazard function.

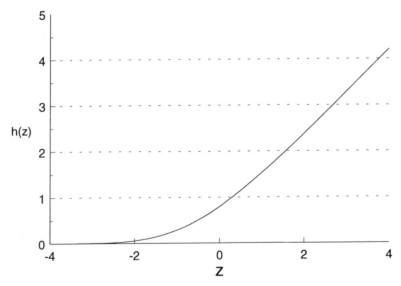

Figure 3.7. The standard normal hazard function.

Example 3.4

Given failure times of 28, 29, 31, 34, and 37 hours, what is the estimated instantaneous failure rate at 27 hours?

Solution

The sample mean is

$$\hat{\mu} = \frac{\sum\limits_{i=1}^{n} x_i}{n} = \frac{28 + 29 + 31 + 34 + 37}{5} = 31.8$$

The sample standard deviation is

$$\hat{\sigma} = \sqrt{\frac{n\sum\limits_{i=1}^{n} x_i^2 - \left(\sum\limits_{i=1}^{n} x_i\right)^2}{n(n-1)}} = \sqrt{\frac{5(5111) - (159)^2}{5(5-1)}} = 3.701$$

The instantaneous failure rate is given by the hazard function, and is estimated by

$$h(27) = \frac{\phi(z)}{\hat{\sigma}[1 - \Phi(z)]} = \frac{\phi\left(\dfrac{27 - 31.8}{3.701}\right)}{3.701\left[1 - \Phi\left(\dfrac{27 - 31.8}{3.701}\right)\right]} = 0.0515$$

3.2.2 The lognormal distribution

The normal and lognormal distributions are closely related. If x is a lognormal random variable, then the variable $y = \ln(x)$ is a normal random variable. The lognormal probability density function is

$$f(x) = \frac{1}{\sigma x \sqrt{2\pi}} \exp\left[-\frac{1}{2}\left(\frac{\ln x - \mu}{\sigma}\right)^2\right], \quad x > 0 \qquad (3.20)$$

The parameters of the lognormal distribution are the location parameter, μ, and the scale parameter σ. The scale parameter is sometimes referred to as the shape parameter. The location parameter can be estimated from the expression

$$\hat{\mu} = \frac{\sum_{i=1}^{n} \ln x_i}{n} \tag{3.21}$$

where n is the sample size.

The scale parameter is estimated from the expression

$$\hat{\sigma} = \sqrt{\frac{n \sum_{i=1}^{n} \ln x_i^2 - \left(\sum_{i=1}^{n} \ln x_i \right)^2}{n(n-1)}} \tag{3.22}$$

The term T_{50} represents the median of the lognormal distribution, and $\ln(T_{50})$ is interchangeable with μ. The lognormal probability density function is shown in Figure 3.8.

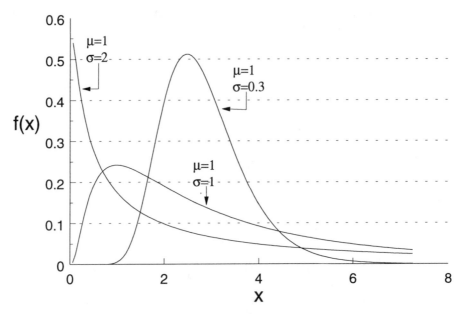

Figure 3.8. Lognormal probability density functions.

The mean of the lognormal distribution is

$$E(x) = \exp\left(\mu + \frac{\sigma^2}{2}\right) = T_{50}e^{\sigma^2/2} \tag{3.23}$$

The variance of the lognormal distribution is

$$V(x) = \left(e^{2\mu+\sigma^2}\right)\left(e^{\sigma^2} - 1\right) = T_{50}e^{\sigma^2}\left(e^{\sigma^2} - 1\right) \tag{3.24}$$

The lognormal reliability function is

$$R(x) = 1 - \Phi\left(\frac{\ln x - \mu}{\sigma}\right), \; x>0 \tag{3.25}$$

The lognormal reliability function is shown in Figure 3.9.

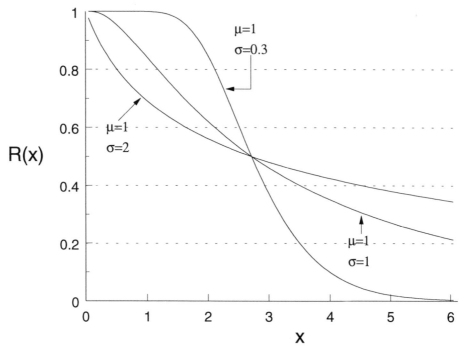

Figure 3.9. Lognormal reliability functions.

The lognormal hazard function is

$$h(x) = \frac{f(x)}{R(x)} = \frac{\phi\left(\frac{\ln x - \mu}{\sigma}\right)}{x\sigma\left[1 - \Phi\left(\frac{\ln x - \mu}{\sigma}\right)\right]} \quad , x > 0 \tag{3.26}$$

The lognormal hazard function, regardless of the parameter values, is initially increasing, then decreases and approaches zero as infinity is approached. For large values of σ ($\sigma > 1.5$) the hazard function increases so quickly, that it may appear on a graph that it is initially decreasing, but this is not the case. The lognormal hazard function is shown in Figure 3.10.

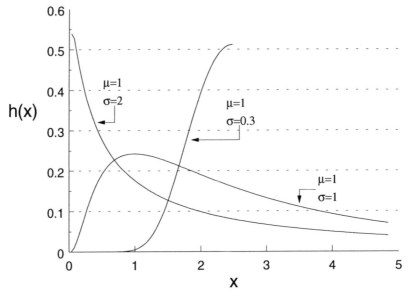

Figure 3.10. Lognormal hazard functions.

Example 3.5

The failure time of a component is lognormally distributed with parameters $\mu = 4$ units and $\sigma = 0.9$. When should the component be replaced if the minimum required reliability for the component is 0.85? What is the value of the hazard function at this time?

Solution

Substituting into the lognormal reliability function gives

$$R(x) = 0.85 = 1 - \Phi\left(\frac{\ln x - 4}{0.9}\right)$$

Simplifying,

$$0.15 = \Phi\left(\frac{\ln x - 4}{0.9}\right)$$

From Appendix A, and linearly interpolating (or from an electronic spreadsheet),

$$\Phi(-1.036) = 0.15$$

The time the component must be replaced to ensure reliability of 0.85 is

$$-1.036 = \frac{\ln x - 4}{0.9}$$

$x = \exp[-1.036(0.9)+4] = 21.5$ units.

The component must be replaced after operating for 21.5 units.
The value of the lognormal hazard function at $x = 21.5$ is

$$h(21.5) = \frac{\phi\left(\dfrac{\ln(21.5) - 4}{0.9}\right)}{(21.5)(0.9)\left[1 - \Phi\left(\dfrac{\ln(21.5) - 4}{0.9}\right)\right]} = 0.014 \text{ failures/unit time.}$$

3.3 Exponential, Poisson, binomial, hypergeometric, and geometric distributions

The exponential distribution is a continuous distribution that is related to the Poisson distribution which is discrete. If the number of failures per unit time is Poisson distributed, then the mean time between failures is exponentially distributed. The exponential distribution has a constant failure rate, and is used to model what is termed the "useful life" of many items. That is, the period after burn-in and before wear-out; the bottom portion of the bathtub curve, when the failure rate is constant. The Poisson distribution is used to describe rates, such as defects per computer chip, defects per automobile, failures per hour, etc.

The binomial, hypergeometric and geometric distributions are discrete distributions used to model situations that have only two possible outcomes. The binomial distribution is a Bernoulli process, and thus, has the following properties:

1. The experiment has n trials,
2. each experiment has two possible outcomes—success or failure,
3. the probability of success or failure is constant for all trials, and
4. each trial is independent.

The hypergeometric distribution is the same as the binomial distribution except the probability of success or failure is not constant for all trials. For example in a lot of 100 items with 10% being defective, the probability of selecting a defective item on the first trial is 10%, but the probability of selecting a defective item on the second trial is 10/99 if a defective item was not selected on the first trial and 9/99 if a defective item was selected on the first trial. To simplify, the binomial distribution assumes replacement, the hypergeometric does not. Another viewpoint is that the binomial distribution applies to sampling from an infinitely large population (replacement has no effect if the sample size is infinite), while the hypergeometric assumes a finite population size.

The geometric distribution is a special case of the negative-binomial distribution. It is used to model the number of trials required to achieve the first success. The negative-binomial is the distribution of the number of trials to achieve a given number of successes.

3.3.1 The exponential distribution

The exponential distribution is a one-parameter, continuous distribution. It is commonly expressed in terms of its mean, θ, and the inverse of its mean, λ.

The exponential probability density function is

$$f(x) = \frac{1}{\theta} e^{-\frac{x}{\theta}} = \lambda e^{-\lambda x} \ , \ x \geq 0 \tag{3.27}$$

where: θ = the distribution mean, and
$\lambda = 1/\theta$ = the failure rate.

The exponential probability density function is shown in Figure 3.11.

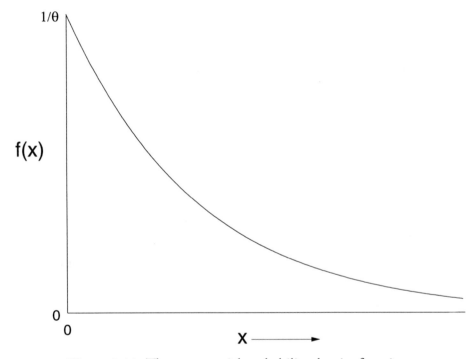

Figure 3.11. The exponential probability density function.

The exponential reliability function is

$$R(x) = e^{-\frac{x}{\theta}} = e^{-\lambda x} \ , \ x \geq 0 \tag{3.28}$$

This is shown in Figure 3.12.

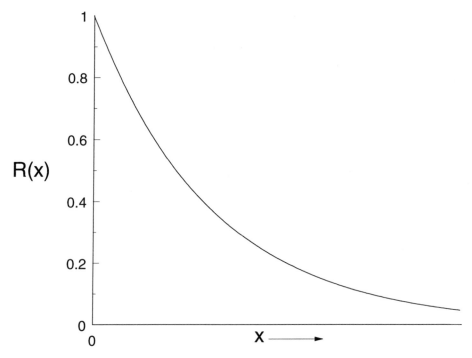

Figure 3.12. The exponential reliability function.

The exponential hazard function is

$$h(x) = \frac{f(x)}{R(x)} = \frac{1}{\theta} = \lambda \qquad\qquad (3.29)$$

The exponential hazard function is constant, as shown in Figure 3.13. A constant failure rate is unique to the exponential distribution, and is responsible for the "lack of memory" property. "Lack of memory" means the probability of failure in a specific time interval is the same regardless of the starting point of that time interval.

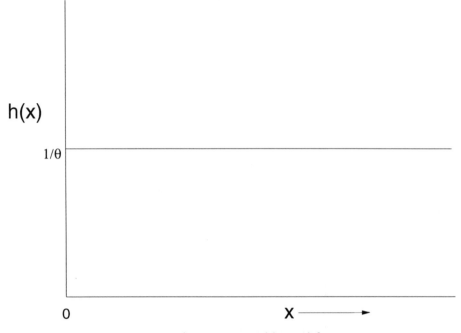

Figure 3.13. The exponential hazard function.

For example, if an item follows the exponential distribution, the probability of failure in the interval $x = 0$ to $x = 20$ is the same as the probability of failure in the interval $x = 100$ to $x = 120$.

The variance of the exponential distribution is

$$V(x) = \theta^2 = \frac{1}{\lambda^2}$$ (3.30)

Example 3.6

What is the probability of an item surviving until $t = 100$ units if the item is exponentially distributed with a mean time between failure of 80 units? Given that the item survived to 200 units, what is the probability of survival until $t = 300$ units? What is the value of the hazard function at 200 units, 300 units?

Solution

The probability of survival until $t = 100$ units is

$$R(100) = e^{-\left(\frac{100}{80}\right)} = 0.2865$$

The probability of survival until $t = 300$ units given survival until $t = 200$ units is[*]

$$R(300,200) = \frac{R(300)}{R(200)} = \frac{e^{-300/80}}{e^{-200/80}} = 0.2865$$

Note that this is equal to the probability of failure in the interval from $t=0$ to $t=100$.

The value of the hazard function is equal to the failure rate and is constant

$$h(t) = \frac{1}{80} = 0.0125$$

3.3.2 The Poisson distribution

The Poisson distribution is used to model occurrence rates, such as defects per item or failures per hour. A Poisson experiment has the following properties:

1. the number of occurrences is independent from period to period—the Poisson process has no memory; and,
2. the probability of an occurrence in a time interval is proportional to the length of the interval.

The Poisson probability density function is

$$P(x,\lambda t) = \frac{e^{-\lambda t}(\lambda t)^x}{x!} , x = 0, 1, 2, 3, \dots, n \tag{3.31}$$

where: $P(x,\lambda t)$ = the probability of exactly x occurrences in the interval λ t, and

λ = the average occurrence rate per unit time.

---

[*] Details on Bayesian analysis are covered in Section 3.8.

The mean and variance of the Poisson distribution are equal and are

$$E(x) = \lambda t \tag{3.32}$$

$$V(x) = \lambda t \tag{3.33}$$

Example 3.7

A computer chip manufacturer averages 7 defects per chip. What is the probability of a chip containing - (a) no defects, (b) 1 defect, (c) less than 3 defects?

Solution

Here, t, the number of computer chips is 1.0.

$\lambda t = 7$, thus, the probability of no defects on a chip is

$$P(0,7) = \frac{e^{-7}(7)^0}{0!} = 0.00091$$

The probability of a chip containing exactly one defect is

$$P(1,7) = \frac{e^{-7}(7)^1}{1!} = 0.00638$$

The probability of less than 3 defects is equal to the sum of exactly 0 defects, exactly 1 defect and exactly 2 defects. The probability of exactly 2 defects is

$$P(2,7) = \frac{e^{-7}(7)^2}{2!} = 0.02234$$

The probability of less than 3 defects is

$$P(x<3,7) = 0.00091 + 0.00638 + 0.02234 = 0.02963$$

Rather than calculating the probability of exactly 0 defects, the probability of exactly 1 defect and the probability of exactly 2 defects, the cumulative Poisson tables in Appendix G could have been utilized.

If the sample size is large and the probability of occurrence is near 0, the Poisson distribution may be used to approximate the binomial distribution. This will be discussed further in the next section.

3.3.3 The binomial distribution

The binomial probability density function is

$$P(x;n,p) = \binom{n}{x} p^x (1-p)^{n-x}, x = 0,\ 1,\ 2,\ 3,\ ...,\ n \qquad (3.34)$$

where: $P(x;n,p)$ = the probability of exactly x successes in n independent trials,

n = the sample size or number of trials, and

p = the probability of success on a single trial.

The mean of the binomial distribution is

$$E(x) = np \qquad (3.35)$$

The variance of the binomial distribution is

$$V(x) = np(1-p) \qquad (3.36)$$

Example 3.8

The probability for successfully launching a certain rocket is 89%. What is the probability of exactly two successful launches in the next three attempts?

Solution

The probability for a successful launch is $p = 0.89$, and the sample size is three attempts, $n = 3$. The probability of exactly two successful attempts is

$$P(2;3,0.89) = \binom{3}{2} 0.89^2 (1-0.89)^{(3-2)} = 0.2614$$

Note that the term $\binom{3}{2}$ is equal to $\left(\dfrac{3!}{2!(3-2)!} \right)$.

Example 3.9

To destroy a military target, at least three missiles must hit the target. The probability of each missile hitting the target is 90%. How many missiles must be launched to ensure, with 99% reliability, that the target will be destroyed?

Solution

The probability of a single missile hitting the target is $p = 0.9$. If four missiles are launched, $n = 4$, and the probability of exactly three missiles hitting the target is

$$P(3;4,0.9) = \binom{4}{3}0.9^3(1-0.9)^{(4-3)} = 0.2916$$

The probability of exactly four missiles hitting the target is

$$P(4;4,0.9) = \binom{4}{4}0.9^4(1-0.9)^{(4-4)} = 0.6561$$

The probability of at least three missiles hitting the target if four are launched is 0.9522 (0.2916 + 0.6561). Thus, launching four missiles does not meet the required reliability, 99%. If five missiles are launched, the probability of exactly three missiles hitting the target is

$$P(3;5,0.9) = \binom{5}{3}0.9^3(1-0.9)^{(5-3)} = 0.0729$$

The probability of exactly four missiles hitting the target is

$$P(4;5,0.9) = \binom{5}{4}0.9^4(1-0.9)^{(5-4)} = 0.3281$$

The probability of exactly five missiles hitting the target is

$$P(5;5,0.9) = \binom{5}{5}0.9^5(1-0.9)^{(5-5)} = 0.5905$$

The probability of at least three missiles hitting the target if five are launched is 0.9915 (0.0729 + 0.3281 + 0.5905). Launching five missiles meets the objective of 99% reliability.

If p is small and n is large, the Poisson distribution can be used to approximate the binomial distribution by replacing λt with np. Note that if p is large the Poisson approximation can also be used by substituting $1-p$ for p and subtracting the resulting probability from 1.0.

Example 3.10

A transistor manufacturer has a failure rate of 3 per 10,000. What is the probability of finding exactly one defect in a random sample of 200 transistors?

Solution

This is a binomial experiment with n = 200 and p = 0.0003. Using a Poisson approximation, λt = (200)(0.0003) = 0.06. The probability of finding exactly one defect in the random sample is

$$P(1,0.06) = \frac{e^{-0.06}(0.06)^1}{1!} = 0.0565$$

Note that it is not necessary for the value of λt to be an integer for the approximation to be valid.

3.3.4 The hypergeometric distribution

The hypergeometric distribution differs from the binomial distribution in that the random sample of n items is selected from a finite population of N items. With the hypergeometric distribution, there is no replacement. If N is large in respect to n ($N>10n$), the binomial distribution is a good approximation to the hypergeometric distribution. The hypergeometric probability density function is

$$P(x; N, n, k) = \frac{\binom{k}{x}\binom{N-k}{n-x}}{\binom{N}{n}}, \quad x = 0, 1, 2, 3, \ldots, n. \tag{3.37}$$

where: $P(x;N,n,k)$ = the probability of exactly x successes in the sample size n, and

k = the number of successes in the population, N.

The mean of the hypergeometric distribution is

$$E(x) = \frac{nk}{N} \tag{3.38}$$

The variance of the hypergeometric distribution is

$$V(x) = \left(\frac{nk}{N}\right)\left(1 - \frac{k}{N}\right)\left(\frac{N-n}{N-1}\right) \tag{3.39}$$

Example 3.11

A manufacturer of televisions produced a lot of 20 sets in which 5 of the sets were shipped with incorrect documentation. If a distributor receives 10 televisions from this lot, what is the probability of the distributor receiving exactly 3 televisions with incorrect documentation?

Solution

The population size is $N = 20$, the sample size is $n = 10$, and the number of successes (a television shipped without documentation is defined as a success in this case) is $k = 5$. The probability of the distributor receiving exactly 3 television sets without documentation is

$$P(3;20,10,5) = \frac{\binom{5}{3}\binom{20-5}{10-3}}{\binom{20}{10}} = 0.3483$$

3.3.5 The geometric distribution

The geometric distribution is used to model the number of trials required to obtain the first success. For the binomial and hypergeometric distributions the number of trials is fixed, and the random variable is the number of successes. For the geometric distribution the number of successes is fixed at one, and the random variable is the number of trials needed to obtain the success. The geometric probability density function is

$$P(x;p) = p(1-p)^{x-1}, \; x = 1, 2, 3, ..., n \tag{3.40}$$

where: $P(x;p)$ = the probability of obtaining the first success on trial number x, and

p = the probability of success on a single trial—all trials are independent.

The mean of the geometric distribution is

$$E(x) = \frac{1}{p} \tag{3.41}$$

The variance of the geometric distribution is

$$V(x) = \frac{1-p}{p^2} \tag{3.42}$$

The probability that the number of trials to achieve the first success is greater than a specified number, n is

$$p(x > n) = (1-p)^n \tag{3.43}$$

If n is large and p is small,

$$p(x > n) \approx e^{-np} \tag{3.44}$$

Example 3.12

A complex electronic system has self diagnostics and does a self check before initializing. On average, the system performs 1.8 self checks before initializing. If each self check is independent, what is the probability that the system will initialize on the third attempt?

Solution

The probability of success per each attempt is

$p=1/1.8 = 0.5556$

The probability of the first success on the third attempt is

$P(3;0.5556) = 0.5556(1-0.5556)^{(3-1)} = 0.1097.$

3.4 The Weibull distribution

The Weibull distribution is a continuous distribution that was publicized by Waloddi Weibull in 1951. Although initially met with skepticism, it has become widely used, especially in the reliability field. The Weibull distribution's popularity resulted from its ability to be used with small sample sizes and its flexibility. In addition to being the most useful density function for reliability calculations, analysis of the Weibull distribution provides the information needed for troubleshooting, classifying failure types, scheduling preventive maintenance and scheduling inspections. The Weibull probability density function is

$$f(x) = \frac{\beta x^{\beta-1}}{\theta^\beta} \exp\left[-\left(\frac{x}{\theta}\right)^\beta\right], x \geq 0 \tag{3.45}$$

where: β = the shape parameter, and
        θ = the scale parameter.

Beta and θ are continuous. The acceptable ranges for these variables are $0 < \beta < \infty$, and $0 < \theta < \infty$.

Typically, β is between 0.5 and 8. As β increases, the mean of the Weibull distribution approaches θ and the variance approaches zero. Theta is also known as the characteristic life because 63.2% of the population fails by the characteristic life point regardless of the value of β. The estimation of β and θ is not straightforward; special techniques such as probability plotting, hazard plotting, or maximum likelihood estimation are required. Methods of parameter estimation are given in Section 3.7

3.4.1 Effects of the shape parameter

By altering the shape parameter, β, the Weibull probability density function takes a variety of shapes. This is demonstrated in Figure 3.14.

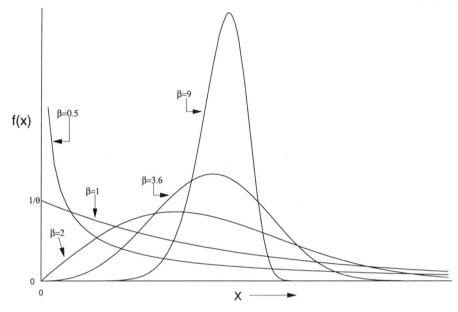

Figure 3.14. Weibull probability density functions.

Note that several of the probability density functions displayed in Figure 3.14 look familiar. The Weibull distribution can be used in a wide variety of situations and dependent on the value of β, is equal to or can approximate several other distributions. For example, if:

β = 1, the Weibull distribution is identical to the exponential distribution

β = 2, the Weibull distribution is identical to the Rayleigh distribution

β = 2.5, the Weibull distribution approximates the lognormal distribution

β = 3.6, the Weibull distribution approximates the normal distribution

Because of this flexibility, there are few observed failure rates that cannot be reasonably modeled by the Weibull distribution. Some specific uses have been:

- The breaking strength of components or the stress required to fatigue metals
- The time to fail for electronic components
- The time to fail for items that wear out, such as automobile tires

- Systems that fail when the weakest component in the system fails

3.4.2 Mean and variance of the Weibull distribution

The mean of the Weibull distribution is

$$E(x) = \theta\Gamma\left(1+\frac{1}{\beta}\right) \tag{3.46}$$

where: $\Gamma(x)$ is the Gamma function and is tabulated in Appendix B.
The variance of the Weibull distribution is

$$V(x) = \theta^2\left[\Gamma\left(1+\frac{2}{\beta}\right) - \Gamma^2\left(1+\frac{1}{\beta}\right)\right] \tag{3.47}$$

If $\beta < 1$, the mean of the Weibull distribution is greater than θ. If $\beta = 1$, the mean of the Weibull distribution is equal to θ. In the case, $\beta > 1$, the mean of the Weibull distribution is less than θ and approaches θ as x increases. The variance of the Weibull distribution decreases and approaches zero as β increases to infinity.

Example 3.13

Determine the mean and variance for a system having a Weibull time to fail distribution with $\beta = 2$ and $\theta = 100$.

Solution

From Appendix B

$$\Gamma\left(1+\frac{1}{2}\right) = \Gamma(1.5) = 0.88623$$

The mean of this distribution is

$$E(x) = (100)\Gamma\left(1+\frac{1}{2}\right) = 100(0.88623) = 88.6$$

The variance of this distribution is

$$V(x) = (100)^2\left[\Gamma\left(1+\frac{2}{2}\right) - \Gamma^2\left(1+\frac{1}{2}\right)\right] = 100^2[\Gamma(2) - \Gamma^2(1.5)] = 2146$$

3.4.3 The Weibull reliability and hazard functions

The Weibull reliability function is

$$R(x) = \exp\left[-\left(\frac{x}{\theta}\right)^{\beta}\right], x > 0 \tag{3.48}$$

Figure 3.15 illustrates the effect of β on the reliability function.

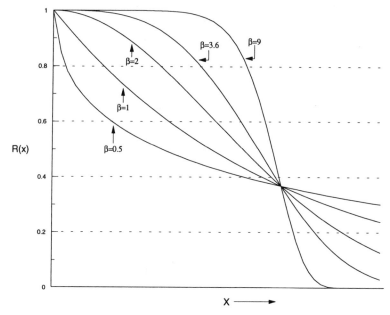

Figure 3.15. Weibull reliability functions.

For the case of $\beta < 1$, the reliability sharply decreases initially and then flattens out. This is the result of infant mortality failures. For the case of $\beta = 1$, the reliability gradually decreases; the result of a constant failure rate. When $\beta > 1$, the reliability slowly decreases initially and then decreases as the characteristic life is approached.

The Weibull hazard function is

$$h(x) = \frac{\beta x^{(\beta-1)}}{\theta^{\beta}}, x > 0 \tag{3.49}$$

The effects of β on the hazard function are demonstrated in Figure 3.16.

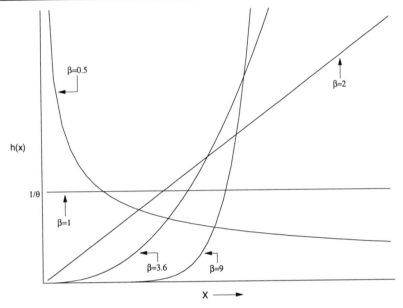

Figure 3.16. Weibull hazard functions.

A shape factor of less than one results in a decreasing failure rate. If $\beta = 1$ the failure rate is constant at a value of $1/\theta$. If $\beta > 1$ the failure rate is increasing; the higher the value of β, the faster the failure rate is increasing.

Example 3.14

What is the probability of survival until time = 40 for a system with a Weibull time to fail distribution having parameters $\beta = 1.8$ and $\theta = 115$? What is the instantaneous failure rate at this time?

Solution

The reliability at time = 40 is

$$R(40) = \exp\left[-\left(\frac{40}{115}\right)^{1.8}\right] = 0.8612$$

The value of the hazard function at time = 40 is

$$h(40) = \frac{(1.8)\left(40^{(1.8-1)}\right)}{115^{1.8}} = 0.0067$$

3.4.4 Relationship to the extreme value distribution

Consider a system consisting of n individual components in series. If one of the components fails, the system fails. In this situation the time to fail for the system is equal to the smallest of the n failure times. This situation may be modeled using extreme value distributions.

The type III asymptotic distribution for the minima is simply the Weibull distribution. The type I asymptotic distribution for maxima and minima, also known as the extreme value distribution (EVD), is closely related to the Weibull distribution.

The EVD reliability function is

$$R(x) = \exp\left[-\exp\left(\frac{x-\delta}{\alpha}\right)\right], \; -\infty < x < \infty \tag{3.50}$$

where: δ = the location parameter, and
$\quad\quad\quad \alpha$ = the scale parameter.

If data that follows a Weibull distribution is transformed by taking the natural logarithm, the result is data that follows the EVD. If $x = \ln(t)$, where t follows a Weibull distribution, x follows the EVD. The parameters of the Weibull distribution and the EVD have the following relationships.

$$\delta = \ln(\theta) \tag{3.51}$$

$$\alpha = \frac{1}{\beta} \tag{3.52}$$

3.5 The gamma and beta distributions

The gamma distribution is a continuous distribution that describes random variables that are bounded at one end. The gamma distribution is often used to model the lifetime of systems. If an event takes place after n exponentially distributed events take place sequentially, the resulting random variable follows a gamma distribution. Mathematically, if

$$y_n = x_1 + x_2 + \ldots + x_n$$

and $x_1, x_2, \ldots, x_n$ are exponentially distributed with identical failure rates, then y_n follows the gamma distribution. Some examples are:

- The time to fail for a system consisting of *n* independent components, with *n-1* components being standby components, where system failure occurs when all *n* components fail
- The time between maintenance actions for a system that requires maintenance after a fixed number of uses

The beta distribution is a continuous distribution that describes the ratio $y_1/(y_1 + y_2)$, where y_1 and y_2 are independent variables that follow the gamma distribution. It is bounded on both ends, and is used to describe random variables constrained to an interval. Because of this, the beta distribution is useful for determining tolerance intervals and for modeling the completion time of tasks in PERT (project evaluation and review technique) simulations.

3.5.1 The gamma distribution

The gamma probability density function is

$$f(x) = \frac{\lambda^\eta}{\Gamma(\eta)} x^{(\eta-1)} e^{-\lambda x} \ , \ x \geq 0, \eta \geq 0, \lambda \geq 0 \tag{3.53}$$

where: η = the shape parameter,
λ = the scale parameter, and
$\Gamma(x)$ = the gamma function and is tabled in Appendix B.

The mean of the gamma distribution is

$$E(x) = \frac{\eta}{\lambda} \tag{3.54}$$

The variance of the gamma distribution is

$$V(x) = \frac{\eta}{\lambda^2} \tag{3.55}$$

The parameters of the gamma distribution can be estimated from the expressions

$$\hat{\lambda} = \frac{\bar{x}}{s^2} \tag{3.56}$$

$$\hat{\eta} = \hat{\lambda}\bar{x} \tag{3.57}$$

where: s^2 = the sample variance and
$\bar{x}$ = the sample mean.

The above equations are based on the method of matching moments. Maximum likelihood estimates are more accurate, but are more complicated.

As seen in Figure 3.17, the gamma probability density function is versatile. When $\eta = 1$, the gamma distribution reduces to the exponential distribution. When η is a positive integer, the gamma distribution is an Erlang distribution, a distribution used in queuing theory. If $\lambda = 2$, then the gamma distribution becomes the chi-square distribution with $v = 2\eta$ degrees of freedom. Also, the gamma distribution becomes normal as η becomes large.

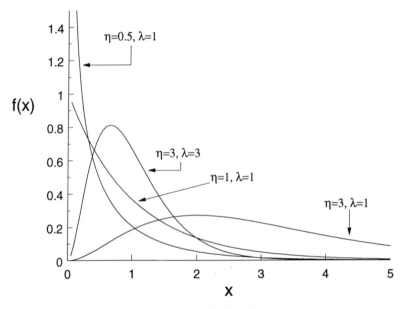

Figure 3.17. Gamma probability density functions.

The gamma reliability function does not exist in closed form unless η is restricted to integer values. For this special case, the gamma reliability function is

$$R(x) = \sum_{k=0}^{\eta-1} \frac{(\lambda x)^k e^{-\lambda x}}{k!}, \; x \geq 0 \tag{3.58}$$

The gamma reliability function is shown in Figure 3.18 for $\lambda = 1$.

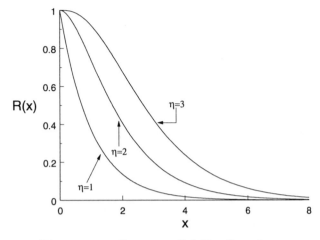

Figure 3.18. Gamma reliability functions.

The gamma hazard function does not exist in closed form unless η is restricted to integer values. For this special case, the gamma hazard function is

$$h(x) = \frac{\dfrac{\lambda^\eta}{\Gamma(\eta)} x^{(\eta-1)} e^{-\lambda x}}{\displaystyle\sum_{k=0}^{\eta-1} \frac{(\lambda x)^k e^{-\lambda x}}{k!}} \ , \ x \geq 0 \tag{3.59}$$

The gamma hazard function is shown in Figure 3.19 for $\lambda = 1$.

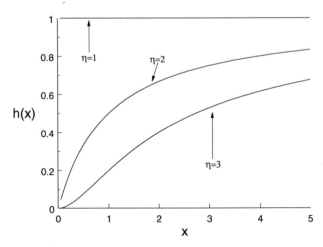

Figure 3.19. Gamma hazard functions.

Example 3.15

The time to fail for a system is gamma distributed with a shape parameter of 2 and a scale parameter of 0.03. What is the probability of survival until $x = 50$ units? What is the value of the hazard function at this time?

Solution

Since η is an integer, the reliability at $x = 50$ units is

$$R(50) = \sum_{k=0}^{2-1} \frac{[0.03(50)]^k e^{-0.03(50)}}{k!} = 0.5578$$

The value of the hazard function at $x = 50$ units is

$$h(50) = \frac{\dfrac{(0.03)^2}{\Gamma(2)} 50^{(2-1)} e^{-(0.03)50}}{0.5578} = 0.1800$$

Example 3.16

A system fails when there are no resistors available. The system is designed with 3 resistors, 2 being standby redundant (the system also has perfect switching). If the resistors have a constant failure rate of 0.0001 hours, what is the probability of system survival to a time of 12,800 hours?

Solution

The resistors have a constant failure rate, thus, they are exponentially distributed. Since the resistors are standby redundant, the time to fail for the system is the sum of the individual failure times for the 3 resistors. The time to fail for this system is described by a gamma distribution with $\lambda = 0.0001$ and $\eta = 3$. The reliability at $t = 12,800$ hours is

$$R(12,800) = \sum_{k=0}^{3-1} \frac{[0.0001(12,800)]^k e^{-0.0001(12,800)}}{k!} = 0.862$$

3.5.2 The beta distribution

The standard beta probability density function is

$$f(x) = \frac{1}{B(p,q)} x^{p-1}(1-x)^{q-1} \, , 0 \leq x \leq 1, p > 0, q > 0 \tag{3.60}$$

where: p and q are shape parameters, and,

$B(p,q)$ is a beta function, and is defined as

$$B(p,q) = \int_0^1 x^{p-1}(1-x)^{q-1} dx = \frac{\Gamma(p)\Gamma(q)}{\Gamma(p+q)} \tag{3.61}$$

The beta probability density function is shown in Figure 3.20.

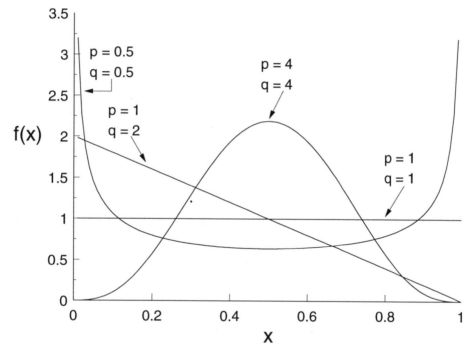

Figure 3.20. Beta probability density functions.

As seen from Figure 3.20, two special cases of the beta distribution are the uniform distribution and the triangular distribution. The beta distribution is quasi-symmetrical; $f(x;p,q)$ is identical to $[1-f(x;q,p)]$. This is shown in Figure 3.21.

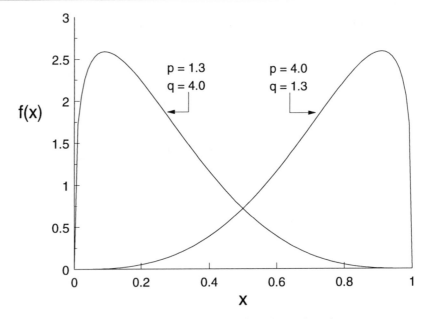

Figure 3.21. Quasi-symmetry of the beta distribution.

The beta distribution is not limited to the range 0 to 1. If x follows the standard beta distribution, then $y = a + bx$ follows the beta distribution with identical parameters as x, but the range is (a,b).

The mean of the beta distribution is

$$E(x) = \frac{p}{(p+q)} \qquad (3.62)$$

The variance of the beta distribution is

$$V(x) = \frac{pq}{(p+q)^2(p+q+1)} \qquad (3.63)$$

Like the gamma distribution, maximum likelihood estimates are the most accurate method of parameter estimation, but are difficult to work with. The moment estimators given below match the accuracy of maximum likelihood estimators if the sample size is large.

$$\hat{p} = \frac{\bar{x}\hat{q}}{1-\bar{x}} \qquad (3.64)$$

$$\hat{q} = \frac{(1-\bar{x})}{s^2}\left[\bar{x}(1-\bar{x}) - s^2\right] \tag{3.65}$$

where: s^2 = the sample variance and

$\bar{x}$ = the sample mean.

The beta reliability function is

$$R(x) = 1 - \frac{\Gamma(p+q)}{\Gamma(p)\Gamma(q)}\int_0^x \tau^{p-1}(1-\tau)^{q-1}d\tau = 1 - I_x(p,q) \,,\, 0 \le x \le 1 \tag{3.66}$$

where $I_x(p,q)$ is the incomplete beta function which is related to the binomial distribution. The incomplete beta function can be read from tables, but it is much easier to use functions contained in electronic spreadsheets (@betai if using Lotus™ 123).

$$I_x(p, q = n - p + 1) = \sum_{i=p}^n \binom{n}{i} x^i (1-x)^{n-i} \tag{3.67}$$

The beta reliability function is shown in Figure 3.22. For the special case when both shape parameters are equal to one, the reliability function is a straight line with slope = 1.

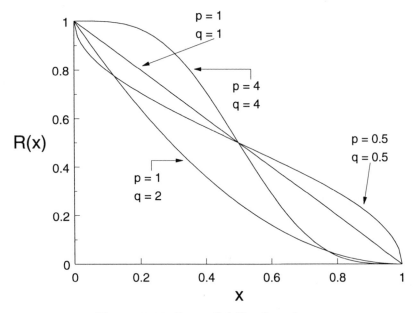

Figure 3.22. Beta reliability functions.

The beta hazard function is

$$h(x) = \frac{\frac{1}{B(p,q)} x^{p-1}(1-x)^{q-1}}{1 - I_x(p,q)} \quad , 0 \le x \le 1 \tag{3.68}$$

The beta hazard function is shown in Figure 3.23. In general, the hazard function increases drastically as x approaches 1.

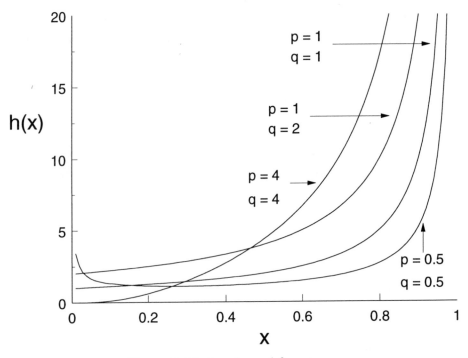

Figure 3.23. Beta hazard functions.

Example 3.17

The strength of a radio signal has been shown to follow a beta distribution over the range 10 units to 50 units with parameters $p = 1.8$ and $q = 2.5$. What is the probability that at any given time the strength of the signal is greater than 38 units?

Solution

Transforming to a standardized beta distribution gives

$$y = \frac{x - 10}{40}$$

For $x = 38$,

$$y = \frac{38 - 10}{40} = 0.7$$

The reliability at $x = 38$ is

$$R(0.7) = 1 - I_{0.7}(1.8, 2.5) = 1 - 0.8838 = 0.1162$$

3.6 Chi-square, *F*, and *t*-distributions

The chi-square, *F*, and *t*-distributions are primarily used as sampling distributions, rather than to model lifetimes. Among other things, these distributions are used to:

- Count the number of failures in an interval
- Determine goodness of fit
- Determine confidence limits
- Draw inferences concerning population means
- Draw inferences concerning population variances

3.6.1 The chi-square distribution

If $y_1, y_2, \ldots, y_v$ are independent, standard normally distributed variables, then

$$\chi^2 = y^2{}_1 + y^2{}_2 + \ldots + y^2{}_v$$

is chi-square distributed with v degrees of freedom (the number of independent variables whose squares are being added). The chi-square distribution is a special case of the gamma distribution with $\lambda = 2$ and $\eta = 2/v$. Since the number of failures in a given interval is an integer by definition, the chi-square distribution may be used to model this phenomenon. This leads to applications involving goodness of fit and the determination of confidence limits.

The chi-square probability density function is

$$f(x) = \frac{1}{2^{v/2} \Gamma(v/2)} x^{(v/2-1)} e^{-x/2} , x > 0 \tag{3.69}$$

The shape of the chi-square distribution is shown in Figure 3.24.

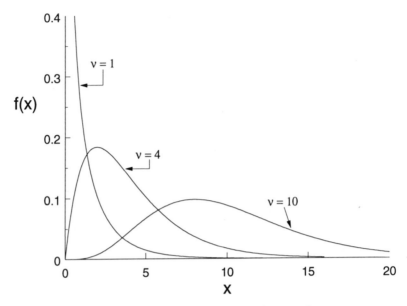

Figure 3.24. Chi-square probability density functions.

The mean of the chi-square distribution is

$$E(x) = v \qquad (3.70)$$

The variance of the chi-square distribution is

$$V(x) = 2v \qquad (3.71)$$

The chi-square distribution has several useful properties:

- The sum of two or more independent chi-square variables is also a chi-square variable with degrees of freedom equal to the sum of the degrees of freedom for the individual variables.
- The ratio of two independent chi-square variables, with degrees of freedom, v_1 and v_2 multiplied by (v_2/v_1) is F distributed.
- If two independent variables are chi-square distributed, the ratio of either of the variables to the sum of both variables is beta distributed.
- As v becomes large, the chi-square distribution approaches normal with mean v and variance $2v$.

3.6.2 The *F* Distribution

The *F* distribution is used to make inferences about means and to construct confidence limits. Given two independent chi-square variables, χ_1^2 and χ_2^2, with degrees of freedom v_1 and v_2, the random variable

$$F = \frac{\chi_1^2 / v_1}{\chi_2^2 / v_2} \tag{3.72}$$

has an *F* distribution with degrees of freedom v_1 and v_2. The probability density function for this variable is

$$f(F) = \left(\frac{\Gamma[(v_1 + v_2)/2](v_1/v_2)^{v_1/2}}{\Gamma(v_1/2)\Gamma(v_2/2)} \right) \left(\frac{F^{v_1/2-1}}{(1 + v_1 F/v_2)^{(v_1+v_2)/2}} \right), \; F > 0 \tag{3.73}$$

The *F* probability density function is shown in Figure 3.25.

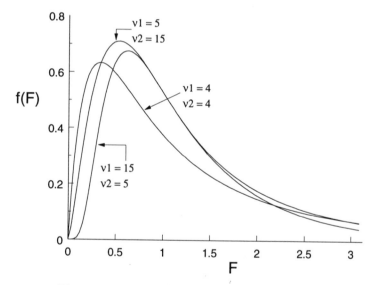

Figure 3.25. F probability density functions.

As seen from Figure 3.25, the shape of the *F* distribution is dependent on the order of degrees of freedom. The degrees of freedom of the chi-square variable in the numerator of *F* is stated first, followed by the degrees of freedom of the chi-square variable in the denominator. If $F_\alpha(v_1, v_2)$ represents the area under the F probability density function, with degrees of freedom v_1 and v_2, to the right of α, then

$$F_{1-\alpha}(v_1,v_2)=\frac{1}{F_\alpha(v_2,v_1)} \tag{3.74}$$

The F distribution is tabled in Appendix E.

The mean of the F distribution is

$$E(F)=\frac{v_2}{v_2-2}, v_2>2 \tag{3.75}$$

Note that the mean of the F distribution is independent of v_1. The variance of the F distribution is

$$V(F)=\frac{2v_2^2(v_1+v_2-2)}{v_1(v_2-2)^2(v_2-4)}, v_2>4 \tag{3.76}$$

If s_1^2 and s_2^2 are the variances of two samples taken from independent, normally distributed populations with variances, σ_1^2 and σ_2^2, and sample sizes, n_1 and n_2, then the statistic

$$F=\frac{s_1^2/\sigma_1^2}{s_2^2/\sigma_2^2} \tag{3.77}$$

is F distributed with $v_1 = n_1-1$ and $v_2 = n_2-1$. Thus, the F distribution is also known as the variance ratio distribution.

Example 3.18

Given a random variable with an F distribution and degrees of freedom of $v_1 = 8$ and $v_2 = 15$, what is the value of F that gives a 5% chance that a random sample will yield a value greater than F? What is the value of F that gives a 95% chance that a random sample will yield a value greater than F?

Solution

For a 5% probability of selecting a value greater than F, this is equivalent to $F_{.05}(8,15)$. From Appendix E, $F_{.05}(8,15) = 2.64$. For a 95% probability of selecting a value greater than F, this is equivalent to $F_{.95}(8,15)$

$$F_{0.95}(8,15)=\frac{1}{F_{0.05}(15,8)}=\frac{1}{3.22}=0.311$$

3.6.3 The *t*-distribution

The *t*-distribution is used to draw inferences concerning means and to construct confidence intervals for means when the variance is unknown, or too few samples are available to utilize the normal distribution. When dealing with large sample sizes, $n > 30$, the sample variance, s^2, is a reasonable estimate of the variance, σ^2. When sample sizes are small, $n < 30$, the error introduced from using s^2 as an estimate of σ^2 causes the statistic

$$t = \frac{\bar{x} - \mu}{s / \sqrt{n}} \tag{3.78}$$

to deviate from the standard normal distribution*. The *t*-distribution is the distribution for the random variable

$$t = \frac{z}{\sqrt{\dfrac{\chi^2}{v}}} \tag{3.79}$$

where: *z* is a standard normal random variable, and

χ^2 is a chi-square random variable with γ degrees of freedom.

The *t*-distribution is a special case of the *F* distribution with $1, \gamma$ degrees of freedom. The *t* probability density function is

$$f(t) = \frac{\Gamma[(v+1)/2]}{\Gamma(v/2)\sqrt{\Pi v}} \left(1 + \frac{t^2}{v}\right)^{-(v+1)/2}, \quad -\infty < t < \infty \tag{3.80}$$

The *t* probability density function is shown in Figure 3.26.

As seen in Figure 3.26, the variance of the *t*-distribution decreases as v increases. Once v is greater than 30, there is almost no change in the variance as v increases, and the *t*-distribution is practically identical to the standard normal distribution.

The mean of the *t*-distribution is

$$E(t) = 0 \tag{3.81}$$

---

* The standard normal deviate is $z = \dfrac{x - \mu}{\sigma}$. $\bar{x}$ is used to approximate μ, and s is used to approximate σ. The central limit theorem states that the standard deviation of an average is inversely proportional to the square root of the number sampled. Thus, the standard normal deviate for a sample of size n is $z = \dfrac{\bar{x} - \mu}{\sigma / \sqrt{n}}$. For more information see Section 3.2.

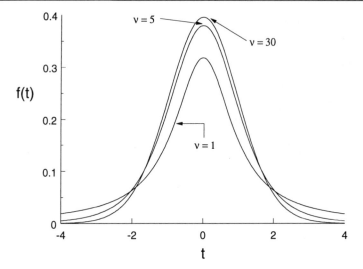

Figure 3.26. *t*-probability density functions.

The variance of the *t*-distribution is

$$V(t) = \frac{v}{v-2}, \, v > 2 \tag{3.82}$$

Example 3.19

A cloth manufacturer guarantees the average strength of a specific material to be 45 units. Each month, 15 specimens are tested, and the computed *t*-statistic must be within $-t_{0.05}$ and $t_{0.05}$ to satisfy the manufacturer's customers. Recently, the strength of the 15 specimens averaged 40 units with a standard deviation of 8, were the specifications met?

Solution

The degrees of freedom is $v = n-1 = 14$. From Appendix F, $t_{0.05} = 1.761$. Thus, $-t_{0.05} = -1.761$. If the average strength of the material is 45 units then,

$$t = \frac{40 - 45}{8/\sqrt{15}} = -2.42$$

This is not within the range -1.761 to 1.761, the manufacturer's process is not producing to the specified strength.

3.7 Parameter estimation

There are many methods available for parameter estimation. In reliability engineering, the most popular methods are:

- Maximum likelihood
- Hazard plotting
- Probability plotting
- Moment estimation

It is desirable for a parameter estimator to have the following properties:

1. Lack of bias—if the expected value of the estimator is equal to the true value of the parameter, it is said to be unbiased.

2. Minimum variance—the smaller the variance of the estimate, the smaller the sample size required to obtain the level of accuracy desired, and the more efficient the estimator. The most efficient estimator is the estimator with minimum variance.

3. Consistency—as the sample size is increased, the value of the estimated parameter becomes closer to the true value of the parameter.

4. Sufficiency—the estimator uses all information available in the data set.

The method used to estimate parameters depends on the type of data or testing involved and the distribution of interest. In addition to the parameter estimation methods listed above, this section describes censored data and presents methods of parameter estimation for the exponential, normal, lognormal, Weibull, and gamma distribution. Methods are presented for complete and censored data.

Parameter estimation techniques are tedious, and computers are often employed to aid in data analysis. Dodson and Kirkland (1994) have developed a comprehensive software package for parameter estimation. The software is capable of maximum likelihood estimation, hazard plotting, probability plotting, and moment estimation. Available distributions are the exponential, Weibull, normal, lognormal, and gamma.

3.7.1 Censored data

A censored data set includes information on failed items and surviving items. Consider the data in Table 3.1. Eight items were placed on test stands. Three of the items failed, and five of the items were removed from testing without failing.

Table 3.1. Example of censored data.

Time to Fail	
35	60 +
45	60 +
55	60 +
60 +	60 +

Obviously, the sample average and the sample standard deviation for the three failed items cannot be used to estimate the parameters of the normal distribution in this case. The sample average is $(35 + 45 + 55)/3 = 45$. The time to fail for each of the remaining five items is greater than 60; the true sample average is considerably greater than 45.

Censoring is described many ways.

Type I Censoring—A test is initiated with a number of items, and the test is terminated after a predetermined time. An example would be to place 100 transistors on test stands and terminate testing after 1,000 hours regardless of the number of failures. This is also known as **time censoring**. In this case, the test time is fixed and the number of failures is the random variable.

Type II Censoring—A test is initiated with a number of items, and the test is terminated after a predetermined number of failures. An example would be to place 100 transistors on test stands and terminate testing after 30 failures regardless of the elapsed time. This is also known as **failure censoring** or **truncation**. In this case, the number of failures is fixed and the testing time is the random variable.

These examples above involve **right** censoring. An item is censored on the right if the failure time is not known, but it is known that the item survived to a known time without failure. If an item is known to be in a failed condition at or before a specific time, but the exact failure time is not known, it is **left** censored.

Single censoring occurs when there is only one censoring point. If 100 transistors are placed on test stands and the test is terminated after 1,000 hours, there is a single censoring point at 1,000 hours. If 20 transistors were removed without failure after 1,000 hours of testing and another 15 transistors were removed without failure after 1,200 hours of testing, there are two censoring points, and the resulting data are **multiple** censored. If exact failure times are not known, but the number of failures in a time interval is recorded, this is **interval** or **grouped data**.

3.7.2 Maximum likelihood estimation

Maximum likelihood is the most widely used method generating estimators. It is based on the principle of determining the parameter(s) value(s) that maximize(s) the probability of obtaining the sample data.

The likelihood function for a given distribution is a representation of the probability of obtaining the sample data. Let $x_1, x_2, ..., x_n$ be independent, random variables from the probability density function $f(x, \theta)$, where θ is the single distribution parameter. Then

$$L(x_1, x_2, ..., x_n; \theta) = f(x_1, \theta) f(x_2, \theta) ... f(x_n, \theta) \tag{3.83}$$

is the joint distribution of the random variables, or the **likelihood function**. The maximum likelihood estimate, $\hat{\theta}$, maximizes the likelihood function. This estimate is asymptotically normal. Often the natural logarithm of the likelihood function is maximized to simplify computations.

The variances of the estimates can be found by inverting the matrix of the negative of the second partial derivatives of the likelihood function, also known as the local information matrix. These estimates are asymptotically normal and the variances obtained from the local information matrix are used to calculate confidence intervals.

3.7.3 Hazard plotting

Hazard plotting is a graphical method of parameter estimation. The cumulative hazard function is transformed to a linear expression, usually by a logarithmic transformation, and plotted. The slope and the intercept of the plot provide the information needed to estimate the parameters of the distribution of interest.

If manually constructing a hazard plot, distribution-specific hazard paper is required. By using hazard paper, the failure times and cumulative hazard function estimates can be plotted directly. With the power of personal computers and electronic spreadsheets, specialized graph paper is no longer needed, as the necessary transformations can be made quickly and easily.

3.7.4 Probability plotting

Probability plotting is a graphical method of parameter estimation. For the assumed distribution, the cumulative distribution function is transformed to a linear expression, usually by a logarithmic transformation, and plotted. If the plotted points form a straight line, the assumed distribution is acceptable, and the slope and the intercept of the plot provide the information needed to estimate the parameters of the distribution of interest. The median rank is usually used to estimate the cumulative distribution function, although there are several alternatives such as the mean rank and the Kaplan-Meier product limit estimator.

If manually constructing a probability plot, distribution-specific probability paper is required. By using probability paper, the failure times and cumulative distribution function estimates can be plotted directly. With the power of personal computers and electronic spreadsheets specialized graph paper is no longer needed, as the necessary transformations can be made quickly and easily.

3.7.5 Moment estimation

Moment estimation is based on the concept of matching the moments of the sample data with the moments defined by the distribution of interest and its parameters. The first moment about the origin

$$E(x) = \begin{cases} \sum_{x} xf(x) & \text{if } x \text{ is discrete} \\ \int_{-\infty}^{\infty} xf(x)dx & \text{if } x \text{ is continuous} \end{cases}$$ (3.84)

is equal to the distribution mean. The second moment about the mean is equal to the distribution variance.

$$E\left[(x - \mu)^2\right] = \begin{cases} \sum_{x} x^2 f(x) - \mu^2 & \text{if } x \text{ is discrete} \\ \int_{-\infty}^{\infty} x^2 f(x)dx - \mu^2 & \text{if } x \text{ is continuous} \end{cases}$$ (3.85)

where μ is the distribution mean.

For some distributions, such as the normal distribution, these moments provide direct estimates of the parameters. For other distributions, such as the Weibull, lognormal and gamma, distribution parameters are estimated by setting the sample moments equal to the theoretical moments and solving for the distribution parameters. The number of moments needed is determined by the number of parameters being estimated. If the distribution has one parameter, this parameter can be estimated by setting Equation 3.84 equal to the sample mean and solving for the parameter. If three parameters are being estimated, three equations are required. The distribution skewness, which is the third moment about the mean, is used with the two equations given above.

3.7.6 Exponential distribution

The simplest method of parameter estimation for the exponential distribution is the method of maximum likelihood. Maximum likelihood provides an unbiased estimate, but provides no indication of goodness of fit. Graphical methods, while more involved, provide a visual goodness of fit test. Often graphical methods will be used in conjunction with maximum likelihood estimation.

3.7.6.1 Maximum likelihood estimation

The exponential probability density function is

$$f(x) = \frac{1}{\theta} e^{-t/\theta}, x \geq 0 \tag{3.86}$$

The maximum likelihood estimation for the parameter θ is

$$\hat{\theta} = \frac{\sum_{i=1}^{n} x_i}{r} \tag{3.87}$$

where: x_i is the ith data point; this may be a failure or a censoring point,

n is the total number of data points both censored and uncensored, and

r is the number of failures.

This estimate is unbiased and is the minimum variance estimator.

Example 3.20

The cycles to fail for seven springs are:

30,183	14,871	35,031	76,321
43,891	31,650	12,310	

Assuming an exponential time to fail distribution, estimate the mean time to fail and the mean failure rate.

Solution

The mean time to fail is

$$\hat{\theta} = \frac{30,183 + 14,871 + 35,031 + 76,321 + 43,891 + 31,650 + 12,310}{7}$$

$$= \frac{244,257}{7} = 34,893.9 \text{ cycles}$$

The mean failure rate is the inverse of the mean time to fail

$$\hat{\lambda} = \frac{1}{34,893.9} = 0.0000287 \text{ failures per cycle}$$

Example 3.21

Assume the data in Example 3.20 represents cycles to fail for seven springs, but an additional 10 springs were tested for 80,000 cycles without failure. Estimate the mean time to fail and the mean failure rate.

Solution

The mean time to fail is

$$\hat{\theta} = \frac{244{,}257 + 10(80{,}000)}{7} = 149{,}179.6 \text{ cycles}$$

The mean failure rate is

$$\lambda = \frac{1}{149{,}179.6} = 0.0000067 \text{ failures per cycle}$$

For a time truncated test a confidence interval for θ is

$$\frac{2\sum_{i=1}^{n} x_i}{\chi^2_{(\alpha/2, 2r+2)}} \le \theta \le \frac{2\sum_{i=1}^{n} x_i}{\chi^2_{(1-\alpha/2, 2r)}} \tag{3.88}$$

Note that the χ^2 degrees of freedom differ for the for the upper and lower limits.

Example 3.22

Fifteen items were tested for 1000 hours. Failures occurred at times 120 hours, 190 hours, 560 hours, and 812 hours. Construct a 90% confidence interval for the mean time to fail and the failure rate.

Solution

This is a time truncated test. The mean life estimate is

$$\hat{\theta} = \frac{120 + 190 + 560 + 812 + 11(1000)}{4} = \frac{12{,}682}{4} = 3{,}170.5$$

For a 90% confidence interval, $\alpha = 0.1$. From Appendix H, $\chi^2_{(0.05,10)} = 18.307$, and $\chi^2_{(0.95,8)} = 2.733$. The 90% confidence interval for θ is

$$\frac{2(12,682)}{18.307} \leq \theta \leq \frac{2(12,682)}{2.733}$$

$$1,385.5 \leq \theta \leq 9,280.6$$

The confidence interval for the failure rate is the inverse of the confidence interval for the mean time to fail.

$$\frac{1}{9,280.6} \leq \lambda \leq \frac{1}{1,385.5}$$

$$0.0001077 \leq \lambda \leq 0.0007217$$

For a failure truncated test a confidence interval for θ is

$$\frac{2\sum_{i=1}^{n} x_i}{\chi^2_{(\alpha/2,2r)}} \leq \theta \leq \frac{2\sum_{i=1}^{n} x_i}{\chi^2_{(1-\alpha/2,2r)}} \tag{3.89}$$

Note that the χ^2 degrees of freedom are the same for the for the upper and lower limits.

Example 3.23

Twelve items were tested with failures occurring at times of 43 hours, 67 hours, 92 hours 94 hours, and 149 hours. At a time of 149 hours, the testing was stopped for the remaining seven items. Construct a 95% confidence interval for the mean time to fail.

Solution

This is a failure truncated test. The mean life estimate is

$$\hat{\theta} = \frac{43 + 67 + 92 + 94 + 149 + 7(149)}{5} = \frac{1488}{5} = 297.6$$

For a 95% confidence interval, $\alpha = 0.05$. From Appendix H, $\chi^2_{(0.025,10)} = 20.483$, and $\chi^2_{(0.975,10)} = 3.247$. The 95% confidence interval for θ is

$$\frac{2(1488)}{20.483} \leq \theta \leq \frac{2(1488)}{3.247}$$

$$145.3 \leq \theta \leq 916.5$$

For failure free testing the one sided lower confidence limit simplifies to

$$\frac{-nt}{\ln \alpha} \leq \theta \tag{3.90}$$

where: t is the testing time,

  ln is the natural logarithm, and

  α is the significance ($\alpha = 0.05$ for a 95% limit).

Example 3.24

Twenty items are tested for 230 hours without failure. Determine a 90% lower confidence limit for θ.

Solution

$$\frac{-20(230)}{\ln(0.1)} = 1{,}997.8 \text{ hours}$$

A confidence interval for reliability is

$$e^{-\frac{x}{\theta_L}} \leq R(x) \leq e^{-\frac{x}{\theta_U}} \tag{3.91}$$

where: θ_L is the lower confidence limit for the mean time to file, and

  θ_U is the upper confidence limit for the mean time to fail.

A confidence interval for percentiles is

$$-\theta_L \ln(1-P) \leq x \leq -\theta_U \ln(1-P) \tag{3.92}$$

where: P is the probability of failure prior to time = x.

3.7.6.2 Hazard Plotting

The exponential cumulative hazard function is

$$H(x) = \frac{x}{\theta} \tag{3.93}$$

If a data set is exponentially distributed, a plot of Equation 3.93 yields a linear fit with a zero intercept and a slope of $1/\theta$. To construct a hazard plot, an estimate for $H(t)$ is needed. The cumulative hazard function is estimated by the cumulative of the inverse of the reverse ranks. For a data set of n points ordered from smallest to largest, the first point has a rank of n, the second $n-1$, etc.

Example 3.25

Construct a hazard plot for the data in Example 3.23.

Solution

Table 3.2 calculates the values necessary for the hazard plot. The plot is shown in Figure 3.27. Note that censored data points are not plotted. The slope of best fit straight line through the data with an intercept of zero is 0.00333. The estimated mean is $\theta = 1/0.00333 = 300.3$.

Table 3.2. Tabulations for an exponential hazard plot.

Time to Fail	Reverse Rank	$h(t)$	$H(t)$
43	12	0.0833	0.0833
67	11	0.0909	0.1742
92	10	0.1000	0.2742
94	9	0.1111	0.3854
149	8	0.1250	0.5104
149 c	7		
149 c	6		
149 c	5		
149 c	4		
149 c	3		
149 c	2		
149 c	1		

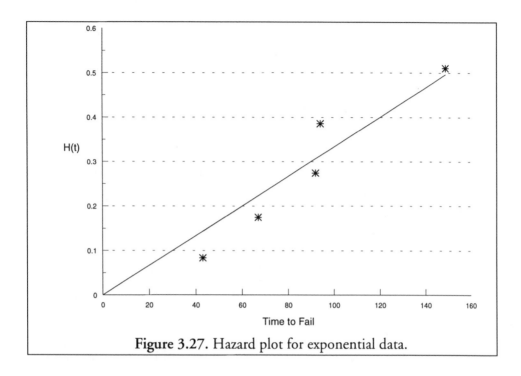

Figure 3.27. Hazard plot for exponential data.

3.7.6.3 Probability plotting

The exponential cumulative distribution function is

$$F(x) = 1 - e^{-\frac{x}{\theta}} \tag{3.94}$$

By manipulation this expression can be transformed to a linear expression

$$\ln\frac{1}{1 - F(x)} = \frac{x}{\theta} \tag{3.95}$$

If a data set follows an exponential distribution, a plot of

$$\ln\frac{1}{1 - F(x)}$$

versus x will be linear with a zero intercept and a slope of $1/\theta$. Before a plot can be constructed, an estimate for $F(x)$ is needed. The cumulative distribution function, $F(x)$, is usually estimated from the median rank, but other estimates such as the mean rank and the Kaplan-Meier product limit estimator are also used. The median rank estimate for $F(x)$ is

$$\hat{F}(x) = \frac{O_i - 0.3}{n + 0.4} \tag{3.96}$$

where O_i is the modified order of failure of the ith data point.

A modified order of failure is only needed if censored data is involved; if not the original order of failure, i, is equivalent to the modified order of failure. The logic for a modified order of failure is as follows. Consider three items; the first was tested for 3 hours and the test was stopped without failure, the second item was tested and failed after 4 hours, and the third item was tested and failed after 4.5 hours. For this data set the failure order is unclear. The first item could have been either the first failure, the second failure or the third failure; thus it is not certain that the first item to fail, the second item, is the first ordered failure. The modified order of failure is computed from the expression

$$O_i = O_{i-1} + I_i \tag{3.97}$$

where I_i is the increment for the ith failure, and is computed from the expression

$$I_i = \frac{(n+1) - O_p}{1 + c} \tag{3.98}$$

where: n is the total number of points in the data set, both censored and uncensored,

c is the number of points remaining in the data set including the current point,

O_p is the order of the previous failure.

An alternative to plotting x versus

$$\ln \frac{1}{1 - F(x)}$$

on conventional graph paper is to plot x versus $F(x)$ on specialized probability paper. The advantage of probability paper is that the values of

$$\ln \frac{1}{1-F(x)}$$

do not have to be computed. With electronic spreadsheets, the disadvantages of probability paper outweigh the advantages. Electronic spreadsheets with built-in statistical functions can quickly make data transformations, determine a best fit straight line using linear regression, and graph the results.

Example 3.26

Construct a probability plot for the data in Example 3.23.

Solution

Table 3.3 contains the calculations necessary for plotting. The probability plot is shown in Figure 3.28. The slope of the best fit straight line through the origin is 0.00304 which estimates the failure rate for the exponential distribution. The mean of the distribution is $\theta = 1/0.00304 = 328.9$.

Table 3.3. Tabulations for exponential probability plotting.

Time to Fail	I_i	O_i	Median Rank, $F(t)$	$\dfrac{1}{1-F(t)}$	$\ln\dfrac{1}{1-F(t)}$
43	1	1	0.0565	1.0598	0.0581
67	2	2	0.1371	1.1589	0.1475
92	3	3	0.2177	1.2784	0.2456
94	4	4	0.2984	1.4253	0.3544
149	5	5	0.3790	1.6104	0.4765
149 c					
149 c					
149 c					
149 c					
149 c					
149 c					
149 c					

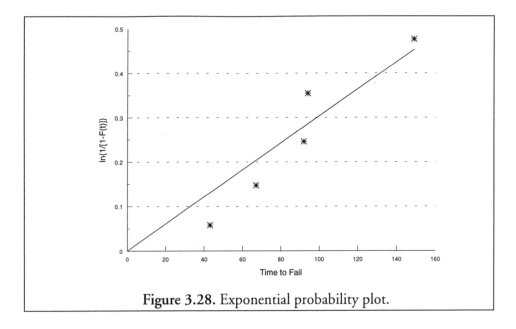

Figure 3.28. Exponential probability plot.

Often, reliability confidence limits are added to probability plots. Upper and lower confidence limits are approximated by 5% and 95% ranks. These ranks can be taken from the rank tables in Appendix C or calculated from the expressions

$$w_\alpha = \frac{\dfrac{j}{n-j+1}}{F_{1-\alpha,2(n-j+1),2j} + \dfrac{j}{n-j+1}}, \alpha \le 0.5 \tag{3.99}$$

$$w_\alpha = \frac{\dfrac{j}{n-j+1}F_{\alpha,2j,2(n-j+1)}}{1 + \dfrac{j}{n-j+1}F_{\alpha,2j,2(n-j+1)}}, \alpha > 0.5 \tag{3.100}$$

where w_α is the $100(1-\alpha)\%$ nonparametric confidence limit,
   j is the failure order,
   n is the total number of data points, both censored and uncensored, and
   $F_{\alpha,v1,v2}$ is the critical value from the F distribution.

When multiple censored data are encountered, the modified failure orders will not be integers, and the rank values will have to be interpolated. The rank values are not plotted against the corresponding failure time. Any deviation of the failure time from the best-fit straight line through the data is considered sampling error, and the time the rank values are plotted against is found by moving parallel to the *x*-axis until the best-fit straight line is intersected. This plotting position is

$$x_i = \theta \ln\left(\frac{1}{1 - F(x_i)}\right)$$

(3.101)

Example 3.27

Construct a probability plot for the previous example including confidence limits.

Solution

Table 3.4 shows the 5% and 95% ranks along with their plotting position for the previous example. A probability plot of this example including confidence limits is shown in Figure 3.29.

Table 3.4. Exponential probability plotting data including confidence limits.

Time to Fail	5% Rank	$\ln\frac{1}{1-5\%\text{Rank}}$	95% Rank	$\ln\frac{1}{1-95\%\text{Rank}}$	Plotting Time
43	0.0043	0.0043	0.2209	0.2496	19.1
67	0.0305	0.0310	0.3387	0.4135	48.5
92	0.0719	0.0746	0.4381	0.5764	80.8
94	0.1229	0.1311	0.5273	0.7493	116.6
149	0.1810	0.1997	0.6091	0.9393	156.7
149 c					
149 c					
149 c					
149 c					
149 c					
149 c					
149 c					

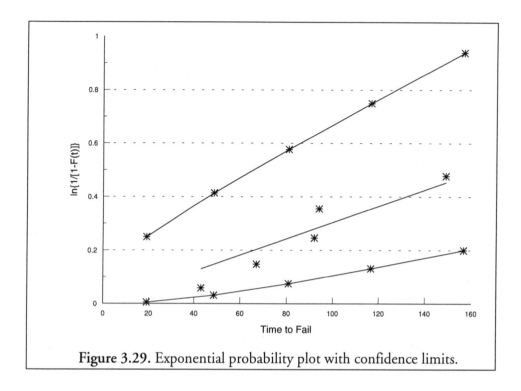

Figure 3.29. Exponential probability plot with confidence limits.

3.7.7 Normal distribution

The normal probability density function is

$$f(x) = \frac{1}{\sigma\sqrt{2\pi}} \exp\left[-\frac{1}{2}\left(\frac{x-\mu}{\sigma}\right)^2 \right], \quad -\infty < x < \infty \qquad (3.102)$$

where: μ is the distribution mean, and

σ is the distribution standard deviation.

If no censoring is involved, the distribution mean is estimated from the expression

$$\hat{\mu} = \bar{x} = \frac{\displaystyle\sum_{i=1}^{n} x_i}{n} \qquad (3.103)$$

where: n is the sample size.

If no censoring is involved, the distribution standard deviation is estimated from the expression

$$\hat{\sigma} = \sqrt{\frac{n\sum\limits_{i=1}^{n} x_i^2 - \left(\sum\limits_{i=1}^{n} x_i\right)^2}{n(n-1)}} \tag{3.104}$$

However, when censored data are involved, parameter estimation becomes complicated. Three popular methods for parameter estimation for the normal distribution when censored data are encountered are (1) maximum likelihood estimation, (2) hazard plotting, and (3) probability plotting. The following sections present each of these alternatives.

3.7.7.1 Maximum likelihood estimation

The maximum likelihood equations for the normal distribution are

$$\frac{\partial L}{\partial \mu} = \frac{r}{\sigma}\left[\frac{\bar{x} - \mu}{\sigma} + \sum_{i=1}^{k} \frac{h(x_i)}{r}\right] = 0 \tag{3.105}$$

$$\frac{\partial L}{\partial \sigma} = \frac{r}{\sigma}\left[\frac{s^2 + (\bar{x} - \mu)^2}{\sigma^2} - 1 + \sum_{i=1}^{k} \frac{z(x_i)h(x_i)}{r}\right] = 0 \tag{3.106}$$

where: r is the number of failures,
k is the number of censored observations,
$\bar{x}$ is the sample mean of the failures,
s is the sample standard deviation for the failures,
$z(x_i)$ is the standard normal deviate

$$z(x_i) = \frac{x_i - \mu}{\sigma}, \text{ and}$$

$h(x_i)$ is the hazard function evaluated at the ith point

$$h(x_i) = \frac{\phi(z(x_i))}{\sigma[1 - \Phi(z(x_i))]}$$

where: $\phi(z(x_i))$ is the standard normal probability density function evaluated at the ith point, and
$\Phi(z(x_i))$ is the standard normal cumulative distribution function evaluated at the ith point.

Note that if no censored data are involved these expressions reduce to the sample mean and the sample standard deviation.

Iterative techniques are necessary to solve Equations 3.105 and 3.106. A standard method based on Taylor series expansions involves repeatedly estimating the parameters until a desired level of accuracy is reached. Estimates of μ and σ are given by the expressions

$$\hat{\mu}_j = \hat{\mu}_{j-1} + h \tag{3.107}$$

$$\hat{\sigma}_j = \hat{\sigma}_{j-1} + k \tag{3.108}$$

where: h is a correction factor for the distribution mean, and

k is a correction factor for the distribution standard deviation.

For each iteration, the correction factors are estimated from the expressions

$$h\frac{\partial^2 L}{\partial \mu^2} + k\frac{\partial^2 L}{\partial \mu \partial \sigma} = -\frac{\partial L}{\partial \mu} \tag{3.109}$$

$$h\frac{\partial^2 L}{\partial \mu \partial \sigma} + k\frac{\partial^2 L}{\partial \sigma^2} = -\frac{\partial L}{\partial \sigma} \tag{3.110}$$

where,

$$\frac{\partial^2 L}{\partial \mu^2} = -\frac{r}{\sigma^2}\left[1 + \sum_{i=1}^{k}\frac{A_i}{r}\right] \tag{3.111}$$

$$\frac{\partial^2 L}{\partial \mu \partial \sigma} = -\frac{r}{\sigma^2}\left[\frac{2(\bar{x}-\mu)}{\sigma} + \sum_{i=1}^{k}\frac{B_i}{r}\right] \tag{3.112}$$

$$\frac{\partial^2 L}{\partial \sigma^2} = -\frac{r}{\sigma^2}\left[\frac{3\{s^2 + (\bar{x}-\mu)^2\}}{\sigma^2} - 1 + \sum_{i=1}^{k}\frac{C_i}{r}\right] \tag{3.113}$$

and

$$A_i = h(x_i)\left[h(x_i) - z(x_i)\right]$$

$$B_i = h(x_i) + z(x_i)A_i$$

$$C_i = z(x_i)\left[h(x_i) + B_i\right]$$

The estimated parameters are asymptotically normal. The variances of the estimates can be found by inverting the local information matrix.

$$F = \begin{bmatrix} -\dfrac{\partial^2 L}{\partial \mu^2} & -\dfrac{\partial^2 L}{\partial \mu \partial \sigma} \\[3mm] -\dfrac{\partial^2 L}{\partial \mu \partial \sigma} & -\dfrac{\partial^2 L}{\partial \sigma^2} \end{bmatrix} \tag{3.114}$$

After inversion, the variances are

$$F^{-1} = \begin{bmatrix} \mathrm{var}(\hat{\mu}) & \mathrm{cov}(\hat{\mu},\hat{\sigma}) \\ \mathrm{cov}(\hat{\mu},\hat{\sigma}) & \mathrm{var}(\hat{\sigma}) \end{bmatrix} \tag{3.115}$$

Approximate $(1-\alpha)100\%$ confidence intervals for the estimated parameters are

$$\hat{\mu} - K_{\alpha/2}\sqrt{\mathrm{var}(\hat{\mu})} \le \mu \le \hat{\mu} + K_{\alpha/2}\sqrt{\mathrm{var}(\hat{\mu})} \tag{3.116}$$

$$\frac{\hat{\sigma}}{\exp\left[\dfrac{K_{\alpha/2}\sqrt{\mathrm{var}(\hat{\sigma})}}{\hat{\sigma}}\right]} \le \sigma \le \hat{\sigma}\exp\left[\dfrac{K_{\alpha/2}\sqrt{\mathrm{var}(\hat{\sigma})}}{\hat{\sigma}}\right] \tag{3.117}$$

where $K_{\alpha/2}$ is the inverse of the standard normal probability density function.

These confidence intervals are approximate, but approach exactness as the sample size increases.

Confidence intervals for reliability can be found using the expressions

$$\mathrm{var}(\hat{z}) \approx \left(\frac{\mathrm{var}(\hat{\mu}) + \hat{z}^2\,\mathrm{var}(\hat{\sigma}) + 2\hat{z}\,\mathrm{cov}(\hat{\mu},\hat{\sigma})}{\hat{\sigma}^2} \right) \tag{3.118}$$

$$\hat{z} - K_{\alpha/2}\sqrt{\mathrm{var}(\hat{z})} \le z \le \hat{z} + K_{\alpha/2}\sqrt{\mathrm{var}(\hat{z})} \tag{3.119}$$

$$1 - \Phi\left(\hat{z} + K_{\alpha/2}\sqrt{\mathrm{var}(\hat{z})}\right) \le R(x) \le 1 - \Phi\left(\hat{z} - K_{\alpha/2}\sqrt{\mathrm{var}(\hat{z})}\right) \tag{3.120}$$

Confidence intervals for percentiles can be found using the expressions

$$\mathrm{var}(\hat{x}) \approx \mathrm{var}(\hat{\mu}) + \hat{z}^2\,\mathrm{var}(\hat{\sigma}) + 2\hat{z}\,\mathrm{cov}(\hat{\mu},\hat{\sigma}) \tag{3.121}$$

$$\hat{x} - K_{\alpha/2}\sqrt{\mathrm{var}(\hat{x})} \le x \le \hat{x} + K_{\alpha/2}\sqrt{\mathrm{var}(\hat{x})} \tag{3.122}$$

Maximum likelihood estimation is tedious and computer routines are often employed. Commercial software is available for these calculations, such as the software developed by Dodson and Kirkland (1994).

3.7.7.2 Hazard Plotting

The normal cumulative hazard function is

$$H(x) = -\ln\left[1 - \Phi\left(\frac{x - \mu}{\sigma}\right)\right] \tag{3.123}$$

where $\Phi(x)$ is the standard normal cumulative distribution function.

By rearranging Equation 3.123, the survival time can be represented as a function of the cumulative hazard function.

$$x = \mu + \sigma\Phi^{-1}\left[1 - e^{-H(x)}\right] \tag{3.124}$$

where $\Phi^{-1}(x)$ is the inverse of the standard normal cumulative distribution function.

It can be seen that by plotting x versus

$$\Phi^{-1}\left[1 - e^{-H(x)}\right]$$

the resulting y-intercept equals μ and the resulting slope equals σ. The hazard function, $h(x)$, is estimated from the inverse of the reverse rank of the ordered failures, and $H(x)$ is the cumulative of the values of $h(x)$. Censored data points are used to compute ranks, but are not included in hazard plots.

An alternative to plotting x versus

$$\Phi^{-1}\left[1 - e^{-H(x)}\right]$$

on conventional graph paper is to plot x versus $H(x)$ on specialized hazard paper. The advantage of hazard paper is that the values of

$$\Phi^{-1}\left[1 - e^{-H(x)}\right]^*$$

do not have to be computed. With sophisticated electronic spreadsheets, the disadvantages of hazard paper outweigh the advantages. Electronic spreadsheets with built-in statistical functions can quickly make data transformations, determine a best fit straight line using linear regression, and graph the results.

---

[*] If using Lotus 123™, the inverse of the standard normal distribution is found with the @function @normal(x,0,1,1).

Example 3.28

Use hazard plotting to determine the parameters of the normal distribution given the following multiple censored data set. A "c" following an entry indicates the censoring.

Time to Fail

150 c	183 c	235
157 c	209	235
167 c	216 c	248 c
179	217 c	257

Solution

Table 3.5 is constructed to obtain the necessary plotting data.

Table 3.5. Tabulations for a hazard plot for the normal distribution.

Time to Fail	Reverse Rank	$h(t)$	$H(t)$	$1-e^{-H(t)}$	$\Phi^{-1}\left[1-e^{-H(t)}\right]$
150 c	12				
157 c	11				
167 c	10				
179	9	0.1111	0.1111	0.1052	−1.2527
183 c	8				
209	7	0.1429	0.2540	0.2243	−0.7578
216 c	6				
217 c	5				
235	4	0.2500	0.5040	0.3959	−0.2640
235	3	0.3333	0.8373	0.5671	0.1691
248 c	2				
257	1	1.0000	1.8373	0.8408	0.9976

Now the five failure times can be plotted against

$$\Phi^{-1}\left[1-e^{-H(t)}\right].$$

This is shown in Figure 3.30. The best fit straight line through the data points was found using linear regression. The *y*-intercept of the best fit straight line through the five points provides an estimate of μ–230.3 in this case, and the slope of the line provides an estimate of σ–32.9 in this case.

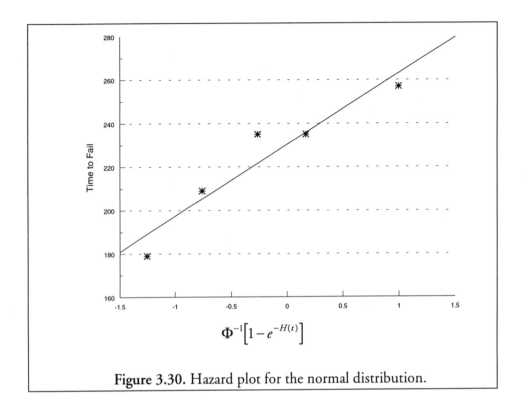

Figure 3.30. Hazard plot for the normal distribution.

3.7.7.3 Probability Plotting

By rearranging the normal cumulative distribution function, a linear expression can be obtained.

$$x = \mu + \sigma\Phi^{-1}[F(x)] \tag{3.125}$$

where: $F(x)$ is the normal cumulative distribution function, and

$\Phi^{-1}(x)$ is the inverse of the standard normal cumulative distribution function.

It can be seen that by plotting x versus

$$\Phi^{-1}[F(x)]$$

the resulting y-intercept equals μ and the resulting slope equals σ. The cumulative distribution function, $F(x)$, is usually estimated from the median rank, but other estimates such as the mean rank and the Kaplan-Meier product limit estimator are also used. Median ranks are estimated using Equations 3.96–3.98 in Section 3.7.6.3.

An alternative to plotting x versus

$$\Phi^{-1}[F(x)]$$

on conventional graph paper is to plot x versus $F(x)$ on specialized probability paper. The advantage of probability paper is that the values of

$$\Phi^{-1}[F(x)]$$

do not have to be computed. With sophisticated electronic spreadsheets, the disadvantages of hazard paper outweigh the advantages. Electronic spreadsheets with built-in statistical functions can quickly make data transformations, determine a best fit straight line using linear regression, and graph the results.

Example 3.29

Use probability plotting to determine the parameters of the normal distribution given the following data set. A "c" following an entry indicates the censoring.

	Time to Fail	
150 c	183 c	235
157 c	209	235
167 c	216 c	248 c
179	217 c	257

Solution

Table 3.6 is constructed to obtain the data for plotting. This data is plotted in Figure 3.31. The slope of this plot is 34.8, which is the estimated value of σ. The y-intercept is 235.3, which is the estimated value of μ.

Table 3.6. Tabulations for a probability plot for normal data.

Time to Fail	I_i	O_i	Median Rank, $F(x)$	$\Phi^{-1}[F(x)]$
150 c				
157 c				
167 c				
179	1.3000	1.3000	0.0806	−1.4008
183 c				
209	1.4625	2.7625	0.1986	−0.8467
216 c				
217 c				
235	2.0475	4.8100	0.3637	−0.3486
235	2.0475	6.8575	0.5288	0.0723
248 c				
257	3.0713	9.9288	0.7765	0.7605

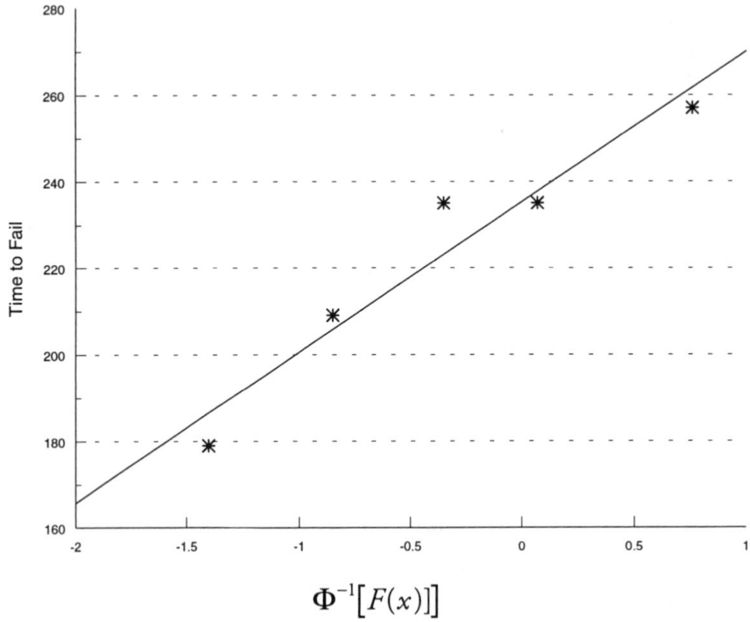

Figure 3.31. Normal probability plot.

Nonparametric confidence limits for reliability can be added to a normal probability plot using 5% and 95% ranks as explained in Section 3.7.6.3. The plotting position for the standard normal inverse of the 5% and 95% ranks is

$$x = \mu + \sigma\Phi^{-1}[F(x)]$$

(3.126)

Note that $F(x)$ is the median rank.

Example 3.30

Construct a probability plot including confidence limits for the previous example.

Solution

Table 3.7 contains the calculations to obtain the confidence limits and their plotting positions.

Table 3.7. Confidence limit calculations for a normal probability plot.

Time to Fail	Failure Order	Median Rank	$\Phi^{-1}[F(x)]$	5% Rank	Interpolated 5% Rank	Φ^{-1} 5% Rank	95% Rank	Interpolated 95% Rank	Φ^{-1} 95% Rank	Plotting Position
	1			0.0043			0.2209			
179	1.3	0.0806	−1.4008		0.0121	−2.2533		0.2562	−0.6550	186.55216
	2			0.0305			0.3387			
209	2.7625	0.1986	−0.8467		0.0620	−1.5379		0.4145	−0.2160	205.83484
	3			0.0719			0.4381			
	4			0.1229			0.5273			
235	4.81	0.3637	−0.3486		0.1700	−0.9543		0.5936	0.2368	223.16872
	5			0.1810			0.6091			
	6			0.2453			0.6848			
235	6.8575	0.5288	0.0723		0.3053	−0.5093		0.7447	0.6580	237.81604
	7			0.3152			0.7547			
	9			0.4727			0.8190			
257	9.9288	0.7765	0.7605		0.5555	0.1397		0.9204	1.4075	261.7654
	10			0.5619			0.9281			

A probability plot including confidence limits is shown in Figure 3.32.

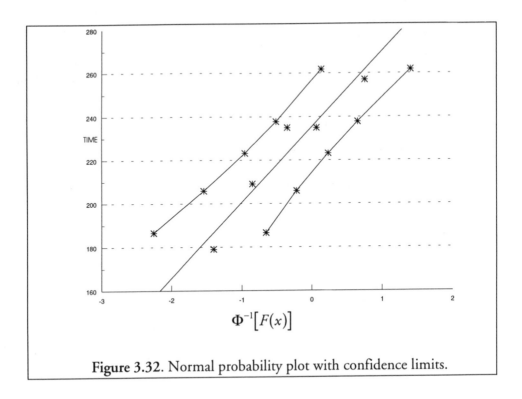

Figure 3.32. Normal probability plot with confidence limits.

3.7.8 Lognormal distribution

The lognormal probability density function is

$$f(x) = \frac{1}{\sigma x \sqrt{2\pi}} \exp\left[-\frac{1}{2}\left(\frac{\ln x - \mu}{\sigma}\right)^2\right], x > 0 \qquad (3.127)$$

where: μ is the location parameter, and
        σ is the shape parameter.

If x is a lognormally distributed random variable, then $y = \ln(x)$ is a normally distributed random variable. The location parameter is equal to the mean of the logarithm of the data points, and the shape parameter is equal to the standard deviation of the logarithm of the data points. Thus, the lognormal distribution does not have to be dealt with as a separate distribution. By taking the logarithm of the data points, the techniques developed for the normal distribution discussed in the previous section can be used to estimate the parameters of the lognormal distribution.

3.7.9 Weibull distribution

The Weibull probability density function is

$$f(x) = \frac{\beta x^{\beta-1}}{\theta^\beta} \exp\left(\frac{x}{\theta}\right)^\beta, x \geq 0 \tag{3.128}$$

where: β is the shape parameter, and
θ is the scale parameter.

In some cases, a three-parameter Weibull distribution provides a better fit than the two-parameter Weibull distribution. The difference in the two distributions is the location parameter, δ, which shifts the distribution along the x-axis. By definition, there is a zero probability of failure for $x < \delta$. Although unusual, the location can be negative; this implies that items were failed prior to testing. The three parameter Weibull distribution is

$$f(x) = \frac{\beta(x-\delta)^{\beta-1}}{\theta^\beta} \exp\left(\frac{x-\delta}{\theta}\right)^\beta, x \geq \delta \tag{3.129}$$

Four methods for estimating the parameters of the Weibull distribution are presented in this section: (1) maximum likelihood estimation, (2) hazard plotting, (3) probability plotting, and (4) matching moments.

3.7.9.1 Maximum likelihood estimation

The maximum likelihood equations for the Weibull distribution are

$$\frac{1}{r}\sum_{i=1}^{r}\ln(x_i) = \left[\sum_{i=1}^{n}x_i^\beta \ln(x_i)\right]\left[\sum_{i=1}^{n}x_i^\beta\right]^{-1} - \frac{1}{\beta} \tag{3.130}$$

$$\hat{\theta} = \left[\frac{1}{r}\sum_{i=1}^{n}x_i^{\hat{\beta}}\right]^{1/\hat{\beta}} \tag{3.131}$$

where: r is the number of failures, and
n is the total number of data points, both censored and uncensored.

Iterative techniques are required to solve Equation 3.130. The estimated parameters are asymptotically normal. The variances of the estimates can be found by inverting the local information matrix. The local information matrix is

$$
F = \begin{bmatrix} -\dfrac{\partial^2 L}{\partial \beta^2} & -\dfrac{\partial^2 L}{\partial \beta \partial \theta} \\[2ex] -\dfrac{\partial^2 L}{\partial \beta \partial \theta} & -\dfrac{\partial^2 L}{\partial \theta^2} \end{bmatrix}
\tag{3.132}
$$

The second partial derivatives of the log-likelihood equation are

$$
\frac{\partial^2 L}{\partial \beta^2} = \sum_r \left[-\frac{1}{\beta} - \left(\frac{x_i}{\theta}\right)^{\beta} \ln^2\left(\frac{x_i}{\theta}\right) \right] + \sum_k \left[-\left(\frac{x_i}{\theta}\right)^{\beta} \ln^2\left(\frac{x_i}{\theta}\right) \right]
\tag{3.133}
$$

$$
\frac{\partial^2 L}{\partial \theta^2} = \sum_r \left[\frac{\beta}{\theta^2} - \left(\frac{x_i}{\theta}\right)^{\beta}\left(\frac{\beta}{\theta^2}\right)(\beta+1) \right] + \sum_k \left[-\left(\frac{x_i}{\theta}\right)^{\beta}\left(\frac{\beta}{\theta^2}\right)(\beta+1) \right]
\tag{3.134}
$$

$$
\frac{\partial^2 L}{\partial \beta \partial \theta} = \sum_r \left\{ -\frac{1}{\theta} + \left(\frac{x_i}{\theta}\right)^{\beta}\left(\frac{1}{\theta}\right)\left[\beta \ln\left(\frac{x_i}{\theta}\right) + 1 \right] \right\}
$$
$$
+ \sum_k \left\{ \left(\frac{x_i}{\theta}\right)^{\beta}\left(\frac{1}{\theta}\right)\left[\beta \ln\left(\frac{x_i}{\theta}\right) + 1 \right] \right\}
\tag{3.135}
$$

where: $\displaystyle\sum_r$ represents summation over all failures, and

$\displaystyle\sum_k$ represents summation over all censored points.

The variances of the estimated parameters are

$$
F^{-1} = \begin{bmatrix} \operatorname{var}(\hat{\beta}) & \operatorname{cov}(\hat{\beta},\hat{\theta}) \\ \operatorname{cov}(\hat{\beta},\hat{\theta}) & \operatorname{var}(\hat{\theta}) \end{bmatrix}
\tag{3.136}
$$

Approximate $(1-\alpha)100\%$ confidence intervals for the estimated parameters are

$$\frac{\hat{\beta}}{\exp\left(\dfrac{K_{\alpha/2}\sqrt{\text{var}(\hat{\beta})}}{\hat{\beta}}\right)} \le \beta \le \hat{\mu} + \hat{\beta}\exp\left(\frac{K_{\alpha/2}\sqrt{\text{var}(\hat{\beta})}}{\hat{\beta}}\right) \tag{3.137}$$

$$\frac{\hat{\theta}}{\exp\left[\dfrac{K_{\alpha/2}\sqrt{\text{var}(\hat{\theta})}}{\hat{\theta}}\right]} \le \theta \le \hat{\theta}\exp\left[\frac{K_{\alpha/2}\sqrt{\text{var}(\hat{\theta})}}{\hat{\theta}}\right] \tag{3.138}$$

where $K_{\alpha/2}$ is the inverse of the standard normal probability density function.

These confidence intervals are approximate, but approach exactness as the sample size increases.

Confidence intervals for reliability can be found using the expressions

$$\exp\left[-\exp\left(u + K_{a/2}\sqrt{\text{var}(u)}\right)\right]$$
$$\le R(x) \le \exp\left[-\exp\left(u - K_{a/2}\sqrt{\text{var}(u)}\right)\right] \tag{3.139}$$

$$u = \beta[\ln(x) - \ln(\theta)] \tag{3.140}$$

$$\text{var}(\hat{u}) \approx \beta^2\left[\left(\frac{\text{var}(\hat{\theta})}{\hat{\theta}^2}\right) + \left(\frac{\hat{u}^2\,\text{var}(\hat{\beta})}{\beta^4}\right) - \left(\frac{2\hat{u}\,\text{cov}(\hat{\beta},\hat{\theta})}{\hat{\beta}^2\hat{\theta}}\right)\right] \tag{3.141}$$

Confidence intervals for percentiles can be found using the expressions

$$e^{y_L} \le \hat{x} \le e^{y_U} \tag{3.142}$$

$$\hat{x} = \hat{\theta}\left[-\ln(1-p)\right]^{1/\hat{\beta}} \tag{3.143}$$

$$y_L = \ln\hat{\theta} + \frac{\ln\left[-\ln(1-p)\right]}{\hat{\beta}} - K_\alpha\sqrt{\text{var}(\hat{y})} \tag{3.144}$$

$$y_U = \ln\hat{\theta} + \frac{\ln\left[-\ln(1-p)\right]}{\hat{\beta}} + K_\alpha\sqrt{\text{var}(\hat{y})} \tag{3.145}$$

$$\mathrm{var}(\hat{y}) = \frac{\mathrm{var}(\hat{\theta})}{\hat{\theta}^2} + \frac{\left\{\ln\left[-\ln(1-p)\right]\right\}^2 \mathrm{var}(\hat{\beta})}{\beta^4}$$

$$-\frac{2\left\{\ln\left[-\ln(1-p)\right]\right\}\mathrm{cov}(\hat{\theta},\hat{\beta})}{\hat{\beta}^2\hat{\theta}}$$

(3.146)

Maximum likelihood estimation is tedious and computer routines are often employed. Commercial software is available for these calculations, such as the software developed by Dodson and Kirkland (1994).

3.7.9.2 Hazard Plotting

The Weibull cumulative hazard function is

$$H(x) = -\ln[1 - F(x)]$$

(3.147)

Replacing $F(x)$ and rearranging gives a linear expression.

$$\ln H(x) = \beta \ln x - \beta \ln \theta$$

(3.148)

By plotting $\ln H(x)$ versus $\ln x$ the resulting slope (censored points are not plotted) provides an estimate of β. The y-intercept of this plot is an estimate of $\beta \ln \theta$. Thus, θ is estimated from the expression

$$\hat{\theta} = \exp\left(-\frac{y_0}{\hat{\beta}}\right)$$

(3.149

where, y_0 is the y-intercept of the hazard plot.

The hazard function $h(x)$ is estimated from the inverse of the reverse rank of the ordered failures; and the cumulative hazard function, $H(x)$, is the cumulative of the values of $h(x)$. An alternative to plotting $\ln H(x)$ versus $\ln x$ is to directly plot $H(x)$ versus x on specialized Weibull hazard paper. The advantage of hazard paper is that logarithmic transformations do not have to be computed. With electronic spreadsheets, these transformations are easily computed, and hazard paper is not needed. Electronic spreadsheets also make fitting a straight line through the data points and constructing the graph easier.

Example 3.31

Determine the parameters of the Weibull distribution using the multiple censored data in the table below. A "c" following an entry indicates censoring.

Time to Fail	
309 c	229
386	104 c
180	217 c
167 c	168
122	138

Solution

Table 3.8 is constructed to obtain the necessary plotting data.

Table 3.8. Tabulations for a hazard plot for the Weibull distribution.

Time to Fail	Reverse Rank	$h(t)$	$H(t)$	$\ln H(t)$	$\ln t$
104 c	10				
122	9	0.1111	0.1111	-2.1972	4.8040
138	8	0.1250	0.2361	-1.4435	4.9273
167 c	7				
168	6	0.1667	0.4028	-0.9094	5.1240
180	5	0.2000	0.6028	-0.5062	5.1930
217 c	4				
229	3	0.3333	0.9361	-0.0660	5.4337
309 c	2				
386	1	1.0000	1.9361	0.6607	5.9558

Now the final two columns of Table 3.8 can be plotted. This plot is shown in Figure 3.33. The slope of the best-fit straight line through the data (found by linear regression) is equal to 2.34 and provides an estimate of β. The y-intercept of the best-fit straight line through the data is −13.004. The estimated scale parameter for the Weibull distribution is

$$\hat{\theta} = \exp\left(-\frac{-13.004}{2.34}\right) = 259.1$$

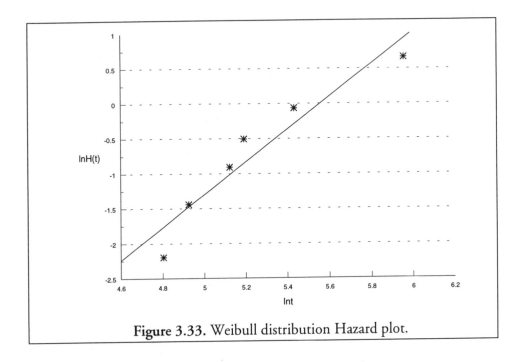

Figure 3.33. Weibull distribution Hazard plot.

3.7.9.3 Probability Plotting

By taking the logarithm of the Weibull cumulative distribution function twice and rearranging,

$$\ln\left[\ln\left(\frac{1}{1-F(x)}\right)\right] = \beta \ln x - \beta \ln\theta \tag{3.150}$$

By plotting

$$\ln\left[\ln\left(\frac{1}{1-F(x)}\right)\right]$$

versus $\ln x$, and fitting a straight line to the points, the parameters of the Weibull distribution can be estimated. The slope of the plot provides an estimate of β, and the y-intercept can be used to estimate θ.

$$\hat{\theta} = \exp\left(-\frac{y_0}{\hat{\beta}}\right) \tag{3.151}$$

The cumulative distribution function, $F(x)$, is usually estimated from the median rank, but other estimates such as the mean rank and the Kaplan-Meier product limit estimator are also used. Median ranks are estimated using Equations 3.96–3.98 in Section 3.7.6.3. Specialized probability paper is available for probability plotting. Using probability paper eliminates the need to transform the data prior to plotting, but this hardly seems necessary with the availability and speed of electronic spreadsheets.

Example 3.32

Determine the parameters of the Weibull distribution using probability plotting for the data in Example 3.31.

Solution

Table 3.9 is constructed to obtain the necessary plotting data.

Table 3.9. Tabulations for a probability plot for the Weibull distribution.

Time to Fail	I_i	O_i	Median Rank, $\hat{F}(t)$	$\ln\left[\ln\left(\dfrac{1}{1-F(t)}\right)\right]$	$\ln t$
104 c					
122	1.1000	1.1000	0.0769	−2.5252	4.8040
138	1.1000	2.2000	0.1827	−1.6008	4.9273
167 c					
168	1.2571	3.4571	0.3036	−1.0167	5.1240
180	1.2571	4.7143	0.4245	−0.5934	5.1930
217 c					
229	1.5714	6.2857	0.5755	−0.1544	5.4337
309 c					
386	2.3571	8.6429	0.8022	0.4827	5.9558

The last two columns of Table 3.9 are plotted in Figure 3.34. The slope of the best-fit straight line through the data (found using linear regression) is 2.41, which is the estimated value of β. The y-intercept of the best-fit straight line through the data is −13.55. The estimated shape parameter is

$$\hat{\theta} = \exp\left(-\frac{-13.55}{2.41}\right) = 276.6$$

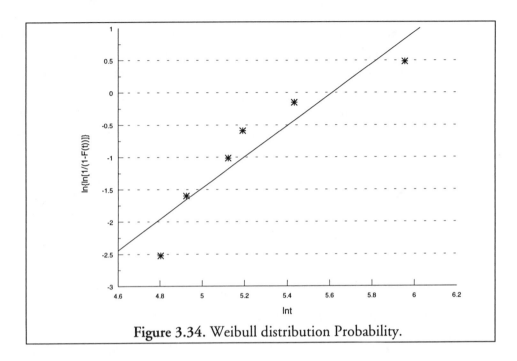

Figure 3.34. Weibull distribution Probability.

Confidence limits can be added to this plot using 5% and 95% ranks as described in Section 3.7.6.3. Plotting position for the 5% and 95% ranks are found from the expression

$$x_i = \theta \left[\ln \left(\frac{1}{1 - F(x)} \right) \right]^{1/\beta} \tag{3.152}$$

3.7.9.4 Matching Moments

The mean of the Weibull distribution is defined as

$$\mu = \theta \Gamma \left(1 + \frac{1}{\beta} \right) \tag{3.153}$$

The variance of the Weibull distribution is

$$\sigma^2 = \theta^2 \left[\Gamma \left(1 + \frac{1}{\beta} \right) - \Gamma^2 \left(1 + \frac{1}{\beta} \right) \right] \tag{3.154}$$

The parameters of the Weibull distribution can be found by equating the two equations above to the sample mean and sample variance of a data set.

Example 3.33

Determine the parameters of the Weibull distribution by matching moments for the following failure times; 34, 56, 71, 43, and 99.

Solution

The sample mean of the five failure times is 60.6, and the sample variance is 655.3. By matching moments, the following two expressions are obtained

$$60.6 = \theta\Gamma\left(1 + \frac{1}{\beta}\right)$$

$$655.3 = \theta^2\Gamma\left[\Gamma\left(1 + \frac{1}{\beta}\right) - \Gamma^2\left(1 + \frac{1}{\beta}\right)\right]$$

Solving these two expressions simultaneously gives approximate values of 2.54 as an estimate of β and 68.3 as an estimate of θ.

3.7.10 Goodness of fit

Before applying a distribution, a test of fit should be applied. There are many goodness-of-fit tests. Some are distribution specific, and some are general. Two popular goodness-of-fit tests, the chi-square test and the Kolmogorov-Smirnov test are of limited value for reliability analysis. The chi-square test requires a large sample size ($n \geq 25$) and cannot be used with multiple censored data, and the Kolmogorov-Smirnov test generally has less power than distribution specific tests.

A general goodness-of-fit test that can be used with multiple censored data is the Hollander-Proschan test. This test is best illustrated with an example. Consider the data in Table 3.10. It is believed that this data follows a Weibull time to fail distribution, and maximum likelihood estimates for the shape and scale parameters are 2.974 and 203.3.

Table 3.10. Example data for goodness-of-fit.

Time to Fail			
42.1 +	105.9	151.3 +	195.6 +
77.8	117.0	157.3	207.0
83.3 +	126.9	163.8	215.3 +
88.7 +	138.7	177.2 +	217.4
101.8	148.9	194.3 +	258.8 +

A + following an observation indicates the item was removed from testing prior to failure.

To test if the Weibull distribution with shape and scale parameters of 2.974 and 203.3 adequately fit this data, follow the steps below.

1. For each **uncensored** observation, use the Kaplan-Meier product limit method to estimate reliability. The Kaplan-Meier reliability estimate is

$$\hat{R}(x_i) = \prod_{i=1}^{i}\left(\frac{n-i}{n-i+1}\right)^{Q_i}$$

(3.155)

   where: Q_i = 1 for uncensored data and 0 for censored data, and
   n is the sample size including both censored and uncensored observations.

2. For each observation and the final observation, uncensored or not, compute the jump of the Kaplan-Meier reliability estimate. The jump for censored observations is zero with the exception of the final observation. The Kaplan-Meier jump is

$$\hat{f}(x_i) = \frac{1}{n}\prod_{j=1}^{i-1}\left(\frac{n-j+1}{n-j}\right)^{1-Q_j}$$

(3.156)

   With the exception of the final observation, if it is censored, the Kaplan-Meier jump can also be estimated from the expression

$$\hat{f}(x_i) = \hat{R}(x_p) - \hat{R}(x_i)$$

(3.157)

   where $\hat{R}(x_p)$ is the Kaplan-Meier reliability estimate for the most previous uncensored point.

3. Calculate the reliability for every observation using the distribution being tested for goodness of fit. For this example, the reliability expression is

$$R_0(x) = e^{-\left(\frac{x}{203.3}\right)^{2.974}}$$

4. For every observation, compute the product of the Kaplan-Meier reliability estimate and the Kaplan-Meier jump.
5. For every observation, raise the reliability computed for the distribution being tested for goodness of fit to the fourth power.
6. For every observation, calculate the difference between reliability using the distribution being tested for goodness of fit for the previous point and the current point. For the first observation this is equal to one minus the reliability using the distribution being tested for goodness of fit.
7. For every observation, multiple the value obtained in step 6 by $n/(n-i+1)$.

The calculations in steps 1–7 are summarized in Table 3.11.

Table 3.11. Summary calculations for steps 1–7.

a Order	b x		c $\frac{n-i}{n-i+1}$	d $\hat{R}(x)$	e Jump	f $R_0(x)$	g $(e)*(f)$	h $R_0^4(x)$	i $R_0^4(x_{i-1})$ $- R_0^4(x_i)$	j $\frac{n-i}{n-i+1}*(i)$
1	42.1	c			0.0000	0.9908	0.0000	0.9637	0.0363	0.0363
2	77.8		0.9474	0.9474	0.0526	0.9442	0.0497	0.7947	0.1690	0.1779
3	83.3	c			0.0000	0.9320	0.0000	0.7546	0.0401	0.0445
4	88.7	c			0.0000	0.9186	0.0000	0.7122	0.0424	0.0499
5	101.8		0.9375	0.8882	0.0592	0.8800	0.0521	0.5997	0.1125	0.1406
6	105.9		0.9333	0.8289	0.0592	0.8661	0.0513	0.5627	0.0370	0.0494
7	117.0		0.9286	0.7697	0.0592	0.8242	0.0488	0.4614	0.1013	0.1447
8	126.9		0.9231	0.7105	0.0592	0.7818	0.0463	0.3735	0.0879	0.1352
9	138.7		0.9167	0.6513	0.0592	0.7256	0.0430	0.2772	0.0963	0.1605
10	148.9		0.9091	0.5921	0.0592	0.6729	0.0398	0.2051	0.0721	0.1312
11	151.3	c			0.0000	0.6601	0.0000	0.1899	0.0152	0.0305
12	157.3		0.8889	0.5263	0.0658	0.6273	0.0413	0.1549	0.0350	0.0778

Continued on next page...

Table 3.11. —*continued...*

a	b	c $\dfrac{n-i}{n-i+1}$	d $\hat{R}(x)$	e Jump	f $R_0(x)$	g (e)*(f)	h $R_0^A(x)$	i $R_0^A(x_{i-1})$ $- R_0^A(x_i)$	j $\dfrac{n-i}{n-i+1}*(i)$
Order	x								
13	163.8		0.8750	0.4605	0.0658	0.5910	0.0389	0.1220	0.0329	0.0822
14	177.2 c				0.0000	0.5145	0.0000	0.0701	0.0519	0.1483
15	194.3 c				0.0000	0.4173	0.0000	0.0303	0.0398	0.1325
16	195.6 c				0.0000	0.4100	0.0000	0.0283	0.0021	0.0082
17	207.0		0.7500	0.3454	0.1151	0.3482	0.0401	0.0147	0.0136	0.0679
18	215.3 c				0.0000	0.3055	0.0000	0.0087	0.0060	0.0399
19	217.4		0.5000	0.1727	0.1727	0.2950	0.0509	0.0076	0.0011	0.0113
20	258.8 c				0.1727	0.1287	0.0222	0.0003	0.0073	0.1460
							0.5244			1.8147

8. The sum of column g is designated as C, and the sum of column j is designated as Y. For this example, $C = 0.5244$ and $Y = 1.8147$.

9. Estimate the standard deviation of C using the expression

$$\hat{\sigma} = \sqrt{\frac{Y}{16}} \qquad (3.158)$$

For this example,

$$\hat{\sigma} = \sqrt{\frac{1.8147}{16}} = 0.3368$$

Note that C is approximately standard normally distributed.

10. Calculate the statistic

$$C^* = \frac{\sqrt{n}(C - 0.5)}{\hat{\sigma}} \qquad (3.159)$$

where n is the total number of observations, censored and uncensored. For this example,

$$C^* = \frac{\sqrt{20}(0.5244 - 0.5)}{0.3368} = 0.3240$$

11. Determine if C^* falls in the acceptable region of the test. For a significance of $\alpha = 0.05$, the acceptable region is $\pm z_{\alpha/2} = \pm 1.96$. For this example, the calculated statistic falls within the acceptable region, and the Weibull distribution with a shape parameter of 2.974 and a scale parameter of 203.3 is considered an adequate model for the data.

3.8 Bayes' probability analysis

The probability of event B_r occurring, given event A has occurred, can be computed using Bayes' theorem

$$P(B_r \setminus A) = \frac{P(B_r)P(A \setminus B_r)}{\sum_{i=1}^{k} P(B_i)P(A \setminus B_i)}, r = 1, 2, ..., k \qquad (3.160)$$

where $B_1, B_2, ..., B_k$ are mutually exclusive events that make up the total sample space, S, and A is an event such that $P(A) \neq 0$.

Example 3.34

Three jars, 1, 2, and 3, each contain two marbles. Jar 1 contains two red marbles, jar 2 contains one red marble and one blue marble, and jar 3 contains two blue marbles. A marble is randomly selected from a randomly selected jar and it is red; what is the probability that the other marble in the same jar is also red?

Solution

The solution is the probability that jar 1 was selected given that a red marble was selected, $P(\text{jar } 1 \setminus \text{red marble})$. Using Bayes' theorem, this can be expressed mathematically as

$$P(\text{jar } 1 \setminus \text{red marble}) = \frac{P(\text{jar } 1)P(\text{red marble} \setminus \text{jar } 1)}{\sum_{i=1}^{3} P(\text{jar } i)P(\text{red marble} \setminus \text{jar } i)}$$

Since there are three jars, the probability of selecting each of the jars, $P(\text{jar } i)$, is 1/3. Given that jar 1 is selected, the probability of selecting a red marble, $P(\text{red marble} \setminus \text{jar } 1)$, is 1. Given that jar 2 is selected, the probability of selecting a red marble, $P(\text{red marble} \setminus \text{jar } 2)$, is 1/2. Given that jar 3 is selected, the probability of selecting a red marble, $P(\text{red marble} \setminus \text{jar } 3)$, is 0. Thus,

$$P(\text{jar } 1 \backslash \text{red marble}) = \frac{\left(\frac{1}{3}\right)(1)}{\left(\frac{1}{3}\right)(1)+\left(\frac{1}{3}\right)\left(\frac{1}{2}\right)+\left(\frac{1}{3}\right)(0)} = \frac{2}{3}$$

A more specific depiction of Bayes' theorem which is often used in reliability is

$$P(A \backslash B) = \frac{P(A \cap B)}{P(B)} \tag{3.161}$$

where A and B are events. If A and B represent the probability of survival to specific times, then the intersection of the two events is the probability of survival to the largest time. Rewriting this expression for reliability,

$$R(t_2 \backslash t_1) = \frac{R(t_2)}{R(t_1)}, t_2 > t_1 \tag{3.162}$$

Example 3.35

The probability of a system surviving until time = 25 is 0.68. The probability of the same system surviving until time = 50 is 0.39. At time = 25 the system is still functional. What is the probability the system will survive until time = 50?

Solution

The probability of survival until time = 50 given survival until time = 25 is

$$R(50 \backslash 25) = \frac{0.39}{0.68} = 0.5735$$

In the above examples, previously known information, such as the color of marbles in each box, was known. This information is known as a **prior** distribution. Bayesian analysis uses the prior distribution along with joint probability density functions to compute the **posterior** distribution, which yields probabilities of events occurring given that other events have occurred.

The posterior probability density function, given survival until t_1 is

$$f(t \setminus t_1) = \frac{f(t)}{R(t_1)}, \quad t_1 < t \tag{3.163}$$

The posterior reliability function, given survival until t_1 is

$$R(t \setminus t_1) = \frac{R(t)}{R(t_1)}, \quad t_1 < t \tag{3.164}$$

Suppose a component has a Weibull time to fail distribution with a shape parameter of 4 and a scale parameter of 100 weeks. Also, suppose that this component has survived for 85 weeks. The **prior** distribution is simply the Weibull distribution with a shape parameter of 4 and a scale parameter of 100 weeks. The **posterior** distribution is derived from the prior distribution given that the component has survived for 85 weeks. The prior and posterior probability density functions for this example are shown in Figure 3.35. The prior and posterior reliability functions for this example are shown in Figure 3.36.

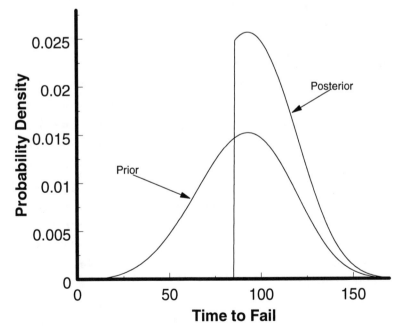

Figure 3.35. Prior and posterior density functions.

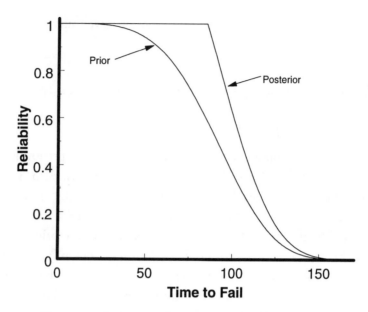

Figure 3.36. Prior and posterior reliability functions.

3.9 Propagation of errors

How can an engineer predict the reliability of the system being designed? A finished product may be a combination of many individual components. And even without the recent emphasis on reduced product development times, it may be infeasible to build prototypes for the purpose of reliability testing. Since statistical information may be available for individual components, the problem is to model the behavior of the system through statistical knowledge of its components. When a variable is a function of several other variables, $y = f(x_1, x_2, \ldots, x_n)$, the procedure of determining the variability of y from knowledge of the variables, $x_1, x_2, \ldots, x_n$, is called **propagation of error**.

This section describes methods for modeling combinations of random variables. The discussion is broken into three parts:

1. properties of means and variances of functions of several variables
2. combinations of random variables that form known distributions, and
3. transformation of random variables.

3.9.1 Properties of means and variances of functions of several variables

Table 3.12 gives the mean and variance for functions of several variables.

Table 3.12. Means and variances of functions of several variables.

Function	Mean	Variance
$y = ax$	$E(y) = aE(x)$	$V(y) = a^2 V(x)$
$y = a + x$	$E(y) = a + E(x)$	$V(y) = V(x)$
$y = x_1 + x_2$	$E(y) = E(x_1) + E(x_2)$	$V(y) = V(x_1) + V(x_2)*$
$y = x_1 - x_2$	$E(y) = E(x_1) - E(x_2)$	$V(y) = V(x_1) + V(x_2)*$
$y = x^2$	$E(y) = [E(x)]^2 + V(x)$	$V(y) = E(x^4) - [E(x^2) + V(x)]^2$
$y = x_1 x_2$	$E(y) = E(x_1)E(x_2)*$	$V(y) = V(x_1)V(x_2) + V(x_2)[E(x_1)]^2 + V(x_1)[E(x_2)]^2 *$
$y = \dfrac{x_1}{x_2}$	$E(y) = E(x_1)E\left(\dfrac{1}{x_2}\right)$	$V(y) = [V(x_1) + E^2(x_1)]E\left(\dfrac{1}{x_2^2}\right) - E^2(x_1)E^2\left(\dfrac{1}{x_2}\right)$

* x_1 and x_2 are independent.

Example 3.36

Determine the expected area and the variance of the area of a rectangle with sides x and y. The variable x is normally distributed with a mean of 20 and a standard deviation of 4; the variable y is normally distributed with a mean of 60 and a standard deviation of 8.

Solution

From Table 3.12, the expected value of the area, $z = xy$ is

$$E(\text{area}) = E(x)E(y) = (20)(60) = 1200$$

The variance of the area is

$$V(\text{area}) = (4^2)(8^2) + (8^2)(20^2) + (4^2)(60^2) = 84{,}224$$

A useful approximation for the mean of a function of several variables is

$$E(y) \approx f(x_1, x_2, \ldots, x_n) + \frac{1}{2}\sum_{i=1}^{n} \frac{\partial^2 f(x_1, x_2, \ldots, x_n)}{\partial x_i^2} V(x_i) \qquad (3.165)$$

The second term of this expression is often ignored, leaving the approximation as

$$E(y) \approx f(x_1, x_2, ..., x_n)$$ (3.166)

A useful approximation for the variance of a function of several variables is

$$V(y) \approx \sum_{i=1}^{n} \left(\frac{\partial f(x_x, x_2, ..., x_n)}{\partial x_i} \right)^2 V(x_i)$$ (3.167)

Example 3.37

The current in a circuit is defined as

$$I = \frac{V}{R}$$

where V is the voltage and R is the resistance. Find the mean current and the variance of the current if the mean voltage is 220 with a standard deviation of 5, and the mean resistance is 4 with a standard deviation of 0.2

Solution

From Equation 3.166,

$$E(I) \approx f(V,R) \approx \frac{220}{4} = 55$$

To utilize Equation 3.167, the partial derivatives of the expression for current are needed.

$$\frac{\partial f}{\partial V} = \frac{1}{R}$$

$$\frac{\partial f}{\partial R} = -\frac{V}{R^2}$$

The approximated variance is

$$V(I) = \left(\frac{1}{4} \right)^2 (5^2) + \left(-\frac{220}{4^2} \right)^2 (0.2^2) = 9.12$$

3.9.2 Combinations of random variables that form well-known distributions

The sum or difference of normally distributed variables is also normally distributed. If x_1 and x_2 are normally distributed with means μ_{x1} and μ_{x2}, and variances σ_{x1}^2 and σ_{x2}^2, then $y = x_1 + x_2$ is normally distributed with a mean of

$$E(y) = \mu_{x1} + \mu_{x2} \tag{3.168}$$

and a variance of

$$V(y) = \sigma_{x1}^2 + \sigma_{x2}^2 + 2\rho\sigma_{x1}\sigma_{x2} \tag{3.169}$$

where ρ is the correlation coefficient, and is defined as

$$\rho = \frac{\text{cov}(x_1, x_2)}{\sigma_{x1}, \sigma_{x2}} \tag{3.170}$$

where $\text{cov}(x_1, x_2)$ is the covariance between variables x_1 and x_2 and is defined as

$$\text{cov}(x_1, x_2) = \int_{-\infty}^{\infty}\int_{-\infty}^{\infty} (x_1 - \mu_1)(x_2 - \mu_2) f(x_1, x_2) dx_1 dx_2 \tag{3.171}$$

The value, $y = x_1 - x_2$, is also normally distributed with a mean of

$$E(y) = \mu_{x1} - \mu_{x2} \tag{3.172}$$

and a variance of

$$V(y) = \sigma_{x1}^2 + \sigma_{x2}^2 - 2\rho\sigma_{x1}\sigma_{x2} \tag{3.173}$$

Note that Equations 3.169 and 3.173 are identical when the correlation coefficient is zero (when the variables are independent).

Example 3.38

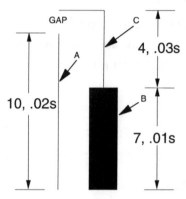

Figure 3.37. Sample fixture.

Referring to Figure 3.37, the sample fixture consists of three parts; the vertical bar to the left (part A), with a mean length of 10 and a standard deviation of 0.02, the solid block (part B), with a mean of length of 7 and a standard deviation of 0.01, and the vertical bar on top of the block (part C) with a mean length of 4 and a standard deviation of 0.03. Determine the expected length and the standard deviation of the identified gap.

Solution

The mean length of the solid block and the vertical bar on top of it is

$E(\text{block and bar}) = 7 + 4 = 11$

There is no reason to believe the length of these parts are not independent, thus, the standard deviation of the length of the solid block and the vertical bar is

$V(\text{block and bar}) = (0.01)^2 + (0.03)^2 = 0.001$

The mean length of the gap is

$E(\text{gap}) = 11 - 10 = 1$

The standard deviation of the gap is

$s = \sqrt{V(\text{gap})} = \sqrt{0.001 + 0.02^2} = 0.0374$

One of the most commonly used statistical principles is the theory of large numbers, also known as the central limit theorem. Simply stated, if

$$y = x_1 + x_2 + ... x_n$$

where x_1, x_2, ..., x_n are independent random variables, then, regardless of the distributions of x_1, x_2, ..., x_n, y will become a normally distributed as n becomes large. In this case, the mean of y is

$$E(y) = E(x_1) + E(x_2) + ... + E(x_n) \qquad (3.174)$$

If x_1, x_2, ..., x_n are independent, the variance of y is

$$V(y) = V(x_1) + V(x_2) + ... + V(x_n) \qquad (3.175)$$

Figures 3.38. 3.39, and 3.40 show the phenomenon of the sum of independent random variables tending to normal as the number of variables being summed increases. A distribution that has a shape much different from normal, the exponential distribution, becomes normal as n increases. Figure 3.38 is the sum of two independent, exponentially distributed variables.

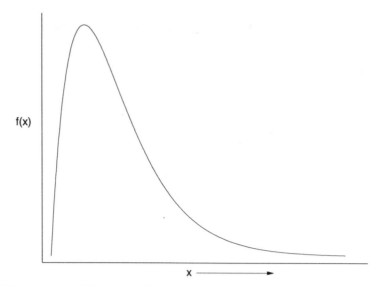

Figure 3.38. The sum of two exponentially distributed variables.

Figure 3.39 is the sum of five independent, exponentially distributed variables.

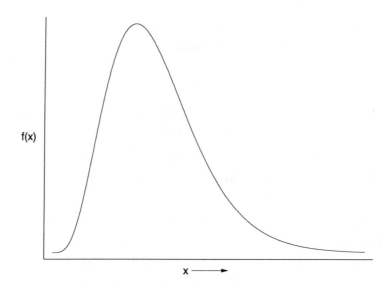

Figure 3.39. The sum of five exponentially distributed variables.

Figure 3.40 is the sum of thirty independent, exponentially distributed variables.

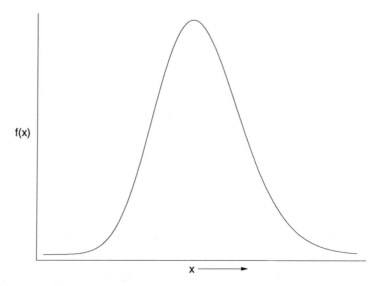

Figure 3.40. The sum of thirty exponentially distributed variables.

The distributions in the previous figures may look familiar. This is because the sum of exponentially distributed random variables is a gamma distributed random variable. Let x_1, x_2, ..., x_n be independent, exponentially distributed random variables with a failure rate of λ. Then $y = x_1$, x_2, ..., x_n follows the gamma distribution with a shape parameter, $\eta = n$ and a scale parameter of λ.

The sum of gamma distributed random variables also follows a gamma distribution. Let x_1, x_2, ..., x_n be independent, gamma distributed random variables with a shape parameter of η and a scale parameter of λ. Then $y = x_1$, x_2, ..., x_n follows the gamma distribution with a shape parameter equal to $m\eta$ and a scale parameter equal to λ.

Example 3.39

A system consisting of 12 components fails after all 12 components fail. The components are standby redundant, and the system has perfect switching. If the components are exponentially distributed with a failure rate of 30 units, what is the reliability function for this system? If the components follow a gamma distribution with a shape parameter of 2 and a scale parameter of 30 units, what is the reliability function for this system?

Solution

The random variable being modeled is

$$y = \sum_{i=1}^{12} x_i$$

Since the individual variables are exponentially distributed, the sum follows a gamma distribution with a shape parameter equal to the individual failure rate, 30, and a shape parameter equal to the number of components, 3. From Section 3.4.1, the gamma reliability function is

$$R(y) = \sum_{k=0}^{11} \frac{(30x)^k e^{-30x}}{k!}$$

If the components had a time to fail that followed a gamma distribution with η = 2, the parameters of the resulting distribution would also be gamma with a shape parameter equal to the sum of the individual shape parameters, which is equal to 24, and a scale parameter equal to the individual failure rate, 30. The resulting reliability function is

$$R(y) = \sum_{k=0}^{23} \frac{(30x)^k e^{-30x}}{k!}$$

The Poisson distribution is also reproductive. The sum of n independent Poisson distributed variables follows a Poisson distribution with a mean equal to the sum of the individual means. For example, if x, y, and z are Poisson distributed with means of 8, 14, and 16, $w = x + y + z$ is Poisson distributed with a mean of 38.

3.9.3 Transformation of random variables

When transforming random variables, if the resulting probability density function is not obvious, it must be computed. For the case of a single random variable, the probability density function for the transformed variable is

$$g(y) = f\left[w(y)\right]\left|\frac{dw}{dy}\right| \tag{3.176}$$

where: $f(x)$ is the probability density function for x,
   $y = u(x)$ is the transformation function, and
   $x = w(y)$ is the inverse of the transformation function, and has only one root.

Example 3.40

The random variable x is exponentially distributed with a failure rate λ. Determine the probability density function for the variable $y = 4x + 12$.

Solution

For this example, the transformation function is $y = 4x + 12$. Thus, the inverse transformation function is

$$x = \frac{y-12}{4}$$

The derivative of the inverse transformation function is

$$\frac{dx}{dy} = \frac{1}{4}$$

The exponential probability density function is

$$f(x) = \lambda e^{-\lambda x}, \; x > 0$$

Substituting into Equation 3.176 gives

$$g(y) = \left(\lambda e^{-\lambda(y-12)/4} \right)\left(\frac{1}{4} \right), \; y > 12$$

The acceptable range for x is 0 to infinity, after transformation, when $x = 0$, $y = 12$, thus, the range of y is 12 to infinity.

If the inverse of the transformation function has more than one root, the probability density function for the transformed variable is

$$g(y) = \sum_{i=1}^{n} f\left[w_i(y) \right] \left| \frac{dw_i}{dy} \right| \tag{3.177}$$

where, n is the number of roots of the inverse transformation function.

Table 3.13 contains some useful transformations of functions involving one variable.

Table 3.13. Transformations involving one random variable.

Transformation Function	Resulting Probability Density Function
$y = a + bx$	$g(y) = \left\|\dfrac{1}{b}\right\| f\left(\dfrac{y-a}{b}\right)$
$y = \dfrac{1}{x}$	$g(y) = \dfrac{1}{y^2} f\left(\dfrac{1}{y}\right)$
$y = e^x$	$g(y) = \left\|\dfrac{1}{y}\right\| f(\ln y)$
$y = \ln x$	$g(y) = e^y f(e^y)$
$y = x^2$	$g(y) = \dfrac{1}{2\sqrt{y}} \left[f(\sqrt{y}) + f(-\sqrt{y}) \right]$
$y = \sqrt{x}$	$g(y) = 2\|y\| f(y^2)$, $y > 0$
$y = x^{1/n}$	$g(y) = \|n y^{n-1}\| f(y^n)$, $y > 0$
$y = x^n$	$g(y) = \left\|\dfrac{1}{n} y^{(1/n)-1}\right\| \displaystyle\sum_{i=1}^{n} f(x_i)$
	$x_1, x_2, \ldots, x_n$ are the roots of $x = y^{1/n}$.
$y = e^{ax}$	$g(y) = \left\|\dfrac{1}{ay}\right\| f\left[\ln(y^{1/a})\right]$

$f(x)$ is the probability density function for x.

Now consider the case where the random variables x_1 and x_2 have a joint probability distribution of $f(x_1, x_2)$ and are transformed to two new random variables, $y_1 = u_1(x_1, x_2)$ and $y_2 = u_2(x_1, x_2)$. If the inverse of the transformation functions, $x_1 = w_1(y_1, y_2)$ and $x_2 = w_2(y_1, y_2)$ have single roots, the joint probability density function for y_1 and y_2 is

$$g(y_1, y_2) = f\left[w_1(y_1, y_2), w_2(y_1, y_2)\right] |J| \tag{3.178}$$

where J is the Jacobian and is defined as the determinant of the partial derivatives;

$$J = \begin{vmatrix} \partial x_1 / \partial y_1 & \partial x_1 / \partial y_2 \\ \partial x_2 / \partial y_1 & \partial x_2 / \partial y_2 \end{vmatrix}$$

In many cases, the transformation is to a single variable, y_1. In this case, simply choose a dummy variable for y_2. When choosing this dummy variable, be sure that y_1 and y_1 are independent; this will simplify the calculations because the joint probability density function for the two variables will be the product of the individual probability density functions.

Some useful transformations for functions of more than one random variable are given in Table 3.14.

Table 3.14. Transformations for functions of more than one random variable.

Transformation Function	Resulting Probability Density Function
$y = x_1 + x_2$	$g(y) = \int f_{x1}(y-z)f_{x2}(z)dz$
$y = x_1 x_2$	$g(y) = \int \left\| \frac{1}{z} \right\| f_{x1}\left(\frac{y}{z}\right)f_{x2}(z)dz$
$y = \dfrac{x_1}{x_2}$	$g(y) = \int \left\| \frac{z}{y^2} \right\| f_{x1}(z)f_{x2}\left(\frac{z}{y}\right)dz$
$y = x_1^2 + x_2^2$	$g(y) = \int \frac{1}{2\sqrt{y-z^2}} f_{x1}(z)f_{x2}\left(\sqrt{y-z^2}\right)dz$
$y = \sqrt{x_1^2 + x_2^2}$	$g(y) = \int \frac{1}{2\sqrt{y^2-z^2}} f_{x1}(z)f_{x2}\left(\sqrt{y^2-z^2}\right)dz$

f_{x1} and f_{x2} are the density functions for the random variables x_1 and x_2.

3.10 Confidence intervals

If two samples of size n are taken from a population, the mean of these two samples will probably be different, and neither will be equal to the population mean. Confidence intervals quantify this variation. For example, a $100(1-\alpha)\%$ confidence interval contains the true population mean $100(1-\alpha)\%$ of the time.

Section 3.7 explains methods for calculating confidence intervals for estimated parameters, reliability and percentiles. This section presents confidence intervals for means, variances, proportions, and the fraction conforming. Tolerance intervals are also presented.

3.10.1 Confidence intervals for the mean and variance

For data that are normally distributed with unknown mean and variance, a $100(1-\alpha)\%$ confidence interval for the mean is

$$\bar{x} - t_{\alpha/2}\frac{s}{\sqrt{n}} < \mu < \bar{x} + t_{\alpha/2}\frac{s}{\sqrt{n}} \tag{3.179}$$

where: $\bar{x}$ is the sample mean,

s is the sample standard deviation, and

$t_{\alpha/2}$ is the critical value of the t-distribution with $\nu = n - 1$ degrees of freedom.

The t-distribution is based on sampling from a normal distribution, but provides good results as long as the distribution is bell-shaped. The t-distribution is tabulated in Appendix F.

If the variance of the population is known or if the sample size is large $(n \geq 25)$, the confidence interval for the population mean is

$$\bar{x} - z_{\alpha/2}\frac{\sigma}{\sqrt{n}} < \mu < \bar{x} + z_{\alpha/2}\frac{\sigma}{\sqrt{n}} \tag{3.180}$$

where: $\bar{x}$ is the sample mean,

σ is the population standard deviation, and

$z_{\alpha/2}$ is the critical value of the standard normal distribution.

Example 3.41

Given the data below, construct a 90% confidence interval for the mean.

12	15	21
22	24	32

Solution

The sample mean is

$$\bar{x} = \frac{12 + 15 + 21 + 22 + 24 + 32}{6} = 21.0$$

The sample standard deviation is

$$s = \sqrt{\frac{n\sum_{i=1}^{n}x_i^2 - \left(\sum_{i=1}^{n}x_i\right)^2}{n(n-1)}} = \sqrt{\left[\frac{6(2894)-(126)^2}{6(6-1)}\right]} = 7.04$$

For a 90% confidence interval, $\alpha = 0.1$. From Appendix F, $t_{0.05}$ with 5 degrees of freedom is 2.015. The 90% confidence interval for the mean is

$$21 - 2.015\frac{7.04}{\sqrt{6}} < \mu < 21 + 2.015\frac{7.04}{\sqrt{6}}$$

$$15.21 < \mu < 26.79$$

Example 3.41

Twenty-eight samples are drawn from a population with a known variance of 3.4. The mean of the sample is 78.7. Construct a 95% confidence interval for the mean.

Solution

From Appendix A, $z_{\alpha/2} = 1.96$. The confidence interval is constructed using the expression

$$78.7 - 1.96\frac{\sqrt{3.4}}{\sqrt{28}} < \mu < 78.7 + 1.96\frac{\sqrt{3.4}}{\sqrt{28}}$$

$$78.0 < \mu < 79.4$$

For data that are normally distributed with sample variance s^2, a $100(1-\alpha)\%$ confidence interval for the variance is

$$\frac{(n-1)s^2}{\chi^2_{\alpha/2,n-1}} \leq \sigma^2 \leq \frac{(n-1)s^2}{\chi^2_{1-(\alpha/2),n-1}} \tag{3.181}$$

where,

$$\chi^2_{\alpha/2,n-1}$$

is the critical value of the chi-square distribution with $n-1$ degrees of freedom.

Example 3.42

Ten boxes of cereal were randomly sampled and weighed. The sample mean was 12.1 ounces and the sample standard deviation was 0.85. Determine a 95% confidence interval for the variance of cereal box weight.

Solution

From Appendix H, the critical values of the chi-square distribution are

$$\chi^2_{0.025,9} = 19.023$$

$$\chi^2_{0.975,9} = 2.70$$

The confidence interval is

$$\frac{9(0.85)^2}{19.023} \leq \sigma^2 \leq \frac{9(0.85)^2}{2.7}$$

$$0.342 \leq \sigma^2 \leq 2.408$$

3.10.2 Confidence Intervals for proportions

A $100(1-\alpha)\%$ confidence interval for a proportion is

$$\frac{2r - 1 + z^2_{\alpha/2} - z_{\alpha/2}\sqrt{\dfrac{(2r-1)(2n-2r+1)}{n} + z^2_{\alpha/2}}}{2(n + z^2_{\alpha/2})}$$

$$\leq \frac{r}{n} \leq \frac{2r + 1 + z^2_{\alpha/2} + z_{\alpha/2}\sqrt{\dfrac{(2r+1)(2n-2r-1)}{n} + z^2_{\alpha/2}}}{2(n + z^2_{\alpha/2})} \tag{3.182}$$

where: r is the number of occurrences in the sample, and
n is the sample size.

If $\hat{p}$ is the proportion of successes in a random sample of size n, and $n\hat{p} \geq 5$ and $n(1-\hat{p}) \geq 5$, then a $100(1-\alpha)\%$ confidence interval is

$$\hat{p} - z_{\alpha/2}\sqrt{\frac{\hat{p}(1-\hat{p})}{n}} \leq p \leq \hat{p} + z_{\alpha/2}\sqrt{\frac{\hat{p}(1-\hat{p})}{n}} \tag{3.183}$$

Example 3.43

In a sample of 500 items 9 were found to be deficient. Determine a 90% confidence interval for the proportion of deficient items.

Solution

From Appendix A, $z_{\alpha/2} = 1.645$. The confidence interval is

$$\frac{19}{500} - 1.645\sqrt{\frac{\frac{19}{500}\left(1 - \frac{19}{500}\right)}{500}} \le p \le \frac{19}{500} + 1.645\sqrt{\frac{\frac{19}{500}\left(1 - \frac{19}{500}\right)}{500}}$$

$$0.0212 \le p \le .05248$$

The beta distribution can also be used to determine a lower confidence limit for the number of occurrences. Appendix D provides the information for determination of a lower reliability confidence limit at confidence levels of 90%, 95%, 99% and 99.5%.

To determine the lower reliability confidence limit without the use of tables requires solving the equation below by trial and error.

$$\alpha = \sum_{i=0}^{r} \left(\frac{\prod\limits_{n+2-i}^{n+1}(n+2-i) \quad i>0}{i!} \quad i=0 \right) \left(R_l\right)^{n+1-i}\left(1 - R_l\right)^i \tag{3.184}$$

where: α is the level of significance ($\alpha = 0.05$ for a 95% limit),

r is the number of failures,

n is the number of trials (successes and failures), and

R_l is the lower reliability confidence limit.

This expression is easily solved with the solver routines included with electronic spreadsheets. Guess at the lower reliability confidence limit and assign this cell as adjustable. In another set of cells, use the guess for R_l to compute the right side of Equation 3.0. Make two constraint cells, with one being α –

the computed right side of Equation 3.0, and the other being the computed right side of Equation 3.0 – α.

Example 3.44

Forty items were tested with 2 failures and 38 successes. Determine the lower reliability confidence limit at 90% confidence.

Solution

From Appendix D, with $n = 40$, $r = 2$, the lower reliability confidence limit at 90% confidence is 0.875.

A $100(1-\alpha)\%$ nonparametric confidence interval for reliability is

$$\frac{n-r}{n-r+(r+1)F_{\alpha/2,2(r+1),2(n-r)}} \leq R \leq \frac{(n-r+1)F_{\alpha/2,2(n-r+1),2r}}{r+(n-r+1)F_{\alpha/2,2(r+1),2r}} \qquad (3.185)$$

where: n is the sample size,

r is the number of failures, and

$F_{\alpha,\nu 1,\nu 2}$ is the critical value of the F-distribution.

Example 3.45

Determine the 80% nonparametric confidence interval for reliability for the data in Example 3.3.

Solution

For a confidence level of 80%, $\alpha = 0.20$. For this example, $n = 40$ and $r = 2$. From Appendix E,

$$F_{0.1,6,76} = 1.8531$$

$$F_{0.1,78,4} = 3.783$$

The 80% confidence interval is

$$\frac{40-2}{40-2+(2+1)1.8531} \leq R \leq \frac{(40-2+1)3.783}{2+(40-2+1)3.783}$$

$$0.8724 \leq R \leq 0.9866$$

3.10.3 Tolerance Intervals

A **tolerance interval** contains $(1-\gamma)\%$ of the observations from a population with $100(1-\alpha)\%$ confidence. Tolerance intervals establish bounds on individual values as opposed to confidence intervals that establish bounds on parameters.

If the population is normally distributed with unknown mean and variance, a $100(1-\alpha)\%$ confidence interval containing $(1-\gamma)\%$ of the observations is

$$\bar{x} \pm ks \qquad\qquad (3.186)$$

where: $\bar{x}$ is the sample mean,

s is the sample standard deviation, and

k is a factor given in Tables I.1a and I.1b in Appendix I.

Tolerance intervals can also be constructed nonparametrically, but the intervals will be wider. The extreme values of the sample contain $100(1-\alpha)\%$ of the population $(1-\gamma)\%$ of the time, where $(1-\gamma)$ is obtained from Table I.2 in Appendix I. Table I.3 in Appendix I contains the sample size required to contain $(1-\gamma)\%$ of the population with $100(1-\alpha)\%$ confidence.

Example 3.46

A fuse-well is being drilled into a warhead, and the fuse-well depths from a random sample of 10 warheads are given below. Assuming a normal population, construct a 99% confidence interval that contains 95% of the population.

12.34	12.37	12.31	12.33	12.24
12.38	12.32	12.32	12.36	12.35

Solution

The sample mean is $\bar{x} = 12.332$, and the sample standard deviation is $s = 0.0397$. From Appendix I, Table I.1 for $\alpha = 0.01$, $\gamma = 0.05$ and $n = 10$, $k = 4.265$. The tolerance interval is

$$12.332 \pm 4.265(0.0397)$$

It can be stated with 99% confidence that 95% of the fuse-well depths will fall in the range from 12.163 to 12.501

3.11 Hypothesis testing

Reliability engineers often make data based decisions about specific systems. For example an engineer might want to scientifically demonstrate that design A has a longer mean time to fail than design B. This can be done with statistical hypothesis testing. First, a null hypothesis is formed. This hypothesis is then tested and will either be rejected or fail to be rejected. If the null hypothesis is not rejected, it does not necessarily mean it is true, rather there is not sufficient evidence to reject it.

The hypothesis being tested is referred to as the **null hypothesis**, H_0. If the null hypothesis is rejected, the **alternative hypothesis**, H_1, is accepted. There is a probability of making incorrect decisions when hypothesis testing. If the null hypothesis is rejected when in reality it is true, this is referred to as **Type I error** or α **error**. If the null hypothesis is not rejected, when in reality it is false, this is referred to as **Type II error** or β **error**. This is shown in the diagram below.

	H0: True	H0: False
Accept H0:	Correct Decision	Type II Error
Reject H0:	Type I Error	Correct Decision

The power of a test is equal to the probability of rejecting the null hypothesis when the alternate hypothesis is true.

3.11.1 Hypothesis tests for means

When testing to determine if a population mean is equal to a specific value, μ_0, the null and alternative hypotheses are

$$H_0: \ \mu = \mu_0,$$

$$H_1: \ \mu \neq \mu_0 \ \text{or} \ \mu < \mu_0 \ \text{or} \ \mu > \mu_0$$

For a two-tailed test, assuming a normal sampling distribution, H_0 is rejected at significance α when the computed t-statistic does not fall in the range from $-t_{\alpha/2,n-1}$ to $t_{\alpha/2,n-1}$. The t-statistic is computed from the expression

$$t = \frac{\bar{x} - \mu_0}{s / \sqrt{n}} \tag{3.187}$$

where: n is the sample size and

s is the sample standard deviation.

If the standard deviation of the population is known, the statistic computed is

$$z = \frac{\bar{x} - \mu_0}{\sigma / \sqrt{n}} \tag{3.188}$$

and the acceptance region is $\pm z_{\alpha/2}$ for a two-tailed test.

When testing to determine if two population means are equal, the null and alternative hypotheses are

$$H_0: \ \mu_1 = \mu_2,$$

$$H_1: \ \mu_1 \neq \mu_2 \ \text{ or } \ \mu_1 < \mu_2 \ \text{ or } \ \mu_1 > \mu_2$$

Assuming the sampling distribution is normally distributed, but the variance is unknown, the statistic tested is

$$t' = \frac{\bar{x}_1 - \bar{x}_2}{\sqrt{s_1^2 / n_1 + s_2^2 / n_2}} \tag{3.189}$$

For a two-tailed test, H_0 is rejected at significance α when the computed t-statistic does not fall in the range from $-t_{\alpha/2}$ to $t_{\alpha/2}$. The degrees of freedom for the statistic are

$$\nu = \frac{\left(s_1^2 / n_1 + s_2^2 / n_2\right)^2}{\dfrac{\left(s_1^2 / n_1\right)^2}{n_1 - 1} + \dfrac{\left(s_2^2 / n_2\right)^2}{n_2 - 1}} \tag{3.190}$$

Assuming the standard deviations of the two populations are equal but unknown, the test statistic is

$$t = \frac{\bar{x}_1 - \bar{x}_2}{s_p \sqrt{1/n_1 + 1/n_2}} \tag{3.191}$$

where

$$s_p = \sqrt{\frac{s_1^2(n_1 - 1) + s_2^2(n_2 - 1)}{n_1 + n_2 - 2}} \tag{3.192}$$

For a two tailed test, H_0 is not rejected at significance α when

$$-t_{\alpha/2, n1+n2-2} < t < t_{\alpha/2, n1+n2-2}$$

When the standard deviation of the two populations is equal and known, the test statistic is

$$z = \frac{\bar{x}_1 - \bar{x}_2}{\sqrt{\sigma_1^2 / n_1 + \sigma_2^2 / n_2}} \qquad (3.193)$$

where σ is the standard deviation of each of the populations.

For a two-tailed test, H_0 is not rejected at significance α when

$$-z_{\alpha/2} < z < z_{\alpha/2}$$

where z is the critical value of the standard normal distribution.

Example 3.47

A new beam is being designed and the design engineer wants to determine if an alloying agent affects strength. Eight beams of Design A, which includes the alloying agent, and 7 beams of design B, which does not include the alloying agent were tested to failure. The results follow. At 5% significance, can the engineer state the beams have equal strength?

Design A		Design B	
89	93	88	93
91	88	87	92
90	87	94	90
92	86	91	97
88	90	94	

Solution

There is no reason to assume the variances are equal, so the tested statistic is

$$t' = \frac{89.4 - 91.78}{\sqrt{2.22^2 / 8 + 3.15^2 / 7}} = -1.67$$

The degrees of freedom for the statistic are

$$v = \frac{\left(s_1^2/n_1 + s_2^2/n_2\right)^2}{\dfrac{\left(s_1^2/n_1\right)^2}{n_1-1} + \dfrac{\left(s_2^2/n_2\right)^2}{n_2-1}}$$

Rounding the above value to $v = 11$, at a significance of 5% from Appendix F, the means of the two designs are accepted as equal if

$$-1.796 < t' < 1.796$$

Thus, the design engineer conclude the strengths are unequal (the design engineer fails to reject the null hypothesis).

When testing to determine if two proportions are equal, the null and alternative hypotheses are

H_0: $p_1 = p_2$,

H_1: $p_1 \neq p_2$ or $p_1 < p_2$ or $p_1 > p_2$

The statistic for testing the difference between two proportions is

$$z = \frac{\hat{p}_1 - \hat{p}_2}{\sqrt{\hat{p}(1-\hat{p})(1/n_1 + 1/n_2)}} \tag{3.194}$$

where

$$\hat{p} = \frac{x_1 + x_2}{n_1 + n_2} \tag{3.195}$$

where: x_1 and x_2 are the number of successes in each of the two samples, and

z is the critical value of the standard normal distribution.

For a two-tailed test, H_0 is not rejected at significance α when

$$-z_{\alpha/2} < z < z_{\alpha/2}$$

3.11.2 Hypothesis tests for variance

If the population being sampled is normal, the chi-square distribution can be used to test if the variance of the distribution is equal to a specific value, σ_0. The hypotheses for this test are

$$H_0: \sigma = \sigma_0$$

$$H_1: \sigma \neq \sigma_0 \ \text{ or } \ \sigma < \sigma_0 \ \text{ or } \ \sigma > \sigma_0$$

The test statistic is

$$\chi^2_{\alpha,v} = \frac{(n-1)s^2}{\sigma_0^2} \tag{3.196}$$

where: n is the sample size

s is the sample standard deviation,

α is the significance, and

v is the degrees of freedom $(n–1)$.

For a two-tailed test, H_0 is not rejected at a significance of α if

$$\chi^2_{1-\alpha/2,v} < \chi^2 < \chi^2_{\alpha/2,v}$$

Example 3.48

A specific type of computer monitor has a normally distributed mean life of 35,000 hours with a standard deviation of 3,000 hours. The manufacturer is testing a new design, and a random sample of 10 monitors has a standard deviation 2,800 hours. Does the new design have a lower standard deviation at 5% significance?

Solution

This is a one tailed test. The hypotheses are

$$H_0: \sigma = 3000$$

$$H_1: \sigma < 3000$$

From Appendix H, with 9 degrees of freedom, the critical value of the chi-square distribution is

$$\chi^2_{1-\alpha} = \chi^2_{0.95} = 3.325$$

The test statistic is

$$\chi^2 = \frac{(10-1)2800^2}{3000^2} = 7.84$$

Since $\chi^2 > \chi^2_{1-\alpha/2}$, the null hypothesis is not rejected, and it cannot be stated that the new design has a lower variance.

When testing to determine if there is a difference in the variance of two populations, assuming the populations are normally distributed, the test statistic is

$$F = \frac{s_1^2}{s_2^2} \tag{3.197}$$

For a two-tailed test, H_0 (the variances of the two populations are equal) is not rejected at a significance of α if

$$F_{1-\alpha,v1,v2} < F < F_{\alpha,v1,v2}$$

where: $v_1 = n_1 - 1$ and
$$v_2 = n_2 - 1$$

Example 3.50

A design engineer is considering two components. Ten Type A components were tested and the sample standard deviation of the strength was 0.092. Fifteen Type B components were tested and the sample standard deviation of the strength was 0.097. At a significance of 0.05, is the variance of the strength of component type A lower than that of component type B?

Solution

This is a one tailed test. The test statistic is

$$F = \frac{0.092^2}{0.097^2} = 0.8996$$

From Appendix E, the critical value of the F-distribution is

$$F_{0.95,9,14} = 0.331$$

Since the calculated statistic is greater than the critical value, it cannot be stated at 5% significance that the two variances are different.

3.12 Exercises

1. Given that a population of components has a normal time to fail distribution with a mean of 400 hours and a standard deviation of 60 hours, graph the probability density function, the reliability function and the hazard function.

2. For the components in Exercise 1, if 200 components are tested for 430 hours, what is the expected number of survivors? What is the expected number of failures between time = 410 and time = 430?

3. For the components in Exercise 1, graphically show the probability of a failure before 425 hours of operation, 410 hours of operation, and from this graph, determine the probability of a failure in the interval from 410 hours of operation to 425 hours of operation.

4. Repeat Exercises 1 & 2 with the components following a lognormal time to fail with the same mean and standard deviation.

5. Given the following probability density function, determine the mean and variance.

$$f(x) = \frac{1}{0.4x\sqrt{2\pi}} \exp\left[-\frac{1}{2}\left(\frac{\ln x - 2}{0.4}\right)^2\right], x > 0$$

6. A population of components has a constant failure rate of 0.003 per hour. What is the probability of failure before 200 hours of operation?

7. What is the value of the exponential probability density function at the intersection with the y-axis?

    a. 0

    b. the failure rate of the distribution

    c. the mean time to fail for the distribution

    d. the variance of the distribution

    e. infinity

    f. none of the above

8. Given the reliability function

$$R(t) = e^{-\frac{t}{\theta}}, t > 0,$$

determine the mean and variance.

9. An automobile manufacturer averages 4 defects per vehicle, what is the probability of an automobile containing (a)no defects, (b) 3 or more defects?

10. The failure rate for a carpet manufacturer is 3.7 per 1000 square yards. What is the probability of finding no defects in a random sample of 100 square yards? Use the Poisson distribution to compute the answer.

11. Repeat Exercise 10 using the binomial distribution to compute the answer.

12. A salesperson has a success rate of 15%. What is the probability of making two successful sales calls in a row.

13. For the sales person in Exercise 12, how many sales calls will have to be made in a day to have a 90% chance of having at least two successful calls?

14. A lot of 15 small military rockets was manufactured, and it is known that two of the rockets received faulty fuses. If four of the rockets are sampled at random, what is the probability that, (a) none of the four have faulty fuses, (b) one or less of the rockets have faulty fuses, and (c) two or less of the rockets have faulty fuses?

15. A certain military rocket has an 84% probability of successfully destroying its intended target. What is the probability that, (a) the first rocket fired at a specified target destroys the target, (b) the second rocket fired at a specified target destroys the target, and (c) the third rocket fired at a specified target destroys the target.

16. A component has the following reliability function

$$R(t) = \exp\left[-\left(\frac{t}{89}\right)^{3.7}\right], t > 0$$

Plot the hazard function.

17. What is the mean and variance of the time to fail for the component in Exercise 16?

18. What is the probability the component in Exercise 16 will fail before time = 80? What is the instantaneous failure rate at this time?

19. A system consists of four identical components, with three being standby redundant. The components have an exponential time-to-fail distribution with a failure rate of 1/235. Determine the probability density function for this system, and determine the system mean time to fail and variance.

20. The sides of a square have an expected length of 8.2 with a variance of 0.74. What is the expected area of this square, and what is the variance of the area?

21. A fixture consists of two pipes, A and B, welded end-to-end. Historically, the average length of pipe A has been 3.7 feet with a standard deviation of 1.2. Historically, the average length of pipe B has been 8.2 feet with a standard deviation of 2.7. What is the average length and standard deviation of the fixture?

22. An component is produced by extruding a shaft and removing a portion of the extrusion. The expected length of the extruded shaft is 23 inches with a standard deviation of 0.3 inches. The expected value for the length removed is 0.6 inches with a standard deviation of 0.09 inches. What is the expected length and standard deviation of the resulting component?

23. The diameter of a rod is normally distributed with mean μ, and standard deviation σ. What is the probability density function for the cross sectional area of the rod?

24. The variable x is exponentially distributed with a mean of 7. If $y = 1/x$, what is the probability density function of y?

25. Given the probability density function

$$f(x) = xe^{-x^2/2}, 0 < x < \infty,$$

(a) prove this is a valid density function, (b) find the reliability function, and (c) find hazard function.

26. Given the hazard function

$$h(x) = c, 0 < x < \infty,$$

determine the reliability and probability density functions.

27. A component has an exponential distribution with a mean time to fail of 500 hours. Given the component survives to 400 hours, what is the probability of the component surviving for an additional 200 hours?

28. A component has a Weibull time to fail distribution with a shape parameter of 4, a scale parameter of 50 and a location parameter of 10. Given the component survives until time = 60 and fails before time = 80, what is the probability of the component surviving until time = 75?

29. Fifty items were tested for 100 hours, and 4 items failed at time = 2, time = 28, time = 59 and time = 81. Assuming an exponential distribution, determine the mean life.

30. Determine a 90% lower confidence limit for the failure rate for the data in Exercise 29.

31. Determine a 90% lower confidence for 99% reliability for the data in Exercise 29.

32. Determine a 90% lower confidence limit for percentiles at time = 40 for the data in Exercise 29.

33. For the data in Exercise 29, determine the parameters of the Weibull distribution using probability plotting.

34. For the data in Exercise 29, determine the parameters of the Weibull distribution using hazard plotting.

35. For the data in Exercise 29, determine the parameters of the Weibull distribution using maximum likelihood estimation.

36. Determine 95% confidence limits for the parameters, reliability at 90% and percentiles at time = 30, for the distribution found in Exercise 35.

37. For the data set below, determine the parameters of the Weibull distribution using probability plotting.

12 c	22 c	15
28	19	30
20 c	31 c	

38. Determine goodness of fit for the distribution found in Exercise 37 using the Hollander-Proschan test.

39. For the data given in Exercise 37, determine the parameters of the lognormal distribution using probability plotting. Include confidence limits on the probability plot using 5% and 95% ranks.

40. For the data given in Exercise 37, determine the parameters of the lognormal distribution using hazard plotting.

41. For the data given in Exercise 37, determine the parameters of the lognormal distribution using maximum likelihood estimation. Determine 95% confidence limits for the parameters.

42. For the data given in Exercise 37, determine the parameters of the normal distribution using maximum likelihood estimation. Determine a 90% confidence interval for 95% reliability.

43. Given the following data, construct a 95% confidence interval for the mean.

45	70	52
78	61	82

44. Construct a 90% confidence interval for the mean of the data in Exercise 43.

45. A random sample of 50 items yielded 40 successes. Determine a 95% confidence interval for the proportion of successes.

46. How many successful launches must occur to demonstrate 95% reliability with 90% confidence with one failed launch?

47. Construct a 95% tolerance interval that contains 95% of the population for the data given in Exercise 43.

48. For the data given in Exercise 43, determine with 10% significance if the population mean is greater than 60.

49. For the data given in Exercise 43, determine with 10% significance if the population mean is less than 60.

50. For the data given in Exercise 43, determine with 10% significance if the population mean is different than 60.

51. For the data given in Exercise 43, determine with 10% significance if the population variance is different than 45.

52. Determine if the mean of population A and B are different given the data below at a significance level of 0.05.

A	B
25	34
33	38
43	39
45	41
51	50
52	58

53. Determine if the variances of populations A and B in Exercise 52 are different at a significance level of 0.1.

3.13 References

Crowder, M. J., A. C. Kimber, R. L. Smith, and T. J. Sweeting. 1991. *Statistical Analysis of Reliability Data*, London: Chapman & Hall.

Dodson, Bryan, and Jack Kirkland. 1994. *The Reliability & Maintenance Analyst*, Auburn Hills, MI: Espinoza Consulting.

Dodson, Bryan. 1994. *Weibull Analysis (with Software)*. Milwaukee, WI: ASQC–Quality Press.

Dodson, B. L., and M. D. Mulcahy. 1992. *Certified Reliability Engineer Examination Study Guide*. Tucson, AZ: Quality Publishing.

Dovich, R. A. 1990. *Reliability Statistics*. Milwaukee, WI: ASQC–Quality Press.

Dovich, R. A. 1992. *Quality Engineering Statistics*. Milwaukee, WI: ASQC–Quality Press.

Hahn, G. J., and S. S. Shapiro. 1967. *Statistical Models in Engineering*. New York: John Wiley & Sons.

Ireson, G. W., and C. F. Coombs. 1988. *Handbook of Reliability Engineering and Management.* New York: McGraw-Hill.

Johnson, N. L., and S. Kotz. 1970. *Distributions in Statistics: Continuous Univariate Distributions-1*. New York: John Wiley & Sons.

Johnson, N. L., and S. Kotz. 1970. *Distributions in Statistics: Continuous Univariate Distributions-2*. New York: John Wiley & Sons.

Juran, J. M., and F. M Gryna. 1988. *Juran's Quality Control Handbook*. New York: McGraw Hill.

Kapur, K. C., and L. R. Lamberson. 1977. *Reliability in Engineering Design*. New York: John Wiley & Sons.

Krishnamoorthi, K. S. 1992. *Reliability Methods for Engineers.* Milwaukee, WI: ASQC–Quality Press.

Lewis, E. E. 1987. *Introduction To Reliability Engineering.* New York: John Wiley & Sons.

O'Conner, P. D. T. 1993. *Practical Reliability Engineering.* New York: John Wiley & Sons.

Shooman, M. L. 1990. *Probabilistic Reliability: An Engineering Approach.* Malabar, FL: Robert E. Krieger.

Sundarajan, C. 1991. *Guide To Reliability Engineering: Data, Analysis, Applications, Implementation, And Management.* New York: Van Nostrand Reinhold.

Tobias, P. A., and D. C. Trindade. 1986. *Applied Reliability.* New York: Van Nostrand Reinhold.

Walpole, R. E., and R. H. Myers. 1989. *Probability and Statistics for Engineers and Scientists.* New York: Macmillan.

♦ ♦ ♦

CHAPTER

4

Prediction, Estimation, and Apportionment Methods

This chapter describes a variety of mathematical models for predicting the reliability of a system. The validity of these models is based on the accuracy of the reliability estimates of the components that compose the models. Methods are presented for obtaining reliability information from public databases and from military standards. After a system has been modeled, it is often desirable to optimize the system. Methods of reliability allocation are also discussed.

4.1 Reliability data sources

When attempting to determine the reliability of a system being designed, it may be infeasible to test all components considered for the design. Component data must be supplied from other sources. A good source of reliability data is often the component manufacturer. In addition to the manufacturer, there are several databases available to the public. Beware that when using reliability data from outside sources environmental conditions can cause great error. Correction factors are typically used to compensate for environmental conditions. Some data bases include correction factors, but some do not.

Data bases available to the public contain three types of data:

1. Raw Data—times to failure, operating hours and/or number of failures are provided. The user must compute failure statistics.

2. Primary, Consolidated Data—failure rates and failure probabilities derived from raw data are provided. Point estimates for mean life with confidence intervals are usually provided.

3. Expert Opinion Data—failure rates and failure probabilities estimated by experts.

Public databases contain a great deal of information, but care must be taken to ensure accuracy. Most databases provide sources of data, limitations, and the methods of statistical analysis used (if any). Be careful to note this information. Some common shortcomings of public databases are:

1. Independent and dependent failures may not be differentiated
2. Primary and secondary failures may not be differentiated
3. Failures due to human error may not be noted
4. Different organizations have different levels of reporting accuracy

Some public databases are

- **FARADA** (Failure Rate Data)—component failure probabilities provided by NASA and the Department of Defense. Available from *Fleet Missile Systems Analysis and Evaluation Group*, Department of Defense, Corona, CA.

- **GIDEP** (Government and Industry Data Exchange Program)—a computerized database with information from a wide variety of components used in the defense industry. The database is operated by GIDEP Operations Center, Department of Defense, Corona, CA, 91720-5000, (714) 736-4677.

- **IEEE Data**—failure probabilities of electrical components based on expert opinion. Available from the *Institute of Electrical and Electronics Engineers*, 345 East 47 Street, New York, NY, 10017-2394, (212) 705-7900.

- **LER Data** (Licensee Event Reports)—failure summaries of components from nuclear power plants. Available from the *Nuclear Regulatory Commission*, Washington, DC

- **NERC** (National Electrical Reliability Council)—component failure data from power plants. Available from the *National Electrical Reliability Council*, New York, NY.

- **NPRD** (Non-electric Parts Reliability Data)—failure data of non-electric components used in military systems. Available from *Rome Air Development Center*, Griffins Air Force Base, NY, 13441-5700, (315) 330-4151.
- **NPRDS** (Nuclear Plant Reliability Data System)—a computerized database of failure data from nuclear power plants. The database is operated by *Southwest Research Institute*, San Antonio, TX.
- **PVP** (Pressure Vessel and Piping)—failure data concerning pressure vessels and piping. This is a technical paper by Bush (1985) and updated periodically.

Another useful source of failure data is Military Handbook - 217 (available from Rome Air Development Center). The purpose of the handbook is to establish and maintain consistent and uniform methods for estimating the inherent reliability of military electronic equipment systems. It provides a common basis for reliability predictions during acquisitions programs and establishes a common basis for comparing and evaluating reliability predictions of related or competitive designs.

The handbook contains two methods for predicting reliability, **Part Stress Analysis** and **Parts Count**. The Part Stress Analysis method requires a greater amount of detailed information and is applicable during the later design phase when actual hardware and circuits are being designed. The Parts Count method requires less information, generally part quantities, quality level and the applicable environment. The Parts Count method is applicable during the early design phase and during proposal formulation, and will generally result in a more conservative estimate.

The Part Stress Analysis method is based on the expression

$$\lambda_p = \lambda_b \Pi_Q \Pi_E \ldots \tag{4.1}$$

where: λ_p is the part failure rate,

λ_b is the base failure rate usually expressed by a model relating the influence of electrical and temperature stresses on the part,

Π_Q is a modification factor for the quality level, and,

Π_E is a modification factor for environmental stresses.

All Π factors modify the base failure rate for the category application and other parameters that affect the part reliability. The Π_E and Π_Q factors are used in virtually all models. Most models also contain other Π factors. The base failure rate models are presented in each part section along with identification of the applicable model factors. All the part models include failure data from both catastrophic and permanent drift failures and are based on a constant failure rate, except for motors which show an increasing failure rate over time. Failures associated with connection of parts into circuit assemblies are not included within the part failure rate models. Information on connection reliability is provided in Sections 16 and 17 of the handbook.

ORACLE is a computer program that aids in the application of the Part Stress Analysis procedure of MIL-HDBK-217. Based on environmental use characteristics, piece part count, thermal and electrical stresses, subsystem repair rates and system configuration, the program calculates piece part, assembly and subassembly failure rates. It also flags over-stressed parts, allows the user to perform tradeoff analyses and provides system mean-time-to-failure and availability. The ORACLE software is available in VAX and DOS versions at replacement tape or disc costs to all Department of Defense organizations, and to contractors for application on specific Department of Defense contracts. The software is available form Rome Laboratory/ERSR, Griffins AFB, NY 13441-5700.

The Parts Count method is based on the expression

$$\lambda_{\text{EQUIP}} = \sum_{i=1}^{n} N_i \left(\lambda_g \Pi_Q \right)_i \qquad (4.2)$$

where: λ_{EQUIP} is the total equipment failure rate (failures per 1 million hours),

λ_g is the generic failure rate for the ith generic part (failures per 1 million hours),

Π_Q is the quality factor for the ith generic part,

N_i is the quantity of the ith generic part, and

n is the number of different generic part categories in the equipment.

4.2 Mathematical models

After component reliability information has been obtained, system reliability can be computed. Most systems can be modeled using reliability block diagrams. The model may be a series system, a parallel system, a standby redundant system, or a combination of the previous.

4.2.1 Series systems

For a series system to operate successfully, all components must operate successfully. A simple series system is shown in Figure 4.1.

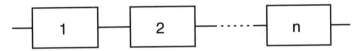

Figure 4.1. Series block diagram.

If each component in the system is independent, the reliability of a series system is

$$R_s = \prod_{i=1}^{n} R_i \tag{4.3}$$

The system hazard function is

$$h_s = \sum_{i=1}^{n} h_i \tag{4.4}$$

If the components in the system are exponentially distributed, the system mean time to fail is

$$MTTF_s = \frac{1}{\sum_{i=1}^{n} \lambda_i} \tag{4.5}$$

where λ_i is the failure rate of the *i*th component.

Example 4.1

Three components each with a reliability of 0.9 are placed in series. What is the reliability of the system?

Solution

The system reliability is the product of the component reliabilities.

$R_s = 0.9^3 = 0.729$

Example 4.2

The components in the system below are exponentially distributed with the indicated failure rates. Develop an expression for the reliability of the system. What is the system reliability at time = 100 hours?

| $\lambda = 0.002$ Hours | $\lambda = 0.002$ Hours | $\lambda = 0.001$ Hours | $\lambda = 0.003$ Hours |

Solution

For the exponential distribution, reliability is defined as

$R(t) = e^{-\lambda t}$

The reliability of the system above is

$R_s(t) = \left(e^{-0.002t}\right)\left(e^{-0.002t}\right)\left(e^{-0.001t}\right)\left(e^{-0.003t}\right) = e^{-0.008t}$

An alternate solution method is to sum the individual values of the hazard function.

$\lambda_s = 0.002 + 0.002 + 0.001 + 0.003 = 0.008$

$R_s = e^{-0.008t}$

At time = 100 hours, the reliability is

$R_s = e^{-0.008(100)} = 0.4493$

4.2.2 Parallel systems

For a parallel system to operate successfully, **at least one** of the components in the system must operate successfully. A general parallel system is shown in Figure 4.2.

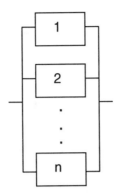

Figure 4.2. Parallel block diagram.

The system above is an **active** parallel system with $n-1$ redundancy. In an active parallel system all components are in operation when the system is in operation. An active parallel system may be a **pure** parallel system or a **shared** parallel system. In a pure parallel system, there is no change in the failure rate of the surviving components after the failure of a companion component. In a shared parallel system, the failure rates of the remaining components change when a companion component fails. An example is an automobile wheel being held on by four bolts. The load is being shared by four bolts, and when one of the bolts fails, the load on the three remaining bolts increases.

In a **passive** parallel system, also known as a **standby redundant** system, only one component functions at a given time. The remaining components do not come into service until required by the failure of other components. A switching device is usually used to transfer operation from one component to another. Passive parallel systems are be discussed in Section 4.2.4.

The reliability of a pure, active parallel system is

$$R_s = 1 - \prod_{i=1}^{n}\left(1 - R_i\right) \tag{4.6}$$

A parallel system consisting of components with n identical components with an exponential time to failure distribution has a mean time to fail of

$$MTBF_s = \sum_{i=1}^{n}\frac{1}{i\lambda} \tag{4.7}$$

where λ is the failure rate of each of the components.

Example 4.3

A system consists of three components. At time = 0, all three components are activated, and as long as at least one of the three components is functional, the system is functional. Write the expression for system reliability if each of the components has an exponential time to fail distribution with mean times to fail of 40 hours, 80 hours and 85 hours. What is the reliability at time = 25 hours?

Solution

This is a system with three components—two in active redundancy The reliability of the system is

$$R_s(t) = 1 - \left(1 - e^{-t/40}\right)\left(1 - e^{-t/80}\right)\left(1 - e^{-t/85}\right)$$

At time = 25 hours, the reliability is

$$R_s(25) = 1 - \left(1 - e^{-25/40}\right)\left(1 - e^{-25/80}\right)\left(1 - e^{-25/85}\right) = 0.9665$$

4.2.3 r-out-of-n systems

Another form of active redundancy is a system consisting of n components in which r of the n components must function for the system to function. An example of this is a four engine aircraft that can maintain flight with only two of the four engines operating. If the reliability, R, of all components is equal, the reliability of an r-out-of-n system is

$$R_s = \sum_{x=r}^{n} \binom{n}{x} R^x (1-R)^{n-x} \tag{4.8}$$

For the special case where the component failure rates are constant, the system mean time to fail is

$$\theta_s = \sum_{i=r}^{n} \frac{1}{i\lambda} \tag{4.9}$$

where: λ is the failure rate of each of the components.

Example 4.4

A system consists of four components. If more than two of the components fail, the system fails. If the components have an exponential time to fail distribution with a failure rate of 0.000388, what is the reliability of the system at time = 300? What is the system mean time to fail?

Solution

This is a 2-out-of-4 system; at least 2 of the 4 components must survive for the system to survive. The reliability of each component is

$$R = e^{-0.000388(300)} = 0.89$$

The reliability of the system is

$$R_s = \sum_{x=2}^{4} \binom{4}{x} R^x (1-R)^{4-x}$$

$$R_s = \left[\frac{4!}{(2!)(4-2)!} \right] (0.89)^2 (1-0.89)^{4-2}$$

$$+ \left[\frac{4!}{(3!)(4-3)!} \right] (0.89)^3 (1-0.89)^{4-3}$$

$$+ \left[\frac{4!}{(4!)(4-4)!} \right] (0.89)^4 (1-0.89)^{4-4}$$

$$= 0.995$$

The system mean time to fail is

$$\theta_s = \sum_{i=2}^{4} \frac{1}{i(0.000388)}$$

$$= \frac{1}{2(0.000388)} + \frac{1}{3(0.000388)} + \frac{1}{4(0.000388)}$$

$$= 2792$$

4.2.4 Standby redundant systems

In a standby redundant system only one component is in operation at a given time, if the on-line component fails, another component is brought on-line. A switching mechanism is usually responsible for bringing a redundant component on-line. A standby redundant system is shown in Figure 4.3.

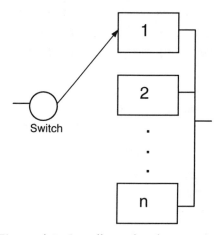

Figure 4.3. Standby redundant system.

In the case of perfect switching and exponential component life distributions, the standby redundant system is modeled by the gamma distribution. This is because the sum of *n* exponentially distributed random variables follows a gamma distribution. For the special case where all components have the same failure rate, λ, the reliability of a standby redundant system with *n* components is

$$R(x) = e^{-\lambda x} \sum_{i=0}^{n-1} \frac{(\lambda x)^i}{i!} \tag{4.10}$$

Example 4.5

Three power supplies are configured in a standby redundant system with perfect switching. The failure rate for each of the power supplies is constant with a mean time between failures of 20,000 hours. What is the probability of the system failing in less than 100,000 hours?

Solution

A constant failure rate indicates an exponential time to fail distribution. The system reliability is

$$R(t) = e^{-0.00005t} \sum_{i=0}^{3-1} \frac{(0.00005t)^i}{i!}$$

The reliability at 100,000 hours is

$$R(t) = e^{-5} \left[\frac{5^0}{0!} + \frac{5^1}{1!} + \frac{5^2}{2!} \right] = 0.1247$$

The probability of a failure in less than 100,000 hours of operation is

P(failure) = 1 − 0.1247 = 0.8753

In many cases, the assumption of perfect switching is unrealistic. For the simple case of two components in standby redundancy with exponential time to fail distributions, the reliability of the system is

$$R_s(x) = e^{-\lambda_a x} + \frac{p\lambda_a}{\lambda_b - \lambda_a} \left(e^{-\lambda_a x} - e^{-\lambda_b x} \right) \tag{4.11}$$

where: p is the reliability of the switch,

λ_a is the failure rate for the primary component, and

λ_b is the failure rate of the standby component.

If the components have identical failure rates, this expression reduces to

$$R_s(x) = e^{-\lambda x} (1 + p\lambda x) \tag{4.12}$$

Example 4.6

In the figure below, components 1 and 2 have exponential time-to-fail distributions with mean failure times of 66,667 hours and 100,000 hours respectively. The reliability of the switch is 0.95. What is the reliability of the system at 10,000 hours?

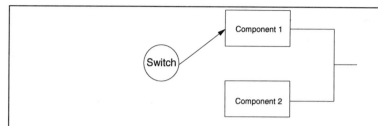

Solution

The system reliability is

$$R_s(t) = e^{-\frac{t}{66,667}} + \frac{0.95\left(\dfrac{1}{66,667}\right)}{\dfrac{1}{100,000} - \dfrac{1}{66,667}}\left(e^{-\frac{t}{66,667}} - e^{-\frac{t}{100,000}}\right)$$

At time = 10,000 hours, this expression is

$$R_s(10,000) = e^{-0.15} - 2.85\left(e^{-0.15} - e^{-0.1}\right) = .9865$$

Now consider the case where the switch is a complex piece of equipment with a constant failure rate, λ_s. For a two-component system, with one component in standby redundancy, the reliability of the system is

$$R_s(x) = e^{-\lambda x}\left[1 + \frac{\lambda}{\lambda_s}\left(1 - e^{-\lambda_s x}\right)\right] \qquad (4.13)$$

where: λ is the failure rate of each of the two components, and
λ_s is the failure rate of the switch.

The reliability of a three-component system with identical failure rates is

$$R_s(t) = e^{-\lambda t}\left[1 + \frac{\lambda}{\lambda_s}\left(1 - e^{-\lambda_s t}\right)\right] + e^{-\lambda t}\left(\frac{\lambda}{\lambda_s}\right)^2\left[1 - e^{-\lambda_s t} - \lambda_s t e^{-\lambda_s t}\right] \qquad (4.14)$$

Example 4.7

Two components with constant failure rates of 0.003 make up a standby redundant system. The device that transfers operation to the second component after failure of the first component has a constant failure rate of 0.0005. Determine the system reliability at time = 400.

Solution

The reliability of this system is

$$R_s(t) = e^{-0.003t}\left[1 + \frac{0.003}{0.0005}\left(1 - e^{-0.0005t}\right)\right]$$

At time = 400, the reliability is

$$R_s(t) = e^{-1.2}\left[1 + 6\left(1 - e^{-0.2}\right)\right] = 0.6288$$

In shared load parallel systems, as one component fails the failure rate of the remaining components increases. For a two-component system with both components having identical, constant failure rates, the system reliability is

$$R_s(x) = e^{-2\lambda_h x} + \frac{2\lambda_h}{2\lambda_h - \lambda_f}\left(e^{-\lambda_f x} - e^{-2\lambda_h x}\right) \tag{4.15}$$

where: λ_h is the half load failure rate (both components operating), and
λ_f is the full load failure rate.

For the special case where $2\lambda_h = \lambda_f$,

$$R_s(x) = e^{-2\lambda_h x} + 2\lambda_h x e^{-\lambda_f x} \tag{4.16}$$

Example 4.8

Two cables support the load of a crane. The failure rate of each of the cables is constant at 0.0007 if both cables are operating properly. The failure rate increases to 0.006 after one cable fails. Determine the reliability at time = 200.

Solution

The reliability of this system is

$$R_s(t) = e^{-2(0.0007)t} + \frac{2(0.0007)}{2(0.0007) - 0.006}\left(e^{-0.006t} - e^{-2(0.0007)t}\right)$$

At time = 200, the reliability is

$$R_s(t) = e^{-0.28} - 0.3043\left(e^{-1.2} - e^{-0.28}\right) = 0.8941$$

For the situations described above, there is no probability of failure of a component while it is in standby mode. Often this is not a valid assumption. The reliability of a system consisting of two components with one being standby redundant is

$$R_s(x) = e^{-\lambda_a x} + \frac{\lambda_a}{\lambda_a - \lambda_b + \lambda_{b,s}}\left[e^{-\lambda_b x} - e^{-(\lambda_a + \lambda_{b,s})x}\right] \tag{4.17}$$

where: λ_a is the failure rate for the primary component,
λ_b is the failure rate of the standby component when it is active, and
$\lambda_{b,s}$ is the failure rate of the standby unit when it is in standby mode.

For the special case where the failure rate of both components is the same in the active mode, the system reliability is

$$R_s(x) = \left(1 + \frac{\lambda}{\lambda_s}\right)e^{-\lambda x} - \frac{\lambda}{\lambda_s}e^{-(\lambda + \lambda_s)x} \tag{4.18}$$

where: λ is the failure rate of each of the components in active mode, and
λ_s is the failure rate of the standby component while in standby mode.

The system mean time to fail is

$$MTTF = \frac{1}{\lambda} + \frac{1}{\lambda_s} - \left(\frac{\lambda}{\lambda_s}\right)\left(\frac{1}{\lambda + \lambda_s}\right) \tag{4.19}$$

Example 4.9

A pump operates continuously with a mean time to fail of 200 hours that follows the exponential distribution. A second, identical pump is placed in standby redundancy, and the mean time to fail while the pump is inactive is 1,000 hours. The standby time to fail is also exponentially distributed. What is the mean time to fail for the system, and what is the system reliability at time = 300 hours?

Solution

The pump failure rate in the active mode is λ = 1/200 = 0.005. The pump failure rate in the standby mode is λ_s = 1/1000 = 0.001. The system mean time to fail is

$$MTTF = \frac{1}{0.005} + \frac{1}{0.001} - \left(\frac{0.005}{0.001}\right)\left(\frac{1}{0.005+0.001}\right) = 366.7$$

The system reliability at time = 300 hours is

$$R_s(300) = \left(1+\frac{0.005}{0.001}\right)e^{-0.005(300)} - \frac{0.005}{0.001}e^{-(0.005+0.001)300} = 0.512$$

4.2.5 Complex systems

In reality many systems are not simple series, parallel or standby redundant systems. They are combinations of these systems. The reliability of these complex systems can be obtained by simplifying the reliability block diagram. Consider the system in Figure 4.4.

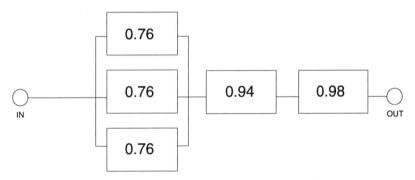

Figure 4.4. Parallel and series combination reliability block diagram.

The three components with reliability of 0.76 are a parallel system. This parallel system is in series with two more components. By reducing the parallel system, a simple series system can be obtained. The reliability of the parallel system is

$$R = 1 - (1-0.76)(1-0.76)(1-0.76) = 0.9862$$

The system in Figure 4.4 can now be shown as

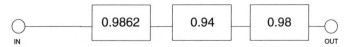

Figure 4.5. Figure 4.4 simplified.

The reliability of this system is

$$R = (0.9862)(0.94)(0.98) = 0.9085$$

Suppose only two of the three components with reliability of 0.76 in Figure 4.4 are required for the system to operate. Now a 2-out-of-3 system is in series with two other components. The reliability of the 2-out-of-3 system is

$$R = \sum_{x=2}^{3} \binom{3}{x} R^x (1-R)^{3-x}$$

$$R = \binom{3}{2} 0.76^2 (1-0.76)^1 + \binom{3}{3} 0.76^3 (1-0.76)^0$$

$$R = 0.415872 + 0.438976 = 0.8548$$

The system can now be shown as three components in series with reliabilities of 0.8548, 0.94 and 0.98. The system reliability is

$$R = (0.8548)(0.94)(0.98) = 0.7874$$

In some cases, the system cannot be simplified as easily. Consider the system in Figure 4.6.

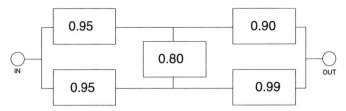

Figure 4.6. Complex reliability block diagram.

There is not an obvious way to simplify this system. By inspection, the component in the center of the diagram plays a key role. If the center component operates, then the system consists of two parallel systems in series. This is shown in Figure 4.7.

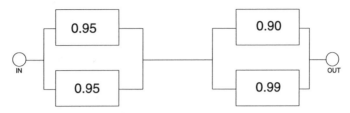

Figure 4.7. Figure 4.6 with the center component functioning.

The reliability of the components in parallel on the left side of Figure 4.7 is

$$R = 1 - (1 - 0.95)(1 - 0.95) = 0.9975$$

The reliability of the other set of parallel components is

$$R = 1 - (1 - 0.9)(1 - 0.99) = 0.999$$

The reliability of the system shown in Figure 4.7 is

$$R = (0.9975)(0.999) = 0.9965$$

Now assume the component in the center of Figure 4.6 fails. The resulting system is shown in Figure 4.8.

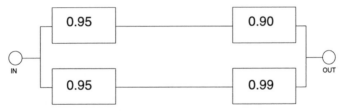

Figure 4.8. Figure 4.6 with center component failed.

Figure 4.8 can be further reduced by computing the reliabilities of the components in series. The reliability of the series system in the top half of Figure 4.8 is

$$R = (0.95)(0.90) = 0.855$$

The reliability of the series system in the bottom half of Figure 4.8 is

$$R = (0.95)(0.99) = 0.9405$$

The reliability of the system shown in Figure 4.8 is

$$R = 1 - (1 - 0.855)(1 - .9405) = 0.9914$$

So far it is known that if the component in the center of Figure 4.6 functions, the reliability of the system is 0.9965; and that if that component fails, the reliability of the system is 0.9914. The system reliability is the reliability of the system given the center component operates properly, multiplied by the probability of the center component operating properly, plus the reliability of the system given the center component fails, multiplied by the probability the center component fails. Since the reliability of the center component is 0.8, the reliability of the system is

$$R = (0.8)(0.9965) + (0.2)(0.9914) = 0.9955$$

4.2.6 Stress-strength systems

If a component has a strength, y, and is subjected to a stress, x, the component fails when $y < x$. If the variables y and x are random and can be described by a probability density function, then the probability of failure can be modeled. Consider Figure 4.9.

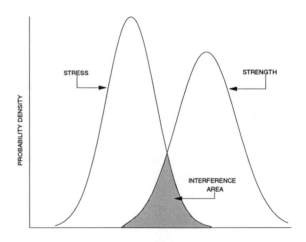

Figure 4.9. Stress-strength interference.

The shaded region of Figure 4.9 is known as the interference area. In the interference area, and only in the interference area, there is a probability of stress being greater than strength. Note that the area in the shaded region of Figure 4.9 is **not** equal to the probability of stress being greater than strength. The general expression for the reliability of a stress-strength system is

$$R = P(\text{stress} < \text{strength}) = \int_0^\infty \int_0^\infty g(y+x)f(x)dxdy \qquad (4.20)$$

where: $g(y)$ is the strength probability density function, and
$f(x)$ is the stress probability density function.

If the probability density functions for stress and strength are both normally distributed and independent, the reliability (the probability that strength is greater than stress) is

$$R = \Phi\left(\frac{\mu_y - \mu_x}{\sqrt{\sigma_y^2 + \sigma_x^2}}\right) \qquad (4.21)$$

where: $\Phi(x)$ is the standard normal cumulative distribution function,
μ_y is the mean strength,
σ_y is the strength standard deviation,
μ_x is the mean stress, and
σ_x is the stress standard deviation.

Example 4.10

The strength of an axle is normally distributed with a mean of 20,000 kPa and a standard deviation of 1,500 kPa. The axle is subjected to a stress that is normally distributed with a mean of 15,000 kPa and a standard deviation of 2,500 kPa. What is the reliability of the axle?

Solution

The axle reliability is

$$R = \Phi\left(\frac{20{,}000 - 15{,}000}{\sqrt{1500^2 + 2500^2}}\right) = \Phi(1.715)$$

> From Appendix A, the area under the standard normal curve to the left of z = 1.715 is 0.9568.

Example 4.11

A component will be subjected to a normally distributed stress with a mean of 65 units and a standard deviation of 8 units. What must the mean strength of the component be if a reliability of 0.999 is required and the standard deviation of the strength is 3 units?

Solution

The first step is to find the inverse of the standard normal distribution function. From Appendix A,

$$0.999 = \Phi(3.0905)$$

From Equation 4.21,

$$3.0905 = \frac{\mu_y - 65}{\sqrt{8^2 + 3^2}}$$

The required mean strength is 91.41 units.

Example 4.12

The strength of a component is normally distributed with an unknown mean and a known variance of 25. Twenty components were randomly selected and tested. The average strength of these 20 components was 150. What is the maximum stress that these components can endure to be 90% confident of a 95% reliability?

Solution

A 90% lower confidence level for the mean strength is found from the expression

$$\mu_{90\%L} = 150 - \left(\frac{1.28}{\sqrt{20}}\right)\sqrt{25} = 148.57$$

The inverse of the standard normal cumulative distribution function, $\Phi(0.95)$, is 1.645. The maximum stress is found from the expression

$$1.645 = \frac{148.57 - x}{\sqrt{25}}$$

$$\mu_x = 140.35$$

4.3 Fault trees

Fault tree analysis provides a formal method of determining the combinations of primary events that result in the occurrence of a specified system level event. H. R. Watson conceived fault-tree analysis while working on safety evaluation for the Minuteman Launch Control System. Watson realized that the logic flow in data processing equipment could be used for analyzing the logic of system failures resulting from component failures.

Fault-trees provide a graphical representation of the system being studied, and their use often results in the discovery of failure combinations that would not have been obvious if other failure identification methods were used. Fault trees are useful for both qualitative and quantitative analyses. Some common uses for fault trees are:

- Root cause failure analysis
- Failure modes and effects analysis
- Preliminary hazard analysis
- Probability calculations

4.3.1 Fault-tree construction

Fault trees are built from gates and events. A list of fault-tree gates is provided in Table 4.1; a list of fault tree events is provided in Table 4.2.

Table 4.1. Fault tree gates.

Symbol	Name	Description
	OR Gate	The event above this gate occurs if **any** of the events below this gate occur. An *OR* gate signifies a union of events.
	AND Gate	The event above this gate occurs if **all** the events below this gate occur. An *AND* gate signifies an intersection of events.
	Exclusive OR Gate	The event above this gate occurs if one of the events below the gate occur and the others do not. The triggering event is specified within the gate.
	Priority AND Gate	The event above this gate occurs if all the events below the gate occur in the order specified. The order may be listed in the gate or in an attached oval. If no order is specified, the default order is left to right.
r	r-out-of-n Gate	The event above this gate occurs if *r* of the *n* events below the gate take place.
	AND NOT Gate	The event above this gate occurs if all the events on a leg without a circle occur, and all the events on a leg with a circle **do not** occur.
	Inhibit Gate	A special type of *AND* gate. The event above this gate transpires if the event listed within the Inhibit gate is satisfied **and** the event below the gate takes place.

Table 4.2. Fault tree events.

Symbol	Name	Description
⬤	Primary event. Also known as a Basic event.	The lowest level of failure possible. Primary events are individual component failures, human errors and software errors.
▭	Conditional Event	Conditional events are dependent on Primary events. They are located above gates in the fault tree.
⌂	House Event	An event that can be turned on or off. If turned on, the probability of occurrence is 1; if turned off, the probability of occurrence is 0. Often used for scenario analysis.
◇	Undeveloped Event	This event has not been defined. Some reasons for not defining an event are; lack of interest, lack of information, or further development will not provide additional understanding.
△	Triangle In	Use to repeat a portion of the tree or to continue the tree on another page.
△	Triangle Out	Used in conjunction with the Triangle In block.

Consider how an automobile might fail to complete a trip. The event under consideration is the failure of the automobile to complete the trip. In the fault tree, this will be the *Top* event, and will be represented by a conditional event.

Simplifying the problem, an automobile fails to complete a trip if

1. two of the five tires go flat (including the spare),
2. the engine fails, or
3. the transmission fails.

For this example, it is assumed all other systems work. This is depicted with a house event. The fault tree for this example is shown in Figure 4.10.

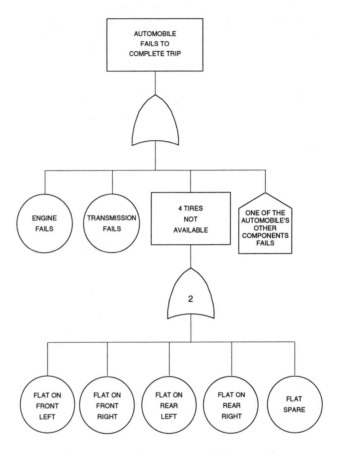

Figure 4.10. Automobile fault tree.

The *Top* event in this fault tree is the conditional event—automobile fails to complete the trip. Following the *Top* event is an *OR* gate. The *Top* event will take place if any of the four events below the *OR* gate take place. Two of these four events are primary events; engine fails and transmission fails. The conditional event, 4 tires not available, is dependent on the outcome of the *r-out-of-n* gate. The number "2" in the *r-out-of-n* gate signifies that two of the five events below the gate must transpire for the conditional event above the gate to occur. The house event is used to indicate if a component not detailed in the fault tree failed. If this house event is turned off, all of the automobile's components not detailed in the fault tree function properly. If turned on, the top event occurs. A logical analysis for this example would be to turn the house event off.

4.3.2 Cut sets and path sets

A **cut set** is a set of primary events that cause the *Top* event to transpire if they **all** transpire. A cut set may be a subset of another cut set. For the automobile trip example: if the engine fails, the transmission fails, there is a flat on the front left tire, there is a flat on the front right, and a flat spare tire, then the automobile will fail to make the trip. Thus, the occurrence of all of these events is a cut set. However, if there is a flat on the front left tire and the front right tire, the automobile also fails to make the trip. The set: flat on front left and flat on front right, is also a cut set.

A **minimum cut set** is a cut set that is no longer a cut set if any events are removed from the cut set. The first cut set mentioned above is not a minimum cut set. Several events were removed (engine fails, transmission fails, left, flat spare) and the set remained a cut set. The cut set: flat on front left and flat on front right, is a minimum cut set. If either of the two events: flat on front left or flat on front right, is removed from the cut set, the remaining event in the set is not sufficient to cause the *Top* event to occur. Thus: the set, flat on front left and flat on front right, is a minimum cut set. The remaining minimum cut sets for this problem are:

1. Engine fails
2. Transmission fails
3. House event turned on
4. Flat on front left and flat on rear left
5. Flat on front left and flat on rear right
6. Flat on front left and flat spare
7. Flat on front right and flat on rear left
8. Flat on front right and flat on right

9. Flat on front right and flat spare
10. Flat on rear left and flat on rear right
11. Flat on rear left and flat spare
12. Flat on rear right and flat spare

Minimum cut sets can be determined intuitively in small fault trees, however, for large trees, quantitative methods are needed. The four most common techniques for determining minimum cut sets are:

1. Use of Boolean algebra
2. The prime number method
3. The binary string bit method
4. The combination testing method

For more information concerning these methods consult Sundararajan (1991).

In some cases the interest is in what prevents the *Top* event from occurring, rather than what causes it to occur. This is done by identifying path sets; the opposite of cut sets. If **none** of the events in a **path set** occur, the *Top* event is prevented from occurring.

A path set, that is no longer a path set if any events are removed from the set, is a **minimum path set**. The minimum path sets for the previous example are (assuming the house event is turned off):

1. a) engine fails and
   b) transmission fails and
   c) flat on front left and
   d) flat on front right and
   e) flat on rear left and
   f) flat on rear right

2. a) engine fails and
   b) transmission fails and
   c) flat on front left and
   d) flat on front right and
   e) flat on rear left and
   f) flat spare

3. a) engine fails and
    b) transmission fails and
    c) flat on front left and
    d) flat on front right and
    e) flat spare rear left and
    f) flat on rear right
4. a) engine fails and
    b) transmission fails and
    c) flat on front left and
    d) flat spare and
    e) flat on rear left
    f) flat on rear right
5. a) engine fails and
    b) transmission fails and
    c) flat spare and
    d) flat on front right and
    e) flat on rear left and
    f) flat on rear right

The fault tree displayed in Figure 4.11 demonstrates the *AND* gate, the *AND NOT* gate, and the Inhibit gate. The *Top* Event is followed by an *AND* gate and takes place only if Event A and Event B take place. Event A is followed by an *AND NOT* gate and transpires if Event 1 occurs and Event 2 does not occur. Event B is followed by an Inhibit gate and occurs if Events 3 and 4 take place.

The fault tree presented in Figure 4.12 illustrates the Exclusive *OR* gate and the Priority *AND* gate. Being followed by an Exclusive *OR* gate, the *Top* Event transpires if either Event A or Event 3 occur, but does not transpire if both Event A and Event 3 occur. Event A takes place if Event 1 and Event 2 take place, but only if Event 1 occurs before Event 2.

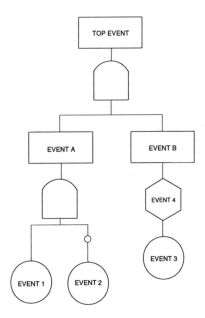

Figure 4.11. Example fault tree.

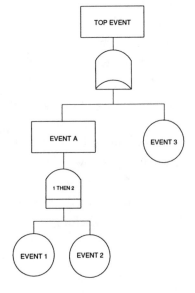

Figure 4.12. Example fault tree.

4.3.3 Quantitative fault tree analysis

If an event does not occur in more than one place in a fault tree, the probability of the *Top* event occurring can be determined by starting at the bottom of the tree and evaluating the probabilities of each branch of the tree. For example, compute the probability of the *Top* Event occurring in the fault tree in Figure 4.13, given the following probabilities for occurrence

1. probability of Event 1 = 0.3,
2. probability of Event 2 = 0.06,
3. probability of Event 3 = 0.12,
4. probability of Event 4 = 0.22, and
5. probability of Event 5 = 0.08.

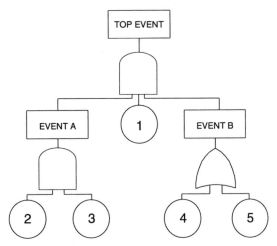

Figure 4.13. Quantitative fault tree example.

Solution

Event A occurs if Events 2 and 3 both occur; the probability of this happening is $(0.06)(0.12) = 0.0072$. Event B occurs if either event 4 or event 5 occur; this probability is $[1-(1-0.22)(1-0.08)] = 0.2824$. The *Top* Event occurs if events A, B and 1 all occur; this probability is $(0.0072)(0.2824)(0.3) = 0.00061$.

Now consider the fault tree in Figure 4.14. This tree is identical to the tree depicted in Figure 4.7, except for two changes; Event 5 has been replaced by event 1, and the gate immediately below the *Top* Event has been changed from an *AND* gate to an *OR gate*. The probability of Events 1–4 occurring is the same as in the previous example.

Because Event 1 appears in more than one location in the fault tree, the branches of the tree are no longer independent. Thus, the method used to solve the previous problem cannot be used.

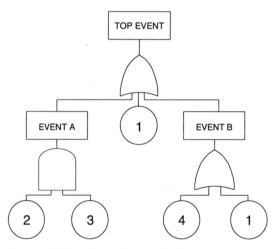

Figure 4.14. Quantitative fault tree example.

The probability of the *Top* Event occurring in a fault tree can be determined if the minimum cut sets for the tree are known. The expression for the probability of the *Top* Event occurring is

$$P_T = \sum_{i=1}^{N} P(C_i) - \sum_{i=1}^{N}\sum_{j=1}^{N} P(C_i \cap C_j)$$
$$+ \sum_{i=1}^{N}\sum_{j=1}^{N}\sum_{k=1}^{N} P(C_i \cap C_j \cap C_k)...+(-1)^{N-1} P\left(\bigcap_{i=1}^{N} C_i\right)$$

(4.22)

where N is the number of minimum cut sets and $P(C_i)$ represents the probability of the minimum cut set i occurring.

Solution

The cut sets for this tree are; (1), (4), (1,2), (1,3), (1,4), (2,3), (2,4), (3,4), (1,2,3), (1,2,4), (1,3,4), (2,3,4), and (1,2,3,4). The minimum cut sets are (1), (4), and (2,3). The probability of each minimum cut set occurring is

Minimum Cut Set	Probability of Occurrence
Event 1	0.3
Event 4	0.22
Event 2 and Event 3	(0.06)(0.12)=0.0072

Using Equation 4.22, the probability of the *Top* Event occurring is:

$$P_T = 0.3 + 0.22 + 0.0072 - (0.3)(0.22) - (0.3)(0.0072)$$
$$- (0.22)(0.0072) + (0.3)(0.22)(0.0072)$$
$$= 0.4579$$

4.4 Monte Carlo Simulation

As seen in the previous sections, reliability modeling can be difficult mathematically. And in many cases, it is impossible to mathematically model the situation desired. Monte Carlo Simulation is a useful tool under these and many other circumstances, such as:

- Verifying analytical solutions
- Studying dynamic situations
- Gaining information about event sequences; often expected values and moments do not provide enough detail
- Determining the important components and variables in a complex system
- Determining the interaction among variables
- Studying the effects of changes without the risk, cost, and time constraints of experimenting on the real system
- Teaching

4.4.1 Random number generators

The heart of any simulation is the generation of random numbers. If a programming language such as, BASIC, C, or FORTRAN is used, random number generators will have to be created. If simulation languages such as, Siman, Slam, Simscript, or GPSS, are used, random number generators are part of the software.

Random numbers from specific distributions are generated by transforming random numbers from the unit, uniform distribution. Virtually all programming languages, as well as electronic spreadsheets, include a unit, uniform random number generator*. Technically, these unit, uniform random number generators are pseudo-random number generators, as the algorithms used to generate them takes away a small portion of the randomness. Nevertheless, these algorithms are extremely efficient and for all practical purposes the result is a set of truly random numbers.

A simple way to generate distribution-specific random numbers is to set the cumulative distribution function equal to a unit, random number and take the inverse. Consider the exponential distribution

$$F(x) = 1 - e^{-\lambda x} \tag{4.20}$$

By setting a random variable uniformly distributed from 0 to 1, r, equal to $F(x)$ and inverting the function, an exponentially distributed random variable, x, with a failure rate of λ is created.

$$r = 1 - e^{-\lambda x}$$

$$1 - r = e^{-\lambda x}$$

$$\ln(1-r) = -\lambda x \tag{4.21}$$

$$x = -\frac{\ln(1-r)}{\lambda}$$

---

* A unit, uniform random variable can be generated using the "RND" function in the BASIC programming language (Visual Basic, Quick Basic, GWBasic, and BASICA), and the "@RAND" function in Lotus™ 123. Microsoft™ Excel includes a random generating tool that allows random numbers to be generated from several distributions.

This expression can be further reduced; the term $1-r$ is also uniformly distributed from 0 to 1. The result is

$$x = -\frac{\ln r}{\lambda} \tag{4.22}$$

Table 4.3 contains some common random number generators.

Table 4.3. Random number generators.

Distribution	Probability Density Function	Random Number Generator
Uniform	$f(x) = \dfrac{1}{b-a}, a \le x \le b$	$x = a + (b-a)r$
Exponential	$f(x) = \lambda e^{-\lambda x}, 0 < x < \infty$	$x = -\dfrac{1}{\lambda} \ln r$
Normal	$f(x) = \dfrac{1}{\sigma\sqrt{2\Pi}} \exp\left[-\dfrac{1}{2}\left(\dfrac{x-\mu}{\sigma}\right)^2\right],$ $-\infty < x < \infty$	$x_1 = \left[\sqrt{-2\ln r_1}\,\cos(2\Pi r_2)\right]\sigma + \mu$ $x_2 = \left[\sqrt{-2\ln r_1}\,\sin(2\Pi r_2)\right]\sigma + \mu$ [†]
Lognormal	$f(x) = \dfrac{1}{\sigma x\sqrt{2\Pi}} \exp\left[-\dfrac{1}{2}\left(\dfrac{\ln x-\mu}{\sigma}\right)^2\right],$ $x > 0$	$x_1 = \left\{\ln\left[\sqrt{-2\ln r_1}\,\cos(2\Pi r_2)\right]\right\}\sigma + \mu$ $x_2 = \left\{\ln\left[\sqrt{-2\ln r_1}\,\sin(2\Pi r_2)\right]\right\}\sigma + \mu$ [†]
Weibull	$f(x) = \dfrac{\beta x^{\beta-1}}{\theta^\beta} \exp\left(\dfrac{x}{\theta}\right)^\beta, x > 0$	$x = \theta(-\ln r)^{1/\beta}$
Poisson	$f(x) = \dfrac{e^{-\lambda t}(\lambda t)^x}{x!}, x = 0,1,2,...,\infty$	$x = \begin{cases} 0, -\dfrac{1}{\lambda}\ln r > t \\ x, \displaystyle\sum_{i=1}^{x} -\dfrac{1}{\lambda}\ln r_i < t < \sum_{i=1}^{x+1} -\dfrac{1}{\lambda}\ln r_i \end{cases}$ [‡]
Chi-square	$f(x) = \dfrac{1}{2^{v/2}\Gamma(v/2)} x^{(v/2-1)}e^{-x/2}, x > 0$	$x = \displaystyle\sum_{i=1}^{v} z_i^2$, z_i is a standard normal random deviate.
Beta	$f(x) = \dfrac{1}{B(p,q)} x^{p-1}(1-x)^{q-1},$ $0 \le x \le 1, p > 0, q > 0$	$x = \dfrac{r^{1/p}}{r^{1/p} + r^{1/q}}$

Continued on next page...

Table 4.3—*continued...*

Distribution	Probability Density Function	Random Number Generator
Gamma	$f(x) = \dfrac{\lambda^n}{\Gamma(\eta)} x^{(\eta-1)} e^{-\lambda x}$, $x \geq 0, \eta \geq 0, \lambda \geq 0$	1. η is a non-integer shape parameter. 2. Let η_1 = the truncated integer root of η. 3. Let $q = -\ln \prod_{j=1}^{\eta_1} r_j$. 4. Let $A = \eta - \eta_1$, and $B = 1-A$. 5. Generate a random number and let $y_1 = r_i^{1/A}$. 6. Generate a random number and let $y_2 = r_{i+1}^{1/B}$ 7. If $y_1 + y_2 \leq 1$ go to 9. 8. Let $i=i+2$ and go to 5. 9. Let $z = y_1 / (y_1 + y_2)$. 10. Generate a random number, r_n. 11. Let $W = -\ln r_n$. 12. $x = (q + zW)\lambda$.
Binomial	$p(x) = \dbinom{n}{x} p^x (1-p)^{n-x}, x = 0, 1, ..., n$	$x = \sum\limits_{i=1}^{n} y_i, \; y_i = \begin{cases} 0, r_i > p \\ 1, r_i \leq p \end{cases}$
Geometric	$p(x) = p(1-p)^{x-1}, x = 1, 2, 3, ...$	$\dfrac{\ln(1-r)}{\ln(1-p)} \leq x \leq \dfrac{\ln(1-r)}{\ln(1-p)} + 1$ [‡]
Student's t	$f(x) = \dfrac{\Gamma[(v+1)/2]}{\Gamma(v/2)\sqrt{\Pi v}} \left(1 + \dfrac{x^2}{v}\right)^{-(v+1)/2}$, $-\infty < x < \infty$	$x = \dfrac{z_1}{\left(\sum\limits_{i=2}^{v+1} \dfrac{z_i^2}{v}\right)^{1/2}}$ z_i is a standard normal random deviate.
F	$f(x) = \left(\dfrac{\Gamma[(v_1 + v_2)/2](v_1/v_2)^{v_1/2}}{\Gamma(v_1/2)\Gamma(v_2/2)}\right)$ $* \left(\dfrac{x^{v_1/2 - 1}}{(1 + v_1 x / v_2)^{(v_1 + v_2)/2}}\right), x > 0$	$x = \dfrac{v_2 \sum\limits_{i=1}^{v_1} z_i^2}{v_1 \sum\limits_{i=v_1+1}^{v_1+v_2} z_i^2}$ z_i is a standard normal random deviate.

[†] Two uniform random numbers must be generated, with the result being two normally distributed random numbers.

[‡] Increase the value of x until the inequality is satisfied.

4.4.2 Simulation modeling

After the desired random number generator(s) have been constructed, the next step is to mathematically model the situation under study. After completing the model, it is important to **validate** and **verify** the model. A valid model is a reasonable representation of the situation being studied. A model is verified by determining that the mathematical and computer model created represents the intended conceptual model.

Enough iterations should be included in the simulation to provide a **steady-state** solution. A steady-state solution is reached when the output of the simulation from one iteration to the next changes negligibly. When calculating means and variances, 1,000 iterations is usually sufficient. If calculating confidence limits, many more iterations are required; after all, for 99% confidence limits the sample size for the number of random deviates exceeding the confidence limit is 1/100th the number of iterations.

Simulation can be used to determine the result of transformations of random variables. Suppose the mean and variance of the product of two normally distributed variables are needed for design purposes. The following BASIC code will produce the desired result. A flowchart for this code is shown in Figure 4.15.

```
REM simulation for the product of two normally distributed variables
e1=100
v1=7
e2=120
v2=16
DEFINT I–L
FOR i = 1 TO 5000
a = RND
b = RND
REM x is normal with mean=e1 and standard deviation=v1
x = (((–2 * LOG(a)) ^ .5) * COS(2 * 3.141592654# * b)) * v1 + e1
REM y is normal with mean=e2 and standard deviation=v2
y = (((–2 * LOG(a)) ^ .5) * SIN(2 * 3.141592654# * b)) * v2 + e2
z = x * y
ztot# = ztot# + z
zsq# = zsq# + z ^ 2
PRINT i
```

```
NEXT i
PRINT "ztot zsq"; ztot#; zsq#
PRINT "mean="; ztot# / 5000
zvar# = (5000 * zsq# – ztot# ^ 2) / (5000 * 4999)
PRINT "variance="; zvar#
```

Note: "RND" generates uniform random deviates on the interval from 0 to 1. The "LOG" function in BASIC represents the natural logarithm.

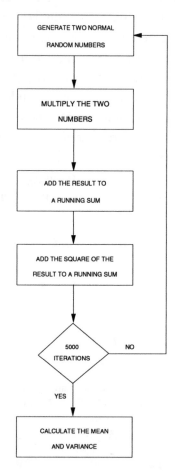

Figure 4.15. Flowchart for the simulation of two normally distributed normal variables.

In the above code, two normal random numbers are generated with the desired parameters and multiplied. This is repeated 5000 times, and the mean and variance of these 5000 random deviates are calculated. The result is a random variable with a mean of 12,009 and a variance of 3,307380.

For the above example, recall that the same result could have been obtained mathematically from the information contained in Section 3.9. A disadvantage of solving this problem mathematically is that there is no information regarding the shape of the resulting distribution.

With electronic spreadsheets, simulations no longer require computer code. The previous example is simulated using *Lotus 123*™ with the following steps*.

1. In cell *A1* place the function @RAND
2. In cell *A2* place the function @RAND
3. In cell *A3* place the formula

   $(((-2*@ln(A1))^{.5})*@cos(2*@pi*A2))*7+100$

4. In cell *A4* place the formula

   $(((-2*@ln(A1))^{.5})*@cos(2*@pi*A2))*7+100$

5. In cell *A5* place the formula

   +A3*A4

6. Copy this row 5,000 times

In the above example, each row in the spreadsheet represents an iteration. The powerful @functions and graphics tools contained in the spreadsheet can then be used for analysis. Note that each change in the spreadsheet causes the random numbers to be changed. It may be helpful to convert the output from formulas to fixed numbers with the "Range Value" command.

Now consider a system consisting of four identical components which are exponentially distributed with a failure rate of 0.8. Three of the components are standby redundant with perfect switching. Information is needed regarding the shape of the resulting distribution. The following code produces four exponentially distributed random variables with a failure rate of 0.8, adds

---

* Microsoft™ Excel can generate normal random variables directly.

them, and writes the result to the file "c:\data."; this process is repeated 5,000 times. A flowchart for this problem is provided in Figure 4.16.

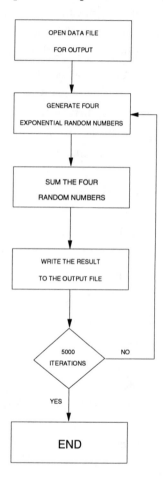

Figure 4.16. Simulation for the sum of exponential random variables.

```
REM simulation for the sum of four exponentially distributed variables
DEFINT I–L
OPEN "c:\data" FOR OUTPUT AS #1 LEN = 256
FOR i = 1 TO 5000
REM x1 is exponential with failure rate = 0.8
x1 = –(1 / .8) * LOG(RND)
REM x2 is exponential with failure rate = 0.8
```

```
x2 = -(1 / .8) * LOG(RND)
REM x3 is exponential with failure rate = 0.8
x3 = -(1 / .8) * LOG(RND)
REM x4 is exponential with failure rate = 0.8
x4 = -(1 / .8) * LOG(RND)
y = x1 + x2 + x3 + x4
PRINT #1, USING "##########.#####"; y
PRINT i
NEXT i
CLOSE
```

By importing the resulting data into an electronic spreadsheet or statistical program, a wide variety of analyses can be done on the data. A histogram of the data produced from the above code is shown in Figure 4.17.

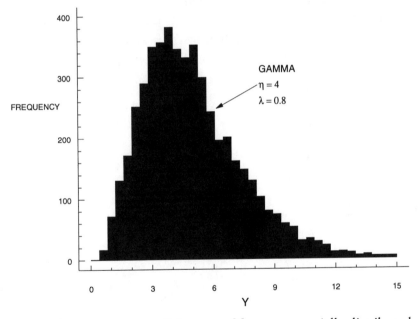

Figure 4.17. Histogram of the sum of four exponentially distributed random variables.

As seen from Figure 4.17, the sum of n exponentially distributed random variables with a failure rate of λ is a random variable that follows the gamma distribution with parameters $\eta = n$ and λ.

This problem is also easily simulated using an electronic spreadsheet. The steps required follow:

1. In cells *A1* through *A4*, place the formula

   $-(1/0.8)*@ln(@rand)$

2. In cell A5 place the formula

   @sum(A1..A4)

3. Copy the contents of row A 5000 times

Again, each row represents an iteration, and the spreadsheet can be used to obtain the desired simulation output.

Now consider a system consisting of three components in series. The components are Weibully distributed with parameters $\beta = 2$, $\theta = 300$; $\beta = 4$, $\theta = 100$; and, $\beta = 0.5$, $\theta = 200$. The code below depicts this situation. Figure 4.18 shows a flowchart for this simulation.

```
REM simulation three Weibully distributed variables in series
DEFINT I–L
DIM x(99)
OPEN "c:\data" FOR OUTPUT AS #1 LEN = 256
FOR i = 1 TO 5000
REM x(1) is Weibull shape parameter=2 and scale parameter=300
x(1) = 300 * (–LOG(RND)) ^ (1 / 2)
REM x(2) is Weibull shape parameter=4 and scale parameter=100
x(2) = 100 * (–LOG(RND)) ^ (1 / 4)
REM x(3) is Weibull shape parameter=0.5 and scale parameter=200
x(3) = 200 * (–LOG(RND)) ^ (1 / .5)
min = 999999999
FOR j = 1 TO 3
IF x(j) < min THEN min = x(j)
NEXT j
y = min
PRINT #1, USING "##########.#####"; y
PRINT i
NEXT i
CLOSE
```

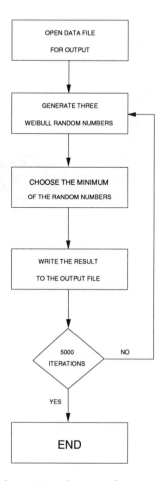

Figure 4.18. Simulation of a series system.

For a series system, the time to fail is the minimum of the times to fail of the components in series. A parallel system could be modeled by altering the above code to take the maximum time to fail of each of the components. Figure 4.19 is a histogram of the resulting data for the series system.

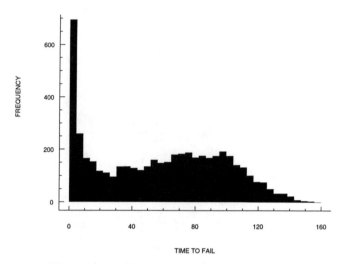

Figure 4.19. Histogram of a series system.

The large number of early failures are caused by the component with the high infant mortality rate ($\beta = 0.5$). The result is a distribution that does not appear to conform to any known distributions. However, with 5,000 points, a reliability function can be built empirically. The result is shown in Figure 4.20.

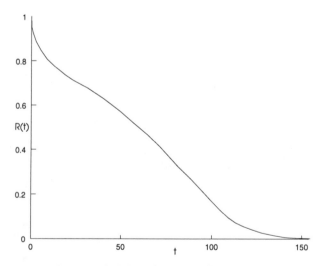

Figure 4.20. Reliability function for a series system.

The following steps are used to simulate the above problem using an electronic spreadsheet:

1. In cell *A1* place the formula

   300*(–@ln(@rand))^(1/2)

2. In cell *A2* place the formula

   100*(–@ln(@rand))^(1/4)

3. In cell *A3* place the formula

   200*(–@ln(@rand))^(1/0.5)

4. In cell *A4* place the formula

   @min(A1..A4)

5. Copy the contents of row *A* 5,000 times.

Now consider a system with two Weibully distributed components, A and B. Component B is standby redundant, and the switching mechanism has a reliability of 95%. The parameters of component A are β = 3, θ = 85. The parameters of component B are β = 4.4, θ = 95. The code below models this system; a flowchart is given in Figure 4.21.

```
REM simulation of a switch for two Weibully distributed variables
DEFINT I–L
OPEN "c:\data" FOR OUTPUT AS #1 LEN = 256
FOR i = 1 TO 5000
REM x is Weibull shape parameter=3 and scale parameter=85
x = 85 * (–LOG(RND)) ^ (1 / 3)
REM y is Weibull shape parameter=4.4 and scale parameter=97
y = 97 * (–LOG(RND)) ^ (1 / 4.4)
s = RND
IF s >= .05 THEN swr = 1 ELSE swr = 0
IF swr = 1 THEN z = x + y ELSE z = x
PRINT #1, USING "##########.#####"; y
PRINT i
NEXT i
CLOSE
```

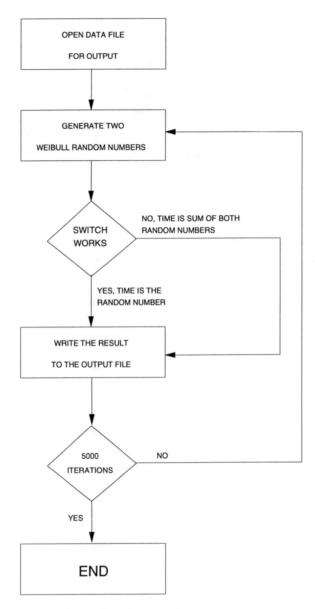

Figure 4.21. Simulation of a switching system.

A histogram of the 5,000 data points written to the data file is shown in Figure 4.22.

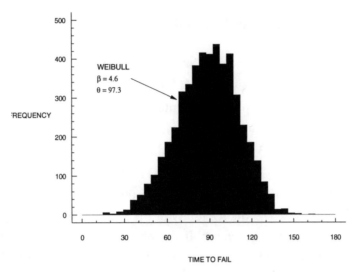

Figure 4.22. Histogram of a switching system.

The histogram shows the time to fail for the system follows a Weibull distribution. The reliability function for this system, built from the 5,000 simulation points, is shown in Figure 4.23.

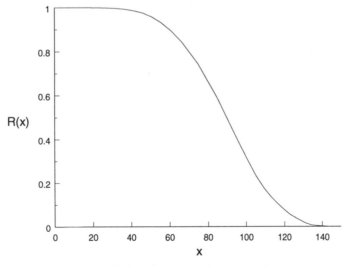

Figure 4.23. Reliability function for a switching system.

This situation can be simulated using an electronic spreadsheet. The required steps follow:

1. In cell A1 place the formula

    85*(@ln(@rand))^(1/3)

2. In cell A@ place the formula

    97*(@ln(@rand))^(1/4.5)

3. In cell A3 place the formula

    @if(@rand<0.05,+A1,+A1+A2)

4. Copy the contents of row A 5,000 times.

In step 4 above, the reliability of the switch is tested using the unit, uniform random number generator. If the unit, uniform random number is less than 0.05, the switch fails, and the time to fail for the system is the time to fail for component A (the value in cell A1). If the switch operates, the system time to fail is the sum of the values in cells A1 and A2.

In summary, simulation is a powerful analytical tool that can be used to model virtually any system. For the above examples 5,000 iterations were used. The number of iterations used should be based on reaching a steady-state condition. Depending on the problem more or less iterations may be needed.

Once simulation is mastered, a danger is that it is overused because of the difficulty involved with mathematical models. Do not be tempted to use simulation before exploring other options. When manipulating models, mathematical models lend themselves to optimization whereas simulation models require trial and error for optimization.

4.5 Markov analysis

Markov analysis is used to model a system that can be defined as a set of states. For example, a system consisting of two components in parallel, A and B, can be defined as having the following four states:

1. Components A and B operating
2. Component A failed and component B operating
3. Component A operating and component B failed
4. Components A and B failed

An important feature of Markov models is that the probability of transition from one state to another in a given time interval is independent of all previous states. Also, the probability of more than one transition in a given interval is assumed to be zero. If the transition rates for the model are constant, the model is homogeneous. If the transition functions are time dependent, the model is non-homogeneous.

Using Markov analysis, the probability of the system being in a specific state at a given time can be determined. This information can be used to determine system performance measures, such as reliability and availability. The probability of a system being in state i at a given time, $P_i(t)$ is found by solving a set of differential equations. The differential equations are derived from the **state transition diagram** or the **transition rate matrix**. The state transition diagram is a graphical representation of the rate of transition from one state to another. For the two-state system described above, assuming component a has a constant failure rate of λ_a and component B has a constant failure rate of λ_b, the state transition diagram is shown in Figure 4.24.

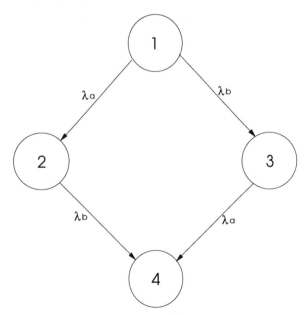

Figure 4.24. Parallel system state transition diagram.

The differential equations needed to describe this system can be determined from the State transition diagram. State 1 has no possibility of being entered, and it is exited with rates of λ_a and λ_b. The differential equation describing this is

$$\frac{dP_1(t)}{dt} = -\lambda_a P_1(t) - \lambda_b P_1(t) \tag{4.23}$$

State 2 is entered from State 1 at a rate of λ_a and exited from with a rate of λ_b. The describing equation is

$$\frac{dP_2(t)}{dt} = \lambda_a P_1(t) - \lambda_b P_2(t) \tag{4.24}$$

State 3 is entered from State 1 at a rate of λ_b and exited from with a rate of λ_a. The describing equation is

$$\frac{dP_3(t)}{dt} = \lambda_b P_1(t) - \lambda_a P_3(t) \tag{4.25}$$

State 4 is entered from State 2 at a rate of λ_b and is entered from State 3 at a rate of λ_a. Since there is no transition from State 4, it is called an **absorbing state**. The differential equation describing State 4 is

$$\frac{dP_4(t)}{dt} = \lambda_b P_2(t) + \lambda_a P_3(t) \tag{4.26}$$

With the exception of the equation describing $P_1(t)$, the equations above are coupled. A drawback of Markov analysis is the difficulty in solving the resulting system of differential equations. However, this problem has been lessened with modern symbolic software such as *Maple*. Modern symbolic processors can quickly solve large systems of differential equations.

Solving the above system of equations yields

$$P_1(t) = e^{-(\lambda_a + \lambda_b)t} \tag{4.27}$$

$$P_2(t) = e^{-\lambda_b t} - e^{-(\lambda_a + \lambda_b)t} \tag{4.28}$$

$$P_3(t) = e^{-\lambda_a t} - e^{-(\lambda_a + \lambda_b)t} \tag{4.29}$$

$$P_4(t) = 1 - e^{-\lambda_a t} - e^{-\lambda_b t} - e^{-(\lambda_a + \lambda_b)t} \tag{4.30}$$

The transition rate matrix displays the same information as the state transition diagram in the form of a matrix. Each value in the matrix, r_{ij}, represents transition rate from state i to state j. For the system described in Figure 4.24, the transition rate matrix is

$$\Lambda = \begin{bmatrix} 0 & \lambda_a & \lambda_b & 0 \\ 0 & 0 & 0 & \lambda_b \\ 0 & 0 & 0 & \lambda_a \\ 0 & 0 & 0 & 0 \end{bmatrix} \tag{4.31}$$

The derivative of the probability of the system being in a given state at a specific time is

$$\frac{dP_i(t)}{dt} = \sum_{k=1}^{n} r_{ki} P_k(t) - \sum_{j=1}^{n} r_{ij} P_i(t) \tag{4.32}$$

The reliability of the system is found with the knowledge of which states are operating states and which states are failure states. The system reliability is probability the system is in an operating state

$$R_s(t) = \sum_{i=1}^{n} U_i P_i(t) \tag{4.33}$$

where: U_i equals 1 if the system operates in state i, and 0 if the state fails in state i.

Stated another way, reliability is the probability the system is not in a failed state

$$R_s(t) = 1 - \sum_{i=1}^{n} V_i P_i(t) \tag{4.34}$$

where: V_i equals 0 if the system operates in state i, and 1 if the state fails in state i.

For the parallel system described earlier, States 1, 2, and 3 represent operating states, and State 4 represents a failed state.

Markov analysis is useful for repairable systems. Consider two components, A and B, in series with failure rates of λ_a and λ_b. When a component fails, it is repaired. The component repair rates are μ_a and μ_b. The system can be defined as having three states:

1. Both components operating
2. Component A failed, component B operating

3. Component A operating, component B failed

The state transition diagram for this system is shown in Figure 4.25.

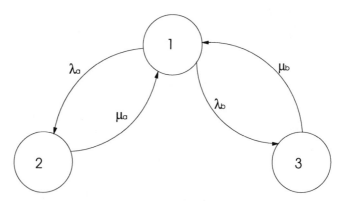

Figure 4.25. Transition state diagram for a repairable system.

The transition rate matrix for this system is

$$\Lambda = \begin{bmatrix} 0 & \lambda_a & \lambda_b \\ \mu_a & 0 & 0 \\ \mu_b & 0 & 0 \end{bmatrix} \tag{4.35}$$

The set of differential equations describing this system is

$$\frac{dP_1(t)}{dt} = -\lambda_a P_1(t) - \lambda_b P_1(t) + \mu_a P_2(t) + \mu_b P_3(t) \tag{4.36}$$

$$\frac{dP_2(t)}{dt} = \lambda_a P_1(t) - \mu_a P_2(t) \tag{4.37}$$

$$\frac{dP_3(t)}{dt} = \lambda_b P_1(t) - \mu_b P_3(t) \tag{4.38}$$

With the above set of equations, the availability of the system can be computed. The system is available if it is in States 1 or 2; it is unavailable if it is in State 3.

In summary, Markov analysis is a powerful modeling tool. It is limited by the difficulty of solving systems of differential equations, but the power of modern symbolic software and numerical routines overcomes the drawback of dealing with systems of differential equations.

4.6 Reliability allocation

When designing, the required system reliability must be translated into sub-system and component reliabilities. This process is called **reliability allocation**. Reliability allocation involves solving the following inequality.

$$f(R_1, R_2, ..., R_n) \geq R_s \tag{4.39}$$

where: R_i is the reliability allocated to the ith sub-system or component,

f is the functional relationship between the components and the system, and

R_s is the required system reliability.

The functional relationship can be derived from reliability modeling, such as block diagrams or fault trees. For complex designs, it may be impossible to determine the functional relationship mathematically. In this case simulation may be used for allocation. Beware that using simulation requires a trial and error type of analysis, and can become time consuming.

When allocating sub-system and component reliabilities, the goal is system optimization. Two common allocation requirements are to:

1. Maximize system reliability while meeting a cost objective
2. Minimize cost while meeting a system reliability objective

Other common constraints when allocating for reliability are limits on weight, temperature, and physical space.

Several algorithms for reliability allocation have been developed, including commercial software, such as SHARPE. Three simple algorithms, the ARINC method, the AGREE method, and a method for repairable systems are presented in this section.

For more complicated allocation problems, dynamic programming may be used. Dynamic programming is a mathematical method for multi-stage decision making. If each component or sub-system is considered a stage, then an apportionment decision can be made at each stage. Dynamic programming is the most general method of reliability allocation, but obtaining solutions is very difficult manually. Computers are usually used to solve dynamic programming problems, and there are several commercial packages available. For further information concerning dynamic programming consult Puterman, 1979.

4.6.1 The ARINC apportionment technique

The ARINC apportionment method assumes all sub-systems are in series and have constant failure rates. The method allocates improved sub-system failure rates based on weighting factors, derived from the present allocation of sub-systems, that satisfy the expression

$$\sum_{i=1}^{n} \lambda_i^* \leq \lambda^* \tag{4.40}$$

where: n is the number of sub-systems,

λ_i^* is the failure rate allocated to sub-system i, and

λ^* is the required system failure rate.

The steps of the algorithm are:

1. Determine the present sub-system failure rates.
2. Compute a weighting factor for each sub-system using the expression

$$w_i = \frac{\lambda_i}{\sum_{i=1}^{n} \lambda_i} \tag{4.41}$$

3. Allocate the new sub-system failure rates using the expression

$$\lambda_i^* = w_i \lambda^* \tag{4.42}$$

Example 4.1

A system which consists of 4 subsystems in series is required to have a reliability of 0.99 for a mission time of 50 hours. Allocate reliability requirements to each of the sub-systems given the following estimates for present sub-system failure rates.

$\lambda_1 = 0.004$ failures / hour

$\lambda_2 = 0.007$ failures / hour

$\lambda_3 = 0.008$ failures / hour

$\lambda_4 = 0.005$ failures / hour

Solution

The weighting factors are

$$w_1 = \frac{0.004}{0.004 + 0.007 + 0.008 + 0.005} = 0.1667$$

$$w_2 = \frac{0.007}{0.004 + 0.007 + 0.008 + 0.005} = 0.2917$$

$$w_3 = \frac{0.008}{0.004 + 0.007 + 0.008 + 0.005} = 0.3333$$

$$w_4 = \frac{0.005}{0.004 + 0.007 + 0.008 + 0.005} = 0.2083$$

Using the exponential reliability function,

$$R^*(0.99) = e^{-\lambda^* 50}$$

Thus, λ^* = 0.000201 failures/hour.

The allocated sub-system failure rates are

$$\lambda_1^* = (0.1667)(0.000201) = 0.0000335 \text{ failures / hour}$$

$$\lambda_2^* = (0.2917)(0.000201) = 0.0000586 \text{ failures / hour}$$

$$\lambda_3^* = (0.3333)(0.000201) = 0.0000669 \text{ failures / hour}$$

$$\lambda_4^* = (0.2083)(0.000201) = 0.0000418 \text{ failures / hour}$$

4.6.2 The AGREE allocation method

The AGREE allocation method determines a minimum acceptable mean life for each component in order to fulfill a minimum acceptable system mean life. It is assumed that sub-systems are in series and have constant failure rates. The method is based on sub-system complexity and considers the relationship between sub-system and system failure. The complexity of a sub-system is defined in terms of modules and their associated circuitry. Modules can be transistors, electron tubes, magnetic amplifiers, etc. Diodes represent half modules, and for computers, where module counts are high, the module count is reduced to compensate for the lower failure rates of digital parts in respect to radio-radar type parts. A sub-system's importance is assigned on a scale from 0 to 1, in proportion to the probability of the system failing if the sub-system fails. An importance factor of 0 indicates the sub-system's failure has no affect on system failure, and an importance factor of 1 indicates certain system failure if the sub-system fails.

Since $e^{-x} \approx 1 - x$ when x is small, the AGREE method allocates failure rates to sub-components using the expression

$$\lambda_i = \frac{n_i \left[-\ln R^*(T) \right]}{\left(\sum_{i=1}^{k} n_i \right) E_i t_i}, \quad i = 1, 2, ..., n \qquad (4.43)$$

where: n_i is the number of modules in the ith sub-system,
   $R^*(T)$ is the required system reliability,
   T is the required mission time for the system,
   t_i is the required operating time for the ith component ,
   E_i is the importance factor for the ith sub-system, and
   k is the number of sub-systems in the system.

The corresponding allocated component reliability is

$$R_i(t_i) = 1 - \frac{\left[R^*(T) \right]^{n_i/N}}{E_i} \qquad (4.44)$$

where: N is the total number of modules in the system $(N = \sum_{i=1}^{k} n_i)$

Example 4.2

A system of 3 sub-systems has a reliability requirement of 0.98 at time = 100 hours. Sub-system 1 is only required to operate for 80 hours and has an importance factor of 0.95. Sub-systems 2 and 3 are required to operate for 100 hours and have importance factors of 1.0. Sub-system 1 consists of 15 modules, Sub-system 2 consists of 30 modules, and Sub-system 3 consists of 20 modules. Use the AGREE method to allocate reliabilities to each of the subsystems.

Solution

From Equation 4.0,

$$\lambda_1 = \frac{15[-\ln 0.98]}{65(0.95)(80)} = 0.0000613$$

$$\lambda_2 = \frac{30[-\ln 0.98]}{65(1.0)(100)} = 0.0000932$$

$$\lambda_3 = \frac{20[-\ln 0.98]}{65(1.0)(100)} = 0.0000622$$

From Equation 4.0,

$$R_1(80) = 1 - \frac{1 - (0.98)^{15/65}}{0.95} = 0.9951$$

$$R_2(100) = 1 - \frac{1 - (0.98)^{30/65}}{1.0} = 0.9907$$

$$R_3(100) = 1 - \frac{1 - (0.98)^{20/65}}{1.0} = 0.9938$$

4.6.3 Repairable systems allocation

The following method allocates failure rates to sub-systems in series with constant failure rates. The allocated sub-system failure rates allow the system to meet an availability objective. It is assumed that all sub-systems are identical and have a constant repair rate of μ. The following steps describe the procedure.

1. Determine the steady-state availability for each sub-system using the expression

$$A_s = \left(A^*\right)^{1/k} \tag{4.45}$$

where: A^* is the required system availability, and
k is the number of sub-systems.

2. Determine the ratio of the allocated failure rate to the repair rate for each sub-system using the expression

$$\theta = \left(\frac{1}{A_s} - 1\right)$$ (4.46)

3. Determine the failure rate allocated to each sub-system using the expression

$$\lambda = \theta\mu$$ (4.47)

where: μ is the repair rate for each of the subsystems.

Example 4.3

Consider a series system composed of 5 independent, identical sub-systems. The repair rate for each of the sub-systems is 0.4, and the required system availability is 0.99. What is the required failure rate for each of the sub-systems?

Solution

The steady-state availability for each of the sub-systems is

$$A_s = (0.99)^{1/5} = 0.998$$

The ratio of the allocated failure rate to the repair rate for each sub-system is

$$\theta = \left(\frac{1}{0.998} - 1\right) = 0.002$$

The failure rate allocated to each sub-system is

$$\lambda = 0.002(0.4) = 0.0008$$

4.7 Software reliability

The information processing industry is growing rapidly. The declining cost of computing hardware has allowed more tasks to be handled by software. Modern products are commonly a combination of hardware and software. Also, more and more computer systems operate in real time, such as machinery controls and reservation systems.

The increase in use of computing systems is matched by an increase in the size and complexity of the computing code used to drive the systems. The reliability of a product or process is a function of the reliability of the system's hardware and its software. Thus, the field of software reliability is becoming increasingly important.

4.7.1 Differences in software and hardware reliability

While the body of knowledge for hardware reliability is well developed, the field of software reliability is relatively new and is still developing. The definition of software reliability is the same as the definition of hardware reliability—the probability of operation for a specified time in a specified environment with no failures. There are several differences in hardware and software reliability:

- Software reliability is not a function of manufacturing. Each set of computer code is identical; there is no manufacturing variability.

- Software does not degrade over time. Mechanical components are subject to wear and degrade with use. Regardless of how much a computer program has been used, it is exactly the same as when it was new, and performs accordingly.

- The **external** environment has no affect on software. Vibration, temperature and other environmental factors may affect computer hardware, but software performance is independent of the external environment. The definition of software reliability refers to the **internal** environment, such as the type of transaction being processed or the hardware the software is operating on.

- All software failures are the result of design errors.

- Software can only be repaired by redesign. Thus, the term maintainability for software is different from the meaning for hardware. Maintainability is a function of the speed and ease with which a computer program can be redesigned.

- Software availability is not used as a performance measure, since most software is not idled during repair.

The techniques for improving software reliability are also different from the conventional techniques used for hardware. Obviously, software reliability cannot be improved with redundancy; any error in the primary code is also contained in the redundant code. Techniques for improving software reliability are:

- Using structured programming
- Using modular programming
- Programming for fault tolerance

Structured programming constrains the programmer to control structures with a single entry point and a single exit point. Thus, the use of GOTO statements are prohibited. Modular programming involves breaking the program into several smaller programs, each as independent as possible. These modules are easier to test and verify. Programs should also be able to tolerate faults. For example, if a user attempts to print a report, but fails to turn on the printer, the program should be able to detect that the printer is not available and notify the user, rather than crash.

4.7.2 Software reliability models

Several models for software reliability have been developed. The two most widely used models are the basic execution time model and the logarithmic Poisson execution time model. Both models have an execution time component and a calendar time component. Only the execution time component is discussed since execution time has been shown to be superior to calendar time for reliability modeling.

4.7.2.1 Basic execution time model

This model assumes failure occurrence is a non-homogeneous Poisson process. That is, at each point in time the occurrence of failures follows a Poisson distribution, and the parameters of the Poisson distribution vary with time. The failure occurrence rate varies with time because faults are being introduced and removed as time passes.

The failure intensity is modeled as a function of the number of failures experienced, and is defined as

$$\lambda(\mu) = \lambda_0\left(1 - \frac{\mu}{v_0}\right) \tag{4.48}$$

where: μ is the expected number of failures at a given point in time,

λ_0 is the initial failure intensity, and

v_0 is the total number of failures that would occur in infinite time.

The rate of change in the failure intensity is

$$\frac{d\lambda}{d\mu} = -\frac{\lambda_0}{v_0} \tag{4.49}$$

The failure rate intensity as a function of time is

$$\lambda(t) = \lambda_0 e^{-\frac{\lambda_0 t}{v_0}} \tag{4.50}$$

The number of failures experienced as a function of execution time is

$$\mu(t) = v_0\left(1 - e^{-\frac{\lambda_0 t}{v_0}}\right) \tag{4.51}$$

Example 4.16

The initial failure intensity for a program was 15 failures per CPU hour, and the program has now experienced 50 failures. Assuming the program will experience 120 failures in an infinite period of time, what is the current failure intensity? What is the rate of change in the failure intensity?

Solution

The current failure intensity is

$$\lambda(\mu) = 15\left(1 - \frac{50}{120}\right) = 8.75 \text{ failures per CPU hour}$$

The rate of change in the failure intensity is

$$\frac{d\lambda}{d\mu} = -\frac{15}{120} = -0.125 \text{ per CPU hour}$$

Example 4.17

For the system in Example 4.16, what is the expected number of failures after 30 hours of execution? What is the expected failure intensity after 30 hours of execution?

Solution

The expected number of failures is

$$\mu(30) = 120 \left(1 - e^{-\frac{15(30)}{120}} \right) = 117.2$$

The expected failure intensity is

$$\lambda(30) = 15 e^{-\frac{15(30)}{120}} = 0.0353 \text{ failures per CPU hour}$$

4.7.2.2 Logarithmic Poisson execution time model

The basic execution time model implies a uniform operational profile. The change in failure rate intensity is constant. The logarithmic Poisson execution time model includes a failure intensity decay parameter that allows a non-uniform operational profile. The failure intensity at a given number of failures is

$$\lambda_i = \lambda_{i-1}(1-\theta) \tag{4.52}$$

where: λ_i is the failure intensity at the ith failure, and
   θ is the failure decay parameter.

The logarithmic Poisson execution time model also assumes failure occurrence is a non-homogeneous Poisson process. The failure intensity as a function of the number of failures experienced is

$$\lambda(\mu) = \lambda_0 e^{-\theta\mu} \tag{4.53}$$

where: μ is the expected number of failures at a given point in time,
   λ_0 is the initial failure intensity,
   v_0 is the total number of failures that would occur in infinite time, and
   θ is the failure intensity decay parameter.

The failure intensity rate of change is

$$\frac{d\lambda}{d\mu} = -\lambda_0 \theta e^{-\theta\mu} = -\lambda\theta \tag{4.54}$$

The failure rate intensity as a function of time is

$$\lambda(t) = \frac{\lambda_0}{\lambda_0\theta t + 1} \tag{4.55}$$

The number of failures experienced as a function of execution time is

$$\mu(t) = \frac{\ln(\lambda_0\theta t + 1)}{\theta} \tag{4.56}$$

Example 4.18

The initial failure intensity for a program was 15 failures per CPU hour, and the program has now experienced 50 failures. The failure intensity decay parameter is 0.03 per failure. Assuming the program will experience 120 failures in an infinite period of time, what is the current failure intensity? What is the rate of change in the failure intensity?

Solution

The current failure intensity is

$$\lambda(\mu) = 15e^{-0.03(50)} = 3.347 \text{ failures per CPU hour}$$

The rate of change in the failure intensity is

$$\frac{d\lambda}{d\mu} = -15(0.03)e^{-0.03(50)} = -0.1004$$

Example 4.19

For the system in Example 4.18, what is the expected number of failures after 30 hours of execution? What is the expected failure intensity after 30 hours of execution?

Solution

The expected number of failures is

$$\mu(t) = \frac{\ln[15(0.03)(30)+1]}{0.03} = 89.1$$

The expected failure rate intensity is

$$\lambda(t) = \frac{15}{15(0.03)(30)+1} = 1.03 \text{ failures per CPU hour}$$

Examples 4.16 and 4.18 are the same with the exception of the failure intensity decay parameter. Figure 4.26 demonstrates the difference in the failure intensity as a function of execution time of the two models.

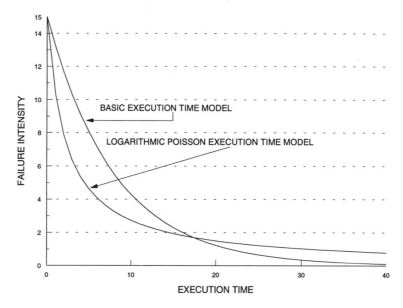

Figure 4.26. Failure intensity as a function of execution time.

Figure 4.27 demonstrates the difference in the expected number of failures as a function of execution time for the two models.

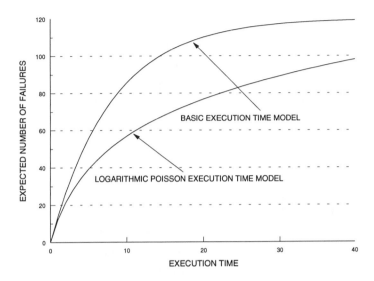

Figure 4.27. Expected cumulative number of failures as a function of execution time.

4.8 Reliability growth

During the design phase a product's reliability usually improves as design changes are made. Also, after a new piece of equipment is installed, its reliability tends to improve as modifications are made and the equipment operation is better understood. Reliability growth is a method of modeling the improvement of reliability over time. Reliability growth can be used to estimate the amount of time required to obtain a reliability goal, or to predict reliability. Note that the software reliability models presented in the previous section are growth models.

There are several reliability growth models; the two discussed in this section are the Duane model and the AMSAA model.

4.8.1 The Duane model

J. T. Duane was one of the first to introduce a reliability growth model. He empirically derived the expression

$$\theta_C = \alpha t^\beta \tag{4.57}$$

where: θ_C is the cumulative mean time between failures, and
$\quad\quad\quad$ β is the slope parameter, and
$\quad\quad\quad$ α is the initial mean time to fail.

By taking the logarithm of Equation 4.57 the following linear expression is found.

$$\ln(\theta_C) = \ln\alpha + \beta \ln t \tag{4.58}$$

The parameters of the Duane model can be found by plotting Equation 4.58.

Example 4.20

Five electronic switches were each tested for 20,000 cycles. After each failure, the root cause was determined, and design changes were made on all 5 switches. The failure data is given in Table 4.4. Determine the Duane model parameters.

Table 4.4. Example data.

Cumulative Cycles	Cumulative Failures
20,000	10
40,000	18
60,000	25
80,000	32
100,000	37

Solution

The parameters are determined by plotting the logarithm of the cumulative failures versus the logarithm of cumulative test cycles. Most authors recommend plotting the cumulative failures versus the cumulative test cycles on log-log paper. This is unnecessary, as the log-transformation can be easily handled with electronic spreadsheets. The electronic spreadsheet can also easily determine the best-fit straight line to the data with built-in regression routines. Table 4.5 contains the information required for the graph.

Table 4.5. Duane model plotting data.

Cumulative Cycles	Cumulative Failures	Cumulative Mean Cycles to Fail	Logarithm of Cumulative Cycles	Logarithm of Cumulative Mean Cycles to Fail
20,000	10	2000	9.9035	7.6009
40,000	18	2222	10.5966	7.7063
60,000	25	2400	11.0021	7.7832
80,000	32	2500	11.2898	7.8240
100,000	37	2703	11.5129	7.9020

A graph of the last two columns of Table 4.5 is shown in Figure 4.28.

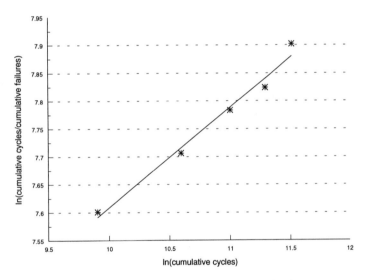

Figure 4.28. Duane reliability growth plot.

The slope of the straight line in Figure 4.28 is $\beta = 0.179$. This can be computed from the graph, or the value can be obtained from an electronic spreadsheet. The *y*-intercept of the graph is 5.81 (again, this can be determined electronically). The initial mean time to fail is

$$\alpha = e^{y \text{ intercept}} \qquad (4.59)$$

$$\alpha = e^{5.814} = 335$$

O'Conner (1991) quantifies the type of reliability improvement program required to achieve a desired slope for the Duane model. They are as follows:

β	Reliability Effort
0–0.2	No priority is given to reliability improvement. Corrective action is only taken for important modes, and it is done with low priority.
0.2	There is routine attention given to reliability improvement. Corrective action is taken for important failure modes.
0.3–0.4	Reliability improvement is a priority. There is analysis and corrective action for all important failure modes.
0.4–0.6	There is a program dedicated to failure elimination. It has top priority, and there is analysis and corrective action for all failures.

The current or instantaneous mean time to fail is

$$\theta_i(t) = \frac{\alpha t^\beta}{(1-\beta)} \tag{4.60}$$

Example 4.21

For the switch in Example 4.20, how long would testing have to continue to obtain a mean cycles to fail of 4,000?

Solution

The Duane reliability growth model for the instantaneous mean cycles to fail for this switch is

$$\theta_i(t) = \frac{335 t^{0.179}}{(1-0.179)}$$

Solving the above expression for time

$$4000 = \frac{335 t^{0.179}}{(1 - 0.179)}$$

$$t = 345,394 \text{ cycles}$$

Using the Duane model, it is estimated that 345,395 cumulative cycles of testing would be required.

4.8.2 The AMSAA Model

The AMSAA (Army Material Systems Analysis Activity) model also assumes a non-homogeneous Poisson process. The instantaneous mean time to fail is

$$\theta_i(t) = \frac{\alpha}{\beta} \left(\frac{t}{\alpha} \right)^{1-\beta} \tag{4.61}$$

where: β is the shape parameter, and
α is the scale parameter.

These parameters can be estimated graphically using the expression

$$\ln[N(t)] = \beta \ln t - \beta \ln \alpha \tag{4.62}$$

where: $N(t)$ is the cumulative number of failures at time = t.

By plotting $\ln[N(t)]$ on the y-axis and $\ln t$ on the x-axis, the slope of the resulting best-fit straight line through the data is the estimated shape parameter, β. The scale parameter is determined using the y-intercept.

$$\alpha = e^{-\frac{y \text{ intercept}}{\beta}} \tag{4.63}$$

Example 4.22

For the data given in Example 4.20, determine the AMSAA growth model parameters, and the number of cycles of testing required to achieve a mean time to fail of 4,000 cycles.

Solution

The data required for plotting is contained in Table 4.6

Table 4.6. AMSAA reliability growth plotting data.

Cumulative Cycles	Cumulative Failures	Logarithm of Cumulative Cycles	Logarithm of Cumulative Failures
20,000	10	9.9035	2.3026
40,000	18	10.5966	2.8904
60,000	25	11.0021	3.2189
80,000	32	11.2898	3.4657
100,000	37	11.5129	3.6109

A plot of the data in Table 4.6 is shown in Figure 4.29.

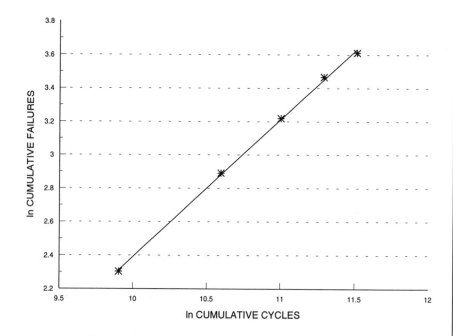

Figure 4.29. AMSAA reliability growth plot.

The slope of the straight line in Figure 4.29 is 0.821, which is equal to the shape parameter, β. The y-intercept of the straight line in Figure 4.29 is -5.815. The scale parameter is

$$\alpha = e^{-\frac{5.81}{0.821}} = 1{,}184$$

The instantaneous mean time to fail is

$$\theta_i(t) = \frac{1184}{0.821} \left(\frac{t}{1184} \right)^{1-0.821}$$

Solving for $\theta_i(t) = 4{,}000$ gives

$$t = 353{,}590 \text{ cycles}$$

4.9 Exercises

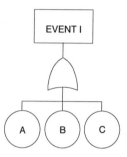

1. What is the probability of Event I occurring in the fault tree above? The probability of A, B, and C occurring is 0.2, 0.4, and 0.3 respectively.
2. For the fault tree in Exercise 1, determine a) all cut sets, b) all minimum cut sets, c) all path sets, and d) all minimum path sets.
3. For the fault tree in Exercise 1, replace the *OR* gate with an *AND* gate and rework the problem.
4. For the fault tree below, determine the minimum cut sets.

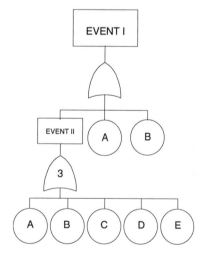

5. For the fault tree to in Exercise 4, determine the probability of Event I occurring given $P(A) = P(B) = P(C) = P(D) = P(E) = 0.15$.

6. For the fault tree below, indicate which of the scenarios below cause Event I to take place.

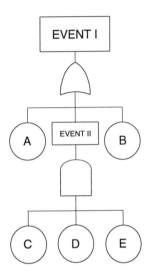

a. Event A transpires
b. Event B transpires
c. Event C transpires
d. Event D transpires
e. Event E transpires
f. Events A and B transpire
g. Events A and C transpire
h. Events A and D transpire
f. Events C, D, and E transpire

7. For the fault tree given in Exercise 6, what is the probability of Event I occurring if P(A) = 0.3, P(B)= 0.09, P(C) = 0.08, P(D) = 0.2, and P(E) = 0.01?

8. Replace the *OR* gate in the fault tree in Exercise 6 with an *AND* gate and repeat Exercise 7.

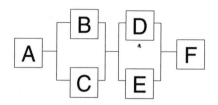

9. Create a fault tree to describe the system above.

10. Determine the minimum cut sets for the fault tree below.

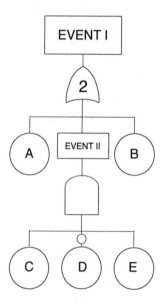

11. Given the following probabilities

$$P(A) = 0.001$$
$$P(B) = 0.02$$
$$P(C) = 0.08$$
$$P(D) = 0.01$$
$$P(E) = 0.06$$

What is the probability of Event I occurring for the fault tree in Exercise 10?

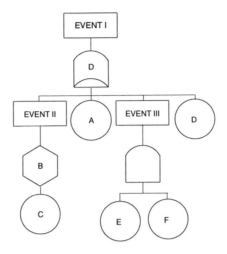

12. For the fault tree above, determine the probability of Event I occurring given

    P(A) = 0.2
    P(B) = 0.3
    P(C) = 0.003
    P(D) = 0.07
    P(E) = 0.08
    P(F) = 0.001

13. Explain why simulation might be used to model a reliability problem.

14. Give some instances when other techniques are more appropriate than simulation

15. Write a simulation to determine the mean time to fail for a system consisting of five components in series, each with exponential times to fail with a mean of 17.

16. For Exercise 15, modify the simulation to find a 95% lower confidence limit for the time to fail.

17. Repeat Exercise 15 with components that follow a Weibull distribution with a shape parameter of 4 and a scale parameter of 90.

18. Identify some public sources for reliability data.

19. What are some limitations of using public reliability data bases?

20. Components A, B, and C are exponentially distributed with mean times to fail of 40 hours, 60 hours, and 75 hours. If these components are in series, what is the reliability of the system at time = 30 hours?

21. What is the mean time to fail for the system described in Exercise 20?

22. If the components in Exercise 20 are in parallel, what is the system reliability at time = 50?

23. What is the system hazard function for the system in described in Exercise 20?

24. Three components with Weibull time to fail distributions are placed in parallel. The Weibull distribution parameters are:

Component	Shape parameter	Scale parameter
A	4	120
B	2	80
C	3.5	100

What is the system reliability at time = 200?

25. A system consists of 4 components with constant failure rates of 0.02. When the system is activated, all 4 components are activated. The system operates as long as at least 2 of the 4 components operate. What is the system reliability at time = 130? What is the system mean time to fail?

26. A system consists of three components. When the system is activated, only one component comes on-line. When the on-line component fails, another component comes on-line. The failure rate for each of the three components is 0.05. What is the system reliability at time = 80?

27. For the system described in Exercise 26, what is the reliability of the system at time = 80 if the mechanism that transfers operation from the on-line component to the standby component has a failure rate of 0.01?

28. Component A has a constant failure rate of 0.02, and component B has a constant failure rate of 0.03. If component A fails, a switch brings component B on-line. The switch has an 8% chance of failing. What is the reliability of this system at time = 100?

29. Two identical components with constant failure rates of 0.09 are activated simultaneously. If one of the components fails, the failure rate of the remaining component increases to 0.14. What is the reliability of this system at time = 20?

30. Three identical components with constant failure rates of 0.09 are activated simultaneously. If one of the components fails, the failure rate of the remaining two components increases to 0.14. If one of the remaining two components fails, the failure rate of the remaining component increases to 0.2. What is the reliability of this system at time = 110?

31. A system consists of two components, A and B, with exponentially distributed mean times to fail of 95 and 85 when they are operating. Component B is brought on-line only if component A fails. Component B has an exponentially distributed mean time to fail of 30 when it is in standby mode. What is the system reliability at time = 150?

32. A system consists of two identical components with a constant failure rate of 0.05 while operating and 0.02 while in standby. When the system in initialized, only one component is operating. When the on-line component fails, the second component is brought on-line. What is the system mean time to fail?

33. What is the reliability of the system below?

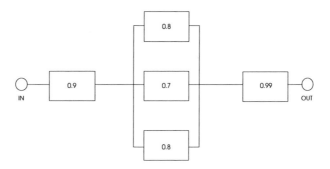

34. What is the reliability of the system below at time = 300?

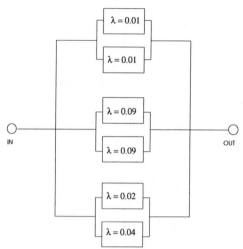

35. In the block diagram below, components A, B, and C have reliability of 0.9, 0.95, and 0.85. What is the reliability of the system?

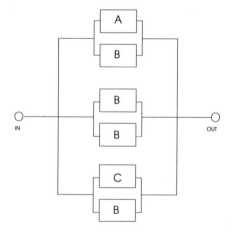

36. A type of beam is normally distributed with a mean strength of 40 and a variance of 0.8. This beam is subjected to a stress which is normally distributed with an average of 38 and a standard deviation of 1.1. What percentage of the beams fail?

37. With manufacturing changes, it is possible to reduce variance of the strength of the beam in the previous exercise. What must this variance be reduced to if only 7% of the beams are allowed to fail?

38. A company is developing a new fiber, and tested 12 specimens to fail. The failure strengths are:

14.2	14.7	15.1
14.4	14.8	15.3
14.6	14.8	15.5
14.6	14.9	15.8

What is the maximum stress that these fibers can withstand to be 90% confident of 95% reliability?

39. Write a flowchart to simulate Exercise 1.

40. Simulate Exercise 1 using an electronic spreadsheet.

41. Write a flowchart to simulate Exercise 4.

42. Simulate Exercise 4 using an electronic spreadsheet, given the probability of Events A, B, C, D and E occurring is 0.01, 0.02, 0.03, 0.04 and 0.05 respectively.

43. Develop the transition rate matrix for the system described in Exercise 20.

44. Develop the set of differential equations to describe the system in Exercise 20.

45. Construct the transition rate diagram and the transition rate matrix for the system described in Exercise 22.

46. A system consists of three sub-systems in series. The system reliability must be at least 0.99 at 80 hours. The three sub-systems have constant failure rates with mean times to fail of 800, 1,000 and 1,200. Allocate reliability requirements to each of the sub-systems using the ARINC method.

47. Given that a computer program will experience 300 failures if run for an infinite period of time, the initial failure intensity is 10 failures per CPU hour, and the program has experienced 30 failures, use the basic execution time model to estimate the current failure intensity, and the rate of change in the failure intensity.

48. For the computer program in Exercise 47, what is the expected number of failures after 50 hours of execution time? What is the failure intensity after 50 hours of execution time?

49. How does software reliability differ form hardware reliability?

50. A pressure valve was tested during development and the following data obtained.

Failure #	Cumulative Time
1	83
2	201
3	385
4	619
5	888
6	1353
7	1776

Determine the parameters of the Duane growth model. What is the expected instantaneous mean time to fail after 1,000 hours of testing?

51. Repeat Exercise 50 using the AMSAA model.

52. The reliability requirement for a system is 0.995 at time = 190. The system is made up of 4 sub-systems with the following characteristics:

Sub-System	Importance Factor	Required Operating Time	Number of Modules
A	1.0	190	30
B	0.8	80	30
C	1.0	15	80
D	0.5	100	45

Use the AGREE method to allocate reliabilities to each sub-system.

53. A system consists of 4 identical components in series with a constant repair rate of 0.09. What is the required mean time to fail for each of the components if a system availability of 0.98 is required?

4.10 References

Bush, S. H. 1985. Statistics of Pressure Vessel and Piping Failures. In *Pressure Vessel and Piping Technology—A Decade of Progress,* edited by C. Sundararajan. New York: American Society of Mechanical Engineers.

Crowder, M. J., A. C. Kimber, R, L. Smith, and T. J. Sweeting. 1991. *Statistical Analysis of Reliability Data.* London: Chapman & Hall.

Dhillon, B. S. 1985. *Quality Control, Reliability, and Engineering Design.* New York: Marcel Dekker.

Dodson, B. L., and M. D. Mulcahy. 1992. *Certified Reliability Engineer Examination Study Guide.* Tucson, AZ: Quality Publishing.

Dovich, R. A. 1990. *Reliability Statistics.* Milwaukee, WI: ASQC–Quality Press.

Hahn, G. J., and S. S. Shapiro. 1967. *Statistical Models in Engineering.* New York: John Wiley & Sons.

Ireson, G. W., and C. F.Coombs. 1988. *Handbook of Reliability Engineering and Management.* New York: McGraw-Hill.

Kapur, K. C., and L. R. Lamberson. 1977. *Reliability in Engineering Design.* New York: John Wiley & Sons.

Kececioglu, D. 1991. *Reliability Engineering Handbook, Volume 2.* Englewood Cliffs, NJ: Prentice Hall.

Krishnamoorthi, K. S. 1992. *Reliability Methods for Engineers.* Milwaukee, WI: ASQC–Quality Press.

Lewis, E. E. 1987. *Introduction To Reliability Engineering.* New York: John Wiley & Sons.

Musa, J., A. Iannino, and K. Okumoto. 1987. *Software Reliability: Measurement, Prediction, Application.* New York: McGraw-Hill.

O'Conner, P. D. T. 1993. *Practical Reliability Engineering.* New York: John Wiley & Sons.

Puterman, M. L. 1979. *Dynamic Programming and Its Applications.* New York: Academic Press.

Shooman, M. L. 1990. *Probabilistic Reliability: An Engineering Approach.* Malabar, FL: Robert E. Krieger.

Sundarajan, C. 1991. *Guide To Reliability Engineering: Data, Analysis, Applications, Implementation, And Management.* New York: Van Nostrand Reinhold.

Tobias, P. A., and D. C. Trindade. 1986. *Applied Reliability.* New York: Van Nostrand Reinhold.

US Department of Defense. *MIL-HDBK-189: Reliability Growth Management.* Philadelphia: Naval Publications and Forms Center.

US Department of Defense. *MIL-HDBK-217: Reliability Prediction of Electronic Equipment.* Philadelphia: Naval Publications and Forms Center.

US Department of Defense. *MIL-HDBK-338: Electronic Reliability Design Handbook.* Philadelphia: Naval Publications and Forms Center.

US Department of Defense. *MIL-HDBK-756: Reliability Modeling and Prediction.* Philadelphia: Naval Publications and Forms Center.

US Department of Defense. *MIL-STD-1556: Government Industry Data Exchange Program (GIDEP).* Philadelphia: Naval Publications and Forms Center.

US Department of Defense. *MIL-STD-1635: Reliability Growth Testing.* Philadelphia: Naval Publications and Forms Center.

♦ ♦ ♦
CHAPTER

5

Reliability Testing

Products are put through many inspections and tests to ensure conformance to requirements and fitness for use. One or more of these evaluations is usually a reliability test. Unlike many quality tests, reliability testing can be time consuming, and is often destructive. There are several types of reliability tests, each with different purposes. MIL-HDBK-781 is an excellent reference for reliability testing. Some common reliability tests are defined below.

Reliability Growth Testing is used at the development stage to model reliability gains. As a product is developed, it may not meet reliability requirements. Some reliability improvements can be made by fine tuning the existing design, but often a design change is required. The new design often results in a lower initial reliability which is improved and eventually exceeds the reliability of the previous design. This process is repeated until reliability requirements are met. The mathematics of reliability growth modeling is discussed in Chapter 4.

Environmental Stress Screening is used to eliminate infant mortality failures. Items are subjected to more harsh environmental conditions than the normal operating environment. The most common stresses include temperature, humidity, vibration and moisture. The stresses are usually cycled during testing, for example, the temperature may be raised from freezing to boiling and back again. MIL-STD-810 provides an excellent reference for environmental stress testing.

Reliability Qualification Testing is used to verify that an item meets its designed reliability. This test is usually an interim step of development: as each subassembly is qualified on the basis of reliability. Sequential testing, truncated testing (described in Chapter 3—see the exponential distribution) and accelerated testing can be used to verify minimum mean time to failure requirements. Qualification testing is also known as design approval testing and demonstration testing.

Acceptance Testing is used to determine if an item is acceptable for use. This test may be conducted by the manufacturer, the purchaser, or both. Sequential testing, truncated testing and accelerated testing can be used to verify minimum mean time to failure requirements.

5.1 Accelerated testing

When items with very high reliability are encountered, the time required to gather failure data can become unreasonable. The time to fail can be reduced by increasing the stress on a component. When this is done, parameters cannot be directly estimated from the test data, and models are required to transform the data or results to normal operating conditions.

While any transformation function could be used to model acceleration, a linear transformation of the time scale is almost always used. Under this assumption, the time to fail under normal operating conditions is

$$t_o = \varepsilon t_\varepsilon \tag{5.1}$$

where: ε is the acceleration factor, and

t_ε is the time to fail under increased stress conditions.

If $f(t)$ represents the probability density function under accelerated conditions, then the probability density function under normal operating conditions is

$$f_o(t) = \frac{1}{\varepsilon} f\left(\frac{t}{\varepsilon}\right) \tag{5.2}$$

The reliability function under normal operating conditions is

$$R_o(t) = R\left(\frac{t}{\varepsilon}\right) \tag{5.3}$$

The hazard function under normal operating conditions is

$$h_o(t) = \frac{1}{\varepsilon} h\left(\frac{t}{\varepsilon}\right) \tag{5.4}$$

Table 5.1 gives transformed reliability functions for several distributions using an acceleration factor of ε.

Table 5.1. Reliability functions with an acceleration factor of ε.

Distribution	Density Function Determined From Accelerated Testing	Reliability Function Under Normal Operating Conditions
Weibull	$f(t) = \dfrac{\beta t^{\beta-1}}{\theta^{\beta}} \exp\left[-\left(\dfrac{t}{\theta}\right)^{\beta}\right]$	$R(t) = \exp\left[-\left(\dfrac{t}{\varepsilon\theta}\right)^{\beta}\right]$
lognormal	$f(t) = \dfrac{1}{\sigma t\sqrt{2\pi}} \exp\left[-\dfrac{1}{2}\left(\dfrac{\ln t - \mu}{\sigma}\right)^{2}\right]$	$R(t) = 1 - \Phi\left(\dfrac{\ln t - \ln \varepsilon - \mu}{\sigma}\right)$
normal	$f(t) = \dfrac{1}{\sigma\sqrt{2\pi}} \exp\left[-\dfrac{1}{2}\left(\dfrac{t - \mu}{\sigma}\right)^{2}\right]$	$R(t) = 1 - \Phi\left(\dfrac{t - \varepsilon\mu}{\varepsilon\sigma}\right)$
exponential	$f(t) = \lambda e^{-\lambda t}$	$R(t) = e^{-\frac{\lambda t}{\varepsilon}}$

Example 5.1

When tested at 180°F, the time to fail for a component was found to follow a Weibull distribution with a shape parameter of 3.5 and a scale parameter of 19.3. The normal operating temperature for the component is 110°F, and the acceleration factor between these two temperatures is known to be 12. Determine the reliability of the component under normal operating conditions at time = 200.

Solution

From Table 5.1 (or Equation 5.3), the expression for reliability under normal operating conditions is

$$R(t) = \exp\left[-\left(\frac{t}{12(193)}\right)^{3.5}\right]$$

At time = 200, the component reliability is

$$R(t) = \exp\left[-\left(\frac{200}{12(19.3)}\right)^{3.5}\right] = 0.550$$

With linear acceleration, the shape of the failure distribution does not change due to acceleration. If the time to fail under accelerated conditions follows a Weibull distribution, the time to fail under normal operation conditions will follow a Weibull distribution with the same shape parameter. This is easily demonstrated with probability plotting. The slope of the probability plot estimates the shape parameter for Weibull probability plots and lognormal probability plots. Thus, if failure data collected under different levels of stress are plotted on the same probability plot, the lines should be parallel (the lines will never be exactly parallel because of sampling error). If parallel lines do not result, either the acceleration is not linear, or the chosen probability density function does not adequately model the data.

Example 5.2

On the same graph, construct a Weibull probability plot for the data obtained under both levels of stress in Table 5.2.

Table 5.2. Time to fail at two levels of stress.

250°F	50°F
3.9	39.2
4.6	48.6
6.1	59.1
7.8	65.5
8.7	70.9
9.5	71.0
9.6	73.7
10.0	76.9
10.1	88.1
10.2	95.8
10.6	99.1
11.8	100.2
12.5	102.4
12.8	107.6
12.9	111.1
13.0	118.6
13.1	123.8
13.2	124.2
13.4	128.9
13.4	131.4
13.5	131.6
13.9	131.9
15.0	139.0
15.1	139.2
15.3	139.8
15.4	144.6
16.3	149.8
16.4	154.8
16.6	155.6
16.8	178.0

Solution

Figure 5.1 shows probability plots for both sets of data. The data set on the right of the figure was obtained under the lower level of stress (50°F).

$$\ln\left[\ln\left(\frac{1}{1-F(t)}\right)\right]$$

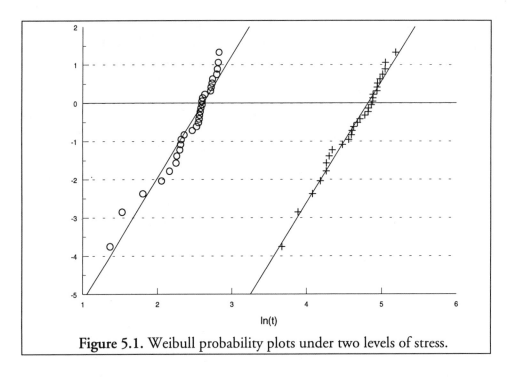

Figure 5.1. Weibull probability plots under two levels of stress.

Figure 5.1 demonstrates linear acceleration; the slope of the two lines is nearly identical.

5.1.1. The Arrhenius model

For the data given in Example 5.2, the acceleration factor can be estimated by taking the ratio of the scale parameters estimated at the two stress levels. If an acceleration factor is needed for another level of stress, testing at that stress level would be required unless there is a way to extrapolate the existing data. This is required in many cases because it is not feasible to test under normal operating conditions due to time constraints.

The Arrhenius model has been shown to accurately model accelerated test data when only thermal stresses are significant. The Arrhenius model is

$$t = ke^{c/T} \tag{5.5}$$

where: t is the time at which a specified portion of the population fails,

k is a constant,

c is a constant, and

T is the absolute temperature (measured in degrees Kelvin or Rankine)[*].

By making a logarithmic transformation, the Arrhenius model can be written as

$$\ln t = \ln k + \frac{c}{T} \qquad (5.6)$$

By plotting this expression, the values of the constants in the Arrhenius model can be determined. Kielpinski and Nelson (1975) have developed optimum test plans for the Arrhenius model. These plans estimate the 10th percentile of the time to failure distribution at the normal operating stress with the greatest possible large sample precision. These plans involve testing at only two temperatures, and Meeker and Hahn (1985) caution their use because the plans do not allow any degrees of freedom for accessing goodness of fit. Meeker and Hahn make the following recommendations for developing an accelerated test plan using the Arrhenius model:

- Restrict testing to a range of temperatures over which there is a good chance that the Arrhenius model adequately represents the data.
- Select a second temperature reasonably removed from the highest temperature.
- Select a low temperature that is as close as possible to the design temperature.
- Apportion more of the available test units to the lower levels of stress.

Example 5.3

A component was tested at four different temperatures, and the estimated Weibull distribution parameters are given below.

Temperature	30°C	50°C	100°C	150°C
β	3.16	3.08	3.14	3.10
θ	912.2	408.9	197.3	104.6

---

[*] Degrees Kelvin is equal to degrees Celsius + 273.16. Degrees Rankine is equal to degrees Fahrenheit + 459.69.

Determine the constants of the Arrhenius model, and assuming 20°C is the normal operating temperature, estimate the acceleration factor for a temperature of 70°C.

Solution

The first step is to estimate a percentile to plot against the absolute temperature. While any percentile is acceptable, for this example, the 10th percentile will be used[*]. This can be done nonparametrically using the rank distribution or a parametric model can be used. Since Weibull parameters have been estimated, the Weibull distribution will be used for this example. The time at which 10% of the population fails is

$$t = \theta\left[-\ln(0.9)\right]^{1/\beta} \tag{5.7}$$

The 10th percentiles are

Temperature	30°C	50°C	100°C	150°C
10th Percentile	447.52	196.93	96.34	50.61

The data required to plot the Arrhenius model are summarized in Table 5.3.

Table 5.3. Arrhenius model plotting data.

10th Percentile	ln(10th Percentile)	Temperature °C	Absolute Temperature °K	Inverse Absolute Temperature
447.52	6.1037	30	303.16	0.0032986
196.93	5.2828	50	323.16	0.0030944
96.34	4.5679	100	373.16	0.0026798
50.61	3.9241	150	423.16	0.0023632

The next step is to plot $1/T$ on the x-axis, $\ln t$ on the y-axis and fit a straight line to the data. This is shown in Figure 5.2. The straight line was fit to the data using least squares regression. The slope of the line is 2207.8 and the y-intercept is −1.3425. Thus, the constants of the Arrhenius model are

---

[*] It is also valid to use the scale parameter in place of the percentile. For example, the scale parameter of the Weibull distribution or the mean of the exponential distribution. See Tobias and Trinidade (1986) for more information.

$$k = e^{y-\text{intercept}} = e^{-1.3425} = 0.2612$$

$$c = \text{ slope } = 2207.8$$

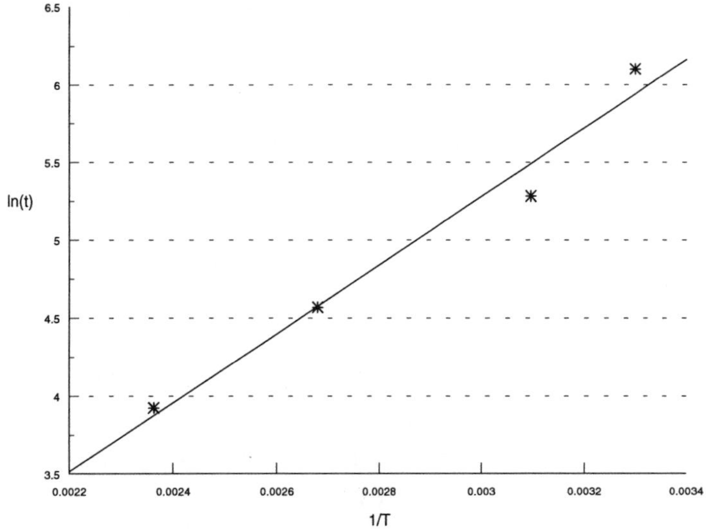

Figure 5.2. Plot of Arrhenius Model.

Assuming the normal operating temperature is 20°C, the acceleration factor at a temperature of 70°C is equal to the ratio of the percentiles at 20°C and 70°C.

$$\varepsilon = \frac{t_{20^0 C}}{t_{70^0 C}}$$

The estimated 10th percentile at 20°C is

$$t_{20^0 C} = 0.2612 e^{2207.8/(20+273.16)} = 487.15$$

The estimated 10th percentile at 70°C is

$$t_{70^0 C} = 0.2612 e^{2207.8/(70+273.16)} = 162.60$$

The acceleration factor at 70°C is

$$\varepsilon_{70^0 C} = \frac{487.15}{162.60} = 2.996$$

5.1.2. Other acceleration models

The Arrhenius model is limited to one type of stress, temperature. When there is more than one type of stress acting on a component, a more complex model is required. Eyring derived the following model based on chemical reaction rates and quantum mechanics.

$$t = aT^{\alpha}e^{b/T}e^{[c+(d/T)]S_1} \tag{5.8}$$

where: t is the time at which a specified portion of the population fails,

  T is the absolute temperature (measured in degrees Kelvin or Rankine,

  α, a, b, c, and d are constants, and

  S_1 is the level of a second stress factor.

With five constants to be estimated for two stress factors in the Eyring model, testing must be conducted under at least five distinct stress combinations. Ideally, more than five testing conditions should be used to demonstrate goodness of fit. Determining the constants is not straight forward, and is best done with mathematical software, such as Mathcad®.

More stress factors may be added to the Eyring model. For example if three stress factors are require, the model would be

$$t = aT^{\alpha}e^{b/T}e^{[c+(d/T)]S_1}e^{[e+(f/T)]S_2} \tag{5.9}$$

Note that for every stress factor added to the model, the values of two additional constants must be estimated. A simpler form of the Eyring model for temperature and voltage has been proposed. The constants α and d are assumed to be zero, and $S_1 = \ln V$, where V is voltage. This simplified model is

$$t = ae^{b/T}V^{-c} \tag{5.10}$$

With this version of the Eyring model, only three constants require estimation, and this can be done with multiple linear regression by linearizing the model.

$$\ln t = \ln a + \frac{b}{T} + c(-\ln V) \tag{5.11}$$

Example 5.4

Testing was conducted on a component at two temperatures and two levels of voltage. The time for 10% of the components to fail is given below. Determine the parameters of the simplified Eyring model.

10th Percentile	Temperature °C	Voltage
253	40	60
148	80	60
97	40	120
61	80	120

Solution

The following table contains the data required for multiple least squares regression.

t	ln(t)	T (°C)	T (°K)	V	1/T (°K)	–ln(V)
253	5.5334	40	313.16	60	0.00319	–4.0943
148	4.9972	80	353.16	60	0.00283	–4.0943
97	4.5747	40	313.16	120	0.00319	–4.7875
61	4.1109	80	353.16	120	0.00283	–4.7875

Using $\ln(t)$ as the dependent variable, and $1/T$ and $-\ln(V)$ as independent variables, multiple least squares regression yields 6.5499 as the *y*-intercept, 1382 as the coefficient for $1/T$ and 1.3309 as the coefficient for $-\ln(V)$. The Eyring model parameters are

$$a = e^{6.5499} = 699.2$$

$$b = 1{,}382$$

$$c = 13{,}309$$

There are many empirically derived acceleration models for voltage, humidity, vibration and other acceleration factors. Ryerson (1966) gives the following empirical relationship for different levels of voltage.

$$\frac{t}{t_\varepsilon} = \left(\frac{V_\varepsilon}{V}\right)^3 \qquad\qquad (5.12)$$

where: t is the time at which a specified portion of the population fails under normal operating conditions,

t_ε is the time at which a specified portion of the population fails under accelerated operating conditions,

V is the normal voltage, and

V_ε is the accelerated level of voltage.

5.2 Sequential testing

There are many occasions when reliability testing is required: at various stages of development, before shipment by the manufacturer, and before acceptance by the customer. Reliability testing may be conducted on individual components, sub-systems, or complete systems. Because of the high cost of reliability testing, in time and materials, sequential testing is usually used to minimize the number of units tested[*]. The truncated tests explained in Chapter 3 may also be used to verify minimum mean time to failure, but they usually require greater sample sizes.

Consider a test of the null hypothesis

$H_0 : \theta = \theta_0$

against the alternate hypothesis

$H_1 : \theta = \theta_1$

Sequential testing utilizes the available data after every failure to make a decision. Three decisions are possible: (1) accept the null hypothesis, (2) reject the null hypothesis, or (3) continue testing. Decisions are based on the likelihood ratio, $L_{1,n} / L_{0,n}$, where

$$L_{k,n} = \prod_{i=1}^{n} f(x_i \backslash \theta_k) \qquad\qquad (5.13)$$

where: $f(x)$ is the probability density function of the variable x, and

---

[*] For information on fixed length testing (to a predetermined length of time, or a predetermined number of failures, consult the section on parameter estimation in Chapter 3. Complete details, including confidence limits and failure free testing are explained.

θ is the parameter being tested.

Sequential test plans have a Type I error (the probability of rejecting the null hypothesis when it is true) of α when $\theta = \theta_0$, and a Type II error (the probability of accepting the null hypothesis when it is not true) that is less than or equal to β when $\theta_1 \leq \theta$.

5.2.1 The binomial distribution

In many instances, the outcome of a reliability test is pass or fail for each of the individual items being tested. This situation can be modeled by the binomial distribution, and for an acceptance test, the hypotheses are

$H_0: p \leq p_0$

$H_1: p > p_0$

where: p is the probability of failure for an item, and

p_0 is the probability of failure such the probability of accepting H_0 is $1-\alpha$, where α is the **Type I error**, or **producer's risk**.

As each item is tested, the decision to continue testing, accept the null hypothesis, or reject the null hypothesis is determined from the expression

$$z = \left(\frac{p_1}{p_0}\right)^y \left(\frac{1-p_1}{1-p_0}\right)^{n-y} \tag{5.14}$$

where: p_1 is the probability of failure such the probability of accepting H_0 is β,

β is **Type II error** or **consumer's risk**,

n is the total number of trials, and

y is the total number of failures.

The test is continued if $A < z < B$, where

$$A = \frac{\beta}{1-\alpha} \tag{5.15}$$

$$B = \frac{1-\beta}{\alpha}$$

The null hypothesis is accepted if $z < A$ and rejected if $z > B$. If neither of these conditions are met, testing continues.

Example 5.5

A sequential test was conducted to test the hypotheses

$$H_0: p \le 0.02$$
$$H_1: p > 0.02$$

The level of producer's risk for the test was 0.05; the level of consumer's risk was 0.1; and $p_1 = 0.1$. The first 3 items tested were successful, and the 4th and 5th items tested failed. Determine the status of the test after the results of each trial were known.

Solution

The values of A and B are

$$A = \frac{0.1}{1 - 0.05} = 0.10526$$

$$B = \frac{1 - 0.1}{0.05} = 18.0$$

The values of z after each trial, and the resulting decisions, are given below.

Trial	z	Decision
1	0.9184	Continue
2	0.8434	Continue
3	0.7746	Continue
4	3.873	Continue
5	19.364	Reject H_0

It is often useful to represent acceptance tests graphically. The test described above can be defined as:

accept H_0 if $c < y$

reject H_0 if $d > y$

continue testing if $c < y < d$

where

$$c = \frac{n\ln\left(\dfrac{1-p_0}{1-p_1}\right)}{\ln\left[\left(\dfrac{p_1}{p_0}\right)\left(\dfrac{1-p_0}{1-p_1}\right)\right]} - \frac{\ln\left(\dfrac{1-\alpha}{\beta}\right)}{\ln\left[\left(\dfrac{p_1}{p_0}\right)\left(\dfrac{1-p_0}{1-p_1}\right)\right]} \qquad (5.16)$$

and

$$d = \frac{n\ln\left(\dfrac{1-p_0}{1-p_1}\right)}{\ln\left[\left(\dfrac{p_1}{p_0}\right)\left(\dfrac{1-p_0}{1-p_1}\right)\right]} + \frac{\ln\left(\dfrac{1-\beta}{\alpha}\right)}{\ln\left[\left(\dfrac{p_1}{p_0}\right)\left(\dfrac{1-p_0}{1-p_1}\right)\right]} \qquad (5.17)$$

Example 5.6

For the test described in Example 5.5 suppose 81 items were tested with the 4th, 18th, 37th, and 73rd items failing while all other items were successful. Show this test graphically.

Solution

This sequential test is shown in Figure 5.3.

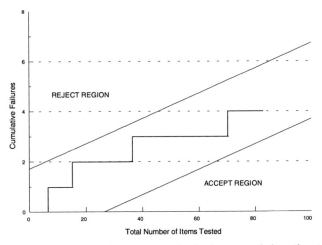

Figure 5.3. Sequential testing with the binomial distribution.

From Figure 5.3 it can be seen that the fewest number of trials required to reject the null hypothesis is 2 (two consecutive failures with no successes). It can also be seen from the figure that the fewest number of trials (all trials being successful) required to accept the null hypothesis is 27. Mathematically, the fewest number of trials required to reject the null hypothesis is

$$f_R = \frac{\ln \beta}{\ln\left[\left(\dfrac{p_1}{p_0}\right)\left(\dfrac{1-p_0}{1-p_1}\right)\right] - \ln\left(\dfrac{1-p_0}{1-p_1}\right)} \tag{5.18}$$

The fewest number of trials required to accept the null hypothesis is

$$f_A = \frac{\ln A}{\ln\left(\dfrac{1-p_1}{1-p_0}\right)} \tag{5.19}$$

The discriminatory power of a sampling plan is shown by its **operating characteristic curve** (OC curve). An OC curve displays the probability of accepting the null hypothesis versus the fraction defective. For binomial sequential sampling, the probability of accepting the null hypothesis is

$$P_a(p) = \frac{B^h - 1}{B^h - A^h} \tag{5.20}$$

where: p is the true fraction defective, and

h is an arbitrary term used to compute p (h usually ranges from -3 to 3) using the expression

$$p = \frac{1 - \left(\dfrac{1-p_1}{1-p_0}\right)^h}{\left(\dfrac{p_1}{p_0}\right)^h - \left(\dfrac{1-p_1}{1-p_0}\right)^h} \tag{5.21}$$

Example 5.7
Construct the OC curve for the sampling plan described in Example 5.5.

Solution

First, a value of −3 is arbitrarily assigned to h, and p is computed. The resulting value of p is then used to compute P_a. The value of h is then increased, and the procedure is repeated until enough values are obtained to construct a graph. Table 5.4 contains the information required to construct an OC curve.

Table 5.4. OC curve computations.

h	p	P_a
−3.0	0.2269	0.001166
−2.6	0.2011	0.002869
−2.2	0.1751	0.007051
−1.8	0.1492	0.017288
−1.4	0.1239	0.042058
−1.0	0.1000	0.100000
−0.6	0.0780	0.223531
−0.2	0.0587	0.435651
0.2	0.0426	0.683413
0.6	0.0297	0.862924
1.0	0.0200	0.950000
1.4	0.0130	0.983252
1.8	0.0082	0.994593
2.2	0.0051	0.998281
2.6	0.0031	0.999457
3.0	0.0018	0.999829

This OC curve is shown in Figure 5.4.

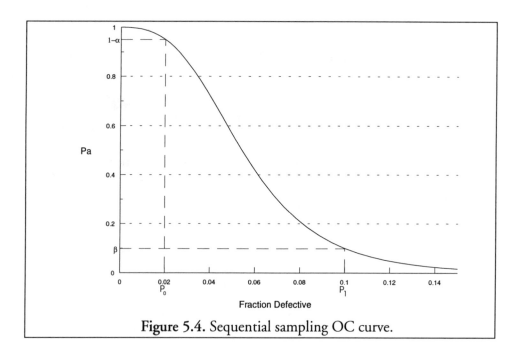

Figure 5.4. Sequential sampling OC curve.

Another characteristic that is valuable when planning a sequential test is the expected number of trials required to reach a decision. This value is a function of the true fraction defective, and is

$$E(p) = \frac{P_a(p)\ln A + \left[1 - P_a(p)\right]\ln B}{p\ln\left(\dfrac{p_1}{p_0}\right) + (1-p)\ln\left(\dfrac{1-p_1}{1-p_0}\right)}$$

(5.22)

This function reaches a maximum between p_0 and p_1, and is relatively flat in this region.

5.2.2 The exponential distribution

In many instances, the time to fail for individual items is available, which provides more information than a simple pass or fail designation and reduces testing time. Assuming an exponential time to fail distribution, a sequential test can be conducted on the cumulative time to fail,

$$T = \sum_{i=1}^{n} t_i \qquad (5.23)$$

where: t_i is the time to fail for the ith item, and

n is the total number of failures.

The test hypotheses are

$H_0: \lambda < \lambda_0$

$H_1: \lambda > \lambda_0$

where: λ is the failure rate of the exponential distribution.

The null hypothesis is accepted if

$$T > \frac{n\ln\left(\dfrac{\lambda_1}{\lambda_0}\right) + \ln\left(\dfrac{\alpha}{1-\beta}\right)}{\lambda_1 - \lambda_0} \qquad (5.24)$$

where: λ_0 is the failure rate such that the probability of accepting H_0 is

$1-\alpha$, and

λ_1 is the failure rate such that the probability of accepting H_0 is

β.

The null hypothesis is rejected if

$$T < \frac{n\ln\left(\dfrac{\lambda_1}{\lambda_0}\right) - \ln\left(\dfrac{\beta}{1-\alpha}\right)}{\lambda_1 - \lambda_0} \qquad (5.25)$$

Testing continues if

$$\frac{n\ln\left(\dfrac{\lambda_1}{\lambda_0}\right) - \ln\left(\dfrac{\beta}{1-\alpha}\right)}{\lambda_1 - \lambda_0} < T < \frac{n\ln\left(\dfrac{\lambda_1}{\lambda_0}\right) + \ln\left(\dfrac{\alpha}{1-\beta}\right)}{\lambda_1 - \lambda_0} \qquad (5.26)$$

Example 5.8

Graphically construct a sequential test plan to test the null hypothesis, $\lambda > 0.02$ units against the alternate hypothesis, $\lambda < 0.02$ units, given $\alpha = 0.05$, $\beta = 0.1$ and $\lambda_1 = 0.025$ units.

Solution

Table 5.5 contains the computations required to construct a graph. The graph is shown in Figure 5.5.

Table 5.5. Exponential sequential test.

Cumulative Time	Failures Reject	Accept Time
0	450	−578
3	584	−444
6	718	−310
9	852	−176
12	986	−43
15	1,120	91
18	1,254	225
21	1,387	359
24	1,521	493
27	1,655	627
30	1,789	761

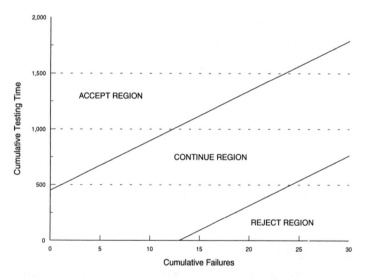

Figure 5.5. Exponential sequential test.

It can be seen from Figure 5.5 that the fastest the null hypothesis can be accepted is to test for 450 units without failure. The fastest the null hypothesis can be rejected is to have 14 consecutive, instantaneous failures.

The OC curve for sequential testing using the exponential distribution is defined by the expression

$$P_a(\lambda) = \frac{B^b - 1}{B^b - A^b} \tag{5.27}$$

where: $P_a(\lambda)$ is the probability of accepting the null hypothesis when λ is the true failure rate,

$B = \dfrac{1-\beta}{\alpha}$,

$A = \dfrac{\beta}{1-\alpha}$, and,

λ is determined by arbitrarily selecting a value of b, and utilizing the expression

$$\lambda = \frac{b(\lambda_1 - \lambda_0)}{\left(\dfrac{\lambda_1}{\lambda_0}\right)^b - 1} \tag{5.28}$$

A typically range for the value of b is from -4 to 4.

Example 5.9

Sketch the OC curve for the test plan described in Example 5.8.

Solution

Table 5.6 contains the computations necessary to sketch the curve. The OC curve is shown in Figure 5.6.

Table 5.6. OC curve computations for an exponential, sequential test.

h	λ	$P_a(\lambda)$
−4.0	0.03388	0.000123
−3.4	0.03197	0.000474
−2.8	0.03013	0.001829
−2.2	0.02836	0.007051
−1.6	0.02664	0.027007
−1.0	0.02500	0.100000
−0.4	0.02342	0.319314
0.2	0.02191	0.683413
0.8	0.02047	0.915945
1.4	0.01909	0.983252
2.0	0.01778	0.996948
2.6	0.01653	0.999457
3.2	0.01535	0.999904

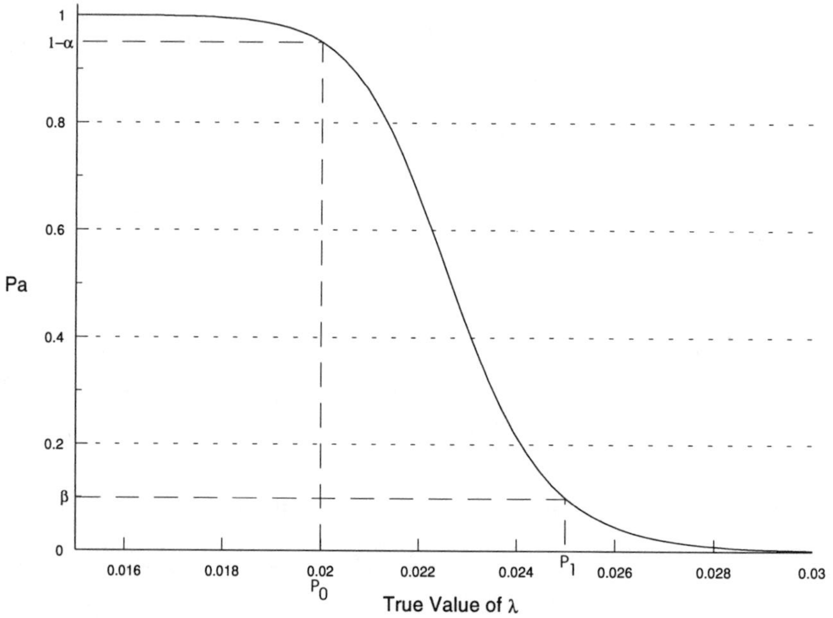

Figure 5.6. OC curve for sequential sampling with the exponential distribution.

The expected number of failures required to reach a decision is a function of the true failure rate, and is

$$E_r(\lambda) = \frac{-c - (d-c)P_a(\lambda)}{s - \frac{1}{\lambda}}, \quad s \neq \frac{1}{\lambda} \tag{5.29}$$

$$E_r(\lambda) = \frac{-cd}{s^2}, \quad s = \frac{1}{\lambda} \tag{5.30}$$

where

$$c = \frac{\ln\left(\frac{\alpha}{1-\beta}\right)}{\lambda_1 - \lambda_0} \tag{5.31}$$

$$d = \frac{\ln\left(\frac{1-\alpha}{\beta}\right)}{\lambda_1 - \lambda_0} \tag{5.32}$$

$$s = \frac{\ln\left(\frac{\lambda_1}{\lambda_2}\right)}{\lambda_1 - \lambda_0} \tag{5.33}$$

The expected time to reach a decision is

$$E_T(\lambda) = \frac{E_r(\lambda)}{\lambda} \tag{5.34}$$

This time represents the cumulative test time for all items. If n items are being tested simultaneously with replacement, the elapsed calendar time required to make a decision is $E_r(\lambda)/n$.

Example 5.10

For the test described in Example 5.8, given the true failure rate is 0.02, determine the expected number of failures to reach a decision, and the expected cumulative testing time to reach a decision.

Solution

The values of c, d and s are

$$c = \frac{\ln\left(\dfrac{0.05}{1-0.1}\right)}{0.025-0.02} = -578.074$$

$$d = \frac{\ln\left(\dfrac{1-0.05}{0.1}\right)}{0.025-0.02} = 450.258$$

$$s = \frac{\ln\left(\dfrac{0.025}{0.02}\right)}{0.025-0.02} = 44.629$$

From the OC curve, $P_a(0.02) = 0.95$. The expected number of failures to reach a decision is

$$E_r(0.02) = \frac{-(-578.074)-(450.258+578.074)0.95}{44.629 - \dfrac{1}{0.02}} = 74.4$$

The total expected testing time to reach a decision is

$$E_T(\lambda) = \frac{74.4}{0.02} = 3720.0$$

5.2.3 The Weibull distribution

There are many instances when it is known that the exponential distribution does not model the time to fail for the testing situation under consideration. If the shape parameter, β, is known, the Weibull distribution can be used in sequential testing. The test hypotheses are

$H_0: \theta > \theta_0$

$H_1: \theta < \theta_0$

where: θ is the scale parameter of the Weibull distribution, and

θ_0 is the scale parameter such that the probability of accepting H_0 is $1-\alpha$.

The test region is defined as

$$nb - c \le \sum_{i=1}^{n} t_i^\beta \le nb + d \qquad (5.35)$$

where

$$a = \frac{1}{\theta_1^\beta} - \frac{1}{\theta_0^\beta} \qquad (5.36)$$

$$b = \frac{(\beta-1)\ln\left(\dfrac{\theta_0}{\theta_1}\right)}{a} \qquad (5.37)$$

$$c = \frac{\ln\left(\dfrac{1-\tau}{\alpha}\right)}{a} \qquad (5.38)$$

$$d = \frac{\ln\left(\dfrac{1-\alpha}{\tau}\right)}{a} \qquad (5.39)$$

and θ_1 is the scale parameter such that the probability of accepting H_0 is τ. The term τ is used to represent consumer's risk because the standard term, β, is used to represent the shape parameter of the Weibull distribution.

Example 5.11

Determine the sequential testing region using the Weibull distribution assuming a shape parameter of 3.0, given θ_0 = 500 hours, θ_1 = 400 hours, α =0.05, and τ = 0.1.

Solution

The calculated values of a, b, c, and d are given below.

$$a = \frac{1}{400^3} - \frac{1}{500^3} = 7.625x10^{-9}$$

$$b = \frac{(3-1)\ln\left(\dfrac{500}{400}\right)}{7.625x10^{-9}} = 5.8529x10^7$$

$$c = \frac{\ln\left(\dfrac{1-0.1}{0.05}\right)}{7.625x10^{-9}} = 3.7907x10^{8}$$

$$d = \frac{\ln\left(\dfrac{1-0.05}{0.1}\right)}{7.625x10^{-9}} = 2.9525x10^{8}$$

The test region is shown graphically in Figure 5.7.

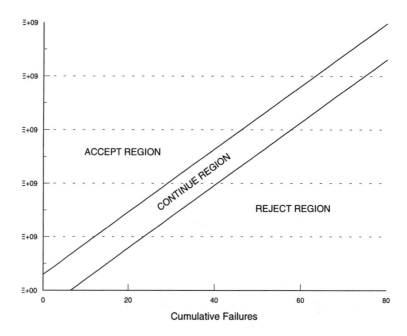

Figure 5.7. Sequential testing with the Weibull Distribution.

Example 5.12

For the test described in Example 5.11, determine the testing time required to accept if there are no failures.

Solution

Using the values of *a*, *b*, *c*, and *d* from the previous example, the testing region is defined as

$$5.8528x10^7 n - 3.7907x10^8 \le \sum_{i=1}^{n} t_i^\beta \le 5.8528x10^7 n + 2.9525x10^8$$

With no failures, $n = 0$, and the null hypothesis is accepted when

$$t^\beta > 2.9525x10^8$$

The testing time required to accept is

$$t = \left(2.9525x10^8\right)^{1/3} = 665.9 \text{ hours.}$$

5.2.4 Bayesian testing with the Weibull distribution

In Example 5.12, note that this is the test time for a single unit. If two units were tested, the total test time would be

$$2\left(t^{3.0}\right) = 2.9525x10^8$$

$$t = \left(\frac{2.9525x10^8}{2}\right)^{1/3.0} = 528.5$$

When using Bayesian analysis with the Weibull distribution, a data transformation can be made, and the result is data that behaves exponentially. The transformation is

$$t^* = t^\beta \tag{5.40}$$

Assuming the value of the shape parameter is equal to β, the maximum likelihood estimate of the scale parameter is

$$\hat{\theta} = \left(\frac{\sum_{i=1}^{n} t_i^\beta}{r}\right)^{1/\beta} \tag{5.41}$$

where: t_i is the time to fail or the time of censoring for the *i*th unit,
   n is the number of units tested, and
   r is the number of failures.

The lower confidence limit for the estimated scale parameter is

$$\theta_{L,\alpha} = \left(\frac{2 \sum_{i=1}^{n} t_i^{\beta}}{\chi^2_{\alpha,2r+2}} \right)^{1/\beta}$$

(5.42)

where: α is the level of significance (α = 0.1 for 90% confidence), and
$\chi^2_{\alpha,\nu}$ is the critical value of the chi-square distribution with significance α, and ν degrees of freedom

This expression assumes testing is discontinued after a predetermined amount of time. If testing is discontinued after a predetermined number failures, the degrees of freedom for the chi-square statistic is $2r$.

The estimated reliability at time t is

$$\hat{R}(t) = e^{\left[-\left(\frac{t}{\hat{\theta}} \right)^{\beta} \right]}$$

(5.43)

The lower confidence limit for reliability at time t is

$$R_{L,\alpha}(t) = e^{\left[-\left(\frac{t}{\theta_{L,\alpha}} \right)^{\beta} \right]}$$

(5.44)

Using the above expressions, it can be seen that the test time required to demonstrate a specified reliability, at time t, with confidence $1-\alpha$, and assuming no units fail, is

$$T = \theta \left(\frac{-\ln \alpha}{n} \right)^{1/\beta}$$

(5.45)

where θ is the characteristic life corresponding to the required reliability at time = t, and is

$$\theta = \frac{t}{\{ -\ln[R(t)] \}^{1/\beta}}$$

(5.46)

From Equation 5.45, it is obvious that the duration of the test time is not directly inversely proportional to the number of units tested. Figure 5.8 shows the relationship between test duration and sample size for a verification test requiring 95% reliability with 90% confidence at 100,000 miles, assuming a shape parameter of 3.

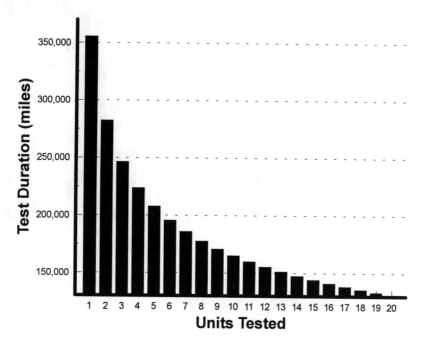

Figure 5.8. Test duration versus number of units tested to ensure 95% reliability with 90% confidence at 100,000 miles, given a shape parameter of 3, and no failures.

From Figure 5.8, it can be seen that the total time on test (test duration X number of units tested), is increasing with the number of units tested. This is shown in Figure 5.9.

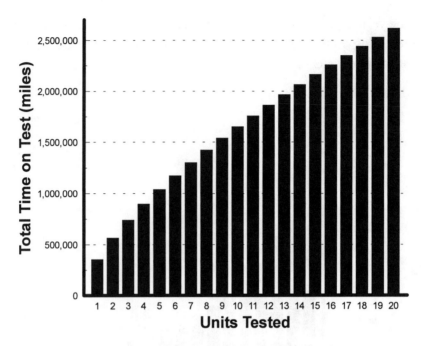

Figure 5.9. Total time on test versus number of units tested to ensure 95% reliability with 90% confidence at 100,000 miles, given a shape parameter of 3, and no failures.

The behavior displayed in Figures 5.8 and 5.9 is unique to the case of a shape parameter greater than 1.0. If the shape parameter is equal to 1, the total time on test required to achieve a specified reliability with a given confidence is independent of the number of units tested. If the shape parameter is less than 1, the total time on test required to achieve a specified reliability with a given confidence decreases as the of the number of units tested increases.

5.3 Exercises

1. Explain the difference between environmental stress testing and acceptance testing.

2. Explain the difference between acceptance testing and qualification testing.

3. Given the density function obtained under accelerated conditions

$$f(t) = \frac{1}{30} \exp\left(-\frac{t}{30}\right)$$

Determine the density function under normal operating conditions, given an acceleration factor of 5.

4. Determine the reliability function under normal operating conditions for the data given in Exercise 3.

5. Determine the hazard function under normal operating conditions for the data given in Exercise 3.

6. What is the reliability of the system given in Exercise 3 under normal operating conditions at time = 50?

7. Graph the reliability of the system given in Exercise 3 under normal operating conditions and accelerated conditions.

8. The acceleration factor for increasing vibration from 50 units to 200 units is 6.4. At a vibration level of 200 units, the time to fail is lognormal with a scale parameter of 0.8 and a location parameter of 3.2. What is the reliability function under normal operating conditions?

9. The time to fail for a component is normally distributed with a mean of 310 and a standard deviation of 42 at a temperature of 130°F. The normal operating temperature is 75°F. What is the reliability function under normal operating conditions given an acceleration factor of 1.8 between temperatures 75°F and 130°F?

10. How can linear acceleration be verified?

11. Given the following temperatures and Weibull distribution parameters, determine the constants of the Arrhenius model.

Temperature	β	θ
70°F	2.84	1021

98°F	2.82	954
23°F	2.86	759
175°F	2.83	631

12. For the data given in Exercise 11, determine the acceleration factor at a temperature of 100°F if the normal operating temperature is 60°F.

13. Given the following data determine the parameters of the Eyring model.

50th Percentile	Temperature	Voltage
45	30°C	20V
38	60°C	20V
35	30°C	40V
29	60°C	40V
33	45°C	30V

14. A sequential test plan is graphically shown in the figure below. What is the fewest number of trials required to reject the null hypothesis?

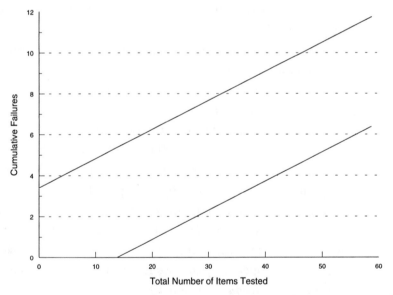

15. For the test plan shown in Exercise 14, what is the fewest number of trials required to accept the null hypothesis?

16. For the test plan shown in Exercise 14, if the first 3 items tested fail, and the next 18 succeed, what is the status of the test?

17. Construct a sequential test plan to test the null hypothesis $p \leq 0.05$ against the alternate hypothesis $p \geq 0.05$, given a producer's risk of 0.05, a consumer's risk of 0.1, and $p_1 = 0.1$.

18. Construct the OC curve for the test plan developed in Exercise 17.

19. For the test plan in Exercise 19, what is the fewest number of trials required to accept the null hypothesis?

20. For the test plan in Exercise 17, what is the fewest number of trials required to reject the null hypothesis?

21. Construct a sequential test plan to test the null hypothesis $\lambda \geq 0.05$ against the alternate hypothesis $\lambda \leq 0.05$, given a producer's risk of 0.05, a consumer's risk of 0.1, and $\lambda_1 = 0.07$.

22. Construct the OC curve for the test plan developed in Exercise 23.

23. What is the expected number of trials required to reach a decision for the test plan developed in Exercise 23?

24. Given a shape parameter of 1.7 for the Weibull distribution, and assuming no failures, how long will 20 items have to be tested to give a reliability of 95% at $t = 100,000$ with 90% confidence.

25. Five items were placed on test stands, one item failed after 42 hours, and the remaining four items were removed after 50 hours. It is known that the time to fail for these items follows a Weibull time to fail with a shape parameter of 2.2. Determine 90% symmetrical limits for the characteristic life.

5.4 References

Dhillon, B. S. 1985. *Quality Control, Reliability, and Engineering Design.* New York: Marcel Dekker.

Dodson, Bryan. 1994. *Weibull Analysis (with Software).* Milwaukee, WI: ASQC–Quality Press.

Dodson, B. L., and M. D. Mulcahy. 1992. *Certified Reliability Engineer Examination Study Guide.* Tucson, AZ: Quality Publishing.

Dovich, R. A. 1990. *Reliability Statistics.* Milwaukee, WI: ASQC–Quality Press.

Ireson, G. W., and C. F.Coombs. 1988. *Handbook of Reliability Engineering and Management.* New York: McGraw-Hill.

Kapur, K. C., and L. R. Lamberson. 1977. *Reliability in Engineering Design.* New York: John Wiley & Sons.

Kielpinski, T. J., and W. Nelson. 1975. Optimum censored accelerated life tests for normal and lognormal life distributions. *IEEE Transactions on Reliability* R-24:310–320.

Krishnamoorthi, K. S. 1992. *Reliability Methods for Engineers.* Milwaukee, WI: ASQC–Quality Press.

Lewis, E. E. 1987. *Introduction To Reliability Engineering.* New York: John Wiley & Sons.

Meeker, W. Q., and G. J. Hahn. 1985. *How to Plan an Accelerated Life Test— Some Practical Guidelines.* Milwaukee, WI: ASQC–Quality Press.

Meeker, W. and Nelson, W. (1976). Optimum accelerated life tests for Weibull and extreme value distributions. *IEEE Transactions on Reliability* R-25:20–24.

Nelson, W. 1990. *Accelerated Testing: Statistical Models, Test Plans and Data Analysis*. New York: John Wiley & Sons.

Shooman, M. L. 1990. *Probabilistic Reliability: An Engineering Approach*. Malabar, FL: Robert E. Krieger.

Tobias, P. A., and D. C. Trindade. 1986. *Applied Reliability*. New York: Van Nostrand Reinhold.

US Department of Defense. *MIL-HDBK-189: Reliability Growth Management*. Philadelphia: Naval Publications and Forms Center.

US Department of Defense. *MIL-HDBK-781: Reliability Test Methods, Plans and Environments for Engineering Development, Qualification and Production*. Philadelphia: Naval Publications and Forms Center.

US Department of Defense. *MIL-STD-810: Environmental Test Methods and Engineering Guidelines*. Philadelphia: Naval Publications and Forms Center.

US Department of Defense. *MIL-STD-1635: Reliability Growth Testing*. Philadelphia: Naval Publications and Forms Center.

♦ ♦ ♦
CHAPTER

6

Maintainability and Availability

Many systems are repairable; when the system fails, it is repaired. Examples are automobiles, dishwashers, most production equipment, etc. Maintainability is a measure of the difficulty to repair the system. More specifically, maintainability is:

> The measure of the ability of a system to be retained in, or restored to, a specified condition when maintenance is performed by personnel having specified skill levels, using prescribed procedures and resources, at each prescribed level of maintenance and repair.

Military Handbook 472 (MIL-HDBK-472) defines six components of maintainability. Figure 6.1 shows the relationship of these components.

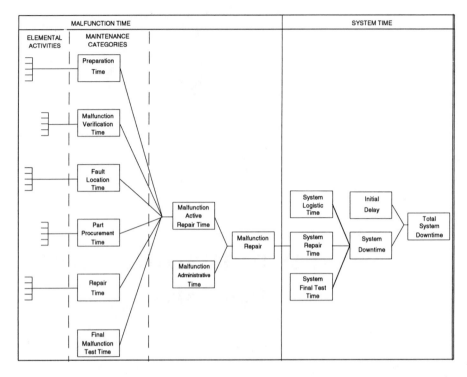

Figure 6.1. Structure of maintainability.

The six components shown in Figure 6.1 are discussed below.

1. **Elemental Activities** are simple maintenance actions of short duration and relatively small variance that do not vary appreciably from one system to another. An example of an elemental activity is the opening and shutting of a door.

2. **Malfunction Active Repair Time** consists of:
   a. Preparation time
   b. Malfunction verification time
   c. Fault location time
   d. Part procurement time
   e. Repair time
   f. Final malfunction test time

Items *a–f* above are composed of elemental activities.

3. **Malfunction Repair Time** consists of:
   a. Malfunction active repair time
   b. Malfunction administrative time
4. **System Repair Time** is the product of malfunction repair time and the number of malfunctions.
5. **System Downtime** includes:
   a. System logistic time
   b. System repair time
   c. System final test time
6. **Total System Downtime** is a combination of the distributions of
   a. Initial delay
   b. System downtime

MIL-HDBK-472 provides a procedure for predicting maintainability based on the structure described above. The philosophy of the procedure is based on the principles of synthesis and transferability. The synthesis principle involves a buildup of downtimes, step-by-step, progressing from the distribution of downtimes of elemental activities through various stages culminating finally with the distribution of system downtime. The transferability principle embodies the concept that data applicable to one type of system can be applied to similar systems, under like conditions of use and environment, to predict system maintainability.

Other useful maintainability references are Military Standard 470, which describes a maintainability program for systems and equipment, and Military Standard 471, which provides procedures for maintainability verification, demonstration, and evaluation.

Availability is a measure of the readiness of a system. More specifically, availability is:

> A measure of the degree to which a system is in an operable and comitable state at the start of a mission when the mission is called for at a random time.

There are three categories of availability.

1. **Inherent Availability** is the ideal state for analyzing availability. It is a function only of the mean time to fail, MTBF, and the mean time to

repair, MTTR; preventive maintenance is not considered. Inherent availability is defined as

$$A_I = \frac{MTBF}{MTBF + MTTR} \tag{6.1}$$

2. **Achieved Availability** includes preventive maintenance as well as corrective maintenance. It is a function of the mean time between maintenance actions, MTMA, and the mean maintenance time, MMT. Achieved availability is defined as

$$A_A = \frac{MTMA}{MTMA + MMT} \tag{6.2}$$

3. **Operational Availability** includes preventive maintenance, corrective maintenance, and delay time before maintenance begins, such as waiting for parts or personnel. It is a function of the mean time between maintenance actions and the mean down time, MDT, and is defined as

$$A_O = \frac{MTMA}{MTMA + MDT} \tag{6.3}$$

It is important to note that the type of availability being described is often not distinguished. Many authors simply refer to "availability," MTTR may be the equivalent of MMT or MDT, and MTBF may be the equivalent MTMA.

6.1 Quantifying maintainability and availability

Maintainability is defined as

$$M(t) = P(T < t) = \int_0^t f(x)dx \tag{6.4}$$

where: $P(T < t)$ is the probability of completing the repairs in time $< T$, and

$f(x)$ is the repair time probability density function.

It has been shown that the lognormal distribution can often be used to model repair times. There are times when repairs are completed quickly, but it is rather uncommon to achieve repair times much shorter than normal. However, in some instances, problems arise causing repairs to take much longer than normal. The skewness of the lognormal distribution models this situation well.

Perhaps the most widely used measure of maintainability is the mean-time-to-repair (MTTR).

$$MTTR = \frac{\sum_{i=1}^{n} \lambda_i \tau_i}{\sum_{i=1}^{n} \lambda_i} \tag{6.5}$$

where: n is the number of sub-systems,

λ_i is the failure rate of the ith sub-system, and

τ_i is the time to repair of the ith unit.

Another useful measure is the median corrective maintenance time (MCMT). This is the time in which half of the maintenance actions can be accomplished; the median of the time to repair distribution. For normally distributed repair times, MTTR = MCMT.

Maximum Corrective Maintenance Time (CMAX%) is the maximum time required to complete a given percentile of maintenance tasks. Unless otherwise specified, CMAX% refers to 95% of all maintenance tasks.

Example 6.1

The time to repair for a system follows a lognormal distribution with a scale parameter of 1.2 and a location parameter of 2.2 Plot the maintainability function for this system, and determine the probability of completing a system repair in less than time = 50.

Solution

The maintainability function is

$$M(t) = \int_0^t f(x)dx$$

In Chapter 3, the lognormal probability density function is given as

$$f(x) = \frac{1}{\sigma x \sqrt{2\pi}} \exp\left[-\frac{1}{2}\left(\frac{\ln x - \mu}{\sigma}\right)^2\right], \quad x > 0$$

---

where: μ is the location parameter, and
σ is the scale parameter.

The integral of this function from 0 to t can be expressed as

$$M(t) = \Phi\left(\frac{\ln t - \mu}{\sigma}\right)$$

where $\Phi(z)$ is the area under the standard normal probability density function to the left of z. This value is tabulated in Appendix A.

The maintainability function is shown in Figure 6.2.

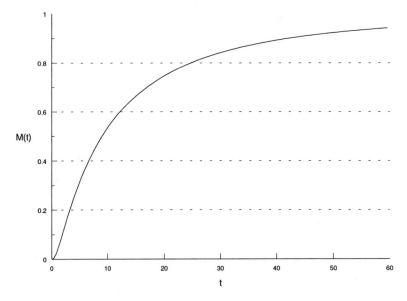

Figure 6.2. Maintainability example.

The probability of completing a repair in less than time = 50 is

$$M(50) = \Phi\left(\frac{\ln 50 - 2.2}{1.2}\right) = \Phi(1.4267) = 0.9232$$

In the special case where the time to fail and the time to repair follow exponential distributions, availability is

$$A(t) = \frac{\mu}{\mu + \lambda} + \frac{\lambda}{\mu + \lambda} e^{-(\mu + \lambda)t} \qquad (6.6)$$

where: μ is the mean repair rate, and

λ is the mean failure rate.

It can be seen from Equation 6.6 that as time increases, availability reaches a steady state of

$$A = \frac{\mu}{\mu + \lambda} \qquad (6.7)$$

This expression is equivalent to

$$A = \frac{\theta}{\theta + \alpha} \qquad (6.8)$$

where: θ is the mean time to fail, and

α is the mean time to repair.

The steady-state availability is independent of the time to fail and time to repair distributions.

The average availability for the period from time = 0 to time = T is equal to the average uptime, which is

$$U(t) = \frac{1}{t} \int_0^t A(s) ds \qquad (6.9)$$

For the special case of exponentially distributed times to fail and repair, this reduces to

$$U(t) = \frac{\mu}{\lambda + \mu} + \frac{\mu}{(\lambda + \mu)^2 t} - \frac{\mu}{(\lambda + \mu)^2 t} e^{-(\lambda + \mu)t} \qquad (6.10)$$

Note that the steady-state uptime is equal to the steady-state availability.

Example 6.2

The time to fail for a component is exponentially distributed with a mean of 25. The time to repair for this component is also exponentially distributed with a mean of 40. Plot availability as a function of time. What is the steady-state availability?

Solution

The mean failure rate is

$$\lambda = \frac{1}{25} = 0.04$$

The mean repair rate is

$$\mu = \frac{1}{40} = 0.025$$

Availability is

$$A(t) = \frac{0.025}{0.025 + 0.04} + \frac{0.04}{0.025 + 0.04} e^{-(0.025+0.04)t}$$

Availability is plotted as a function of time in Figure 6.3.

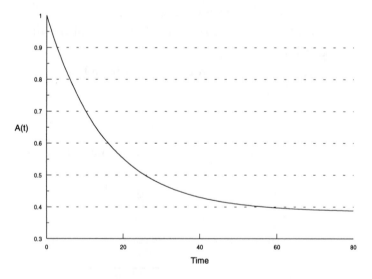

Figure 6.3. Availability as a function of time.

The steady-state availability is

$$A = \frac{25}{25 + 40} = 0.3846$$

This is verified by Figure 6.3.

To determine system availability, it is important to specify the operating assumptions. With the trivial assumption that all components in the system remain operating while failed components are repaired, system availability for a series system consisting of n components is

$$A_s(t) = \prod_{i=1}^{n} A_i(t) \tag{6.11}$$

This assumption is obviously not valid in many circumstances. Consider a six-stand rolling mill. It is impossible to operate five stands while repairing the other stand. Equation 6.11 also requires that n repairmen be available. If the $n-1$ operating components continue to run while the failed component is being repaired, it is possible to have all n components in a failed state.

Assuming all components remain running while the failed component is being repaired makes more sense for a parallel system. The purpose of redundant components is to prevent system failure or downtime. Using this assumption, and assuming n repairmen are available, the availability of a system with n systems in parallel is

$$A_s(t) = 1 - \prod_{i=1}^{n} \left[1 - A_i(t)\right] \tag{6.12}$$

Example 6.3

Five components in series each have a mean time to fail that is normally distributed, with a mean of 60 hours, and a standard deviation of 10. The mean time to repair of each of these components is exponentially distributed with a mean of 30 hours. There are five, repairmen and components are only removed from service during repair time (if the system is down because component number 1 failed, components 2–5 continue to operate). What is the system steady-state availability?

Solution

The steady-state availability of each component is

$$A = \frac{60}{60 + 30} = 0.6667$$

The system steady-state availability is

$$A_s = (0.6667)^5 = 0.1317$$

Example 6.4

Rework Example 6.3 assuming the five components are in parallel.

Solution

The system steady-state availability is

$$A_s = 1 - (1 - 0.6667)^5 = 0.9959$$

As stated earlier, the assumption that all components in a series system continue to operate even though the failure of one component causes a system failure does not often apply to series systems. More often, all components are shut down until the failed item is repaired. Then, the entire system is brought on-line. In this case, system availability can be computed from the system mean time to fail and the system mean time to repair.

Example 6.5

Assuming exponential distributions for the mean time between failures and the mean time to repair for all components, compute the steady-state system availability of the series system shown below. All components are idled when the system fails.

MTBF = 20	MTBF = 30	MTBF = 25
MTTR = 15	MTTR = 19	MTTR = 22

Solution

The system mean time between failures is

$$MTBF_s = \frac{1}{\frac{1}{20}+\frac{1}{30}+\frac{1}{25}} = 8.1081$$

The system mean time to repair is found by computing the weighted average of each component's mean repair time and the percentage of system failures caused by that component.

Component	MTBF	Failure Rate	MTTR	Weighted Average
1	20	0.05	15	0.75
2	30	0.0333	19	0.6333
3	25	0.04	22	0.88
Total		0.1233		2.2633

The system mean time to repair is

$$MTTR_s = \frac{2.2633}{0.1233} = 18.3560$$

The steady-state system availability is

$$A_s = \frac{8.1081}{8.1081+18.356} = 0.3061$$

Assuming all components continued to operate when the system fails, the system availability would be found by computing the product of the component availabilities.

Component	MTBF	MTTR	Availability
1	20	15	0.5714
2	30	19	0.6122
3	25	22	0.5319

System availability in this case is

$$A_s = (0.5714)(0.6122)(0.5319) = 0.1861$$

which is substantially less than the availability achieved by shutting the remaining components down during a system failure.

6.2. Preventive maintenance

In some cases, it is possible to prevent failures with preventive maintenance. The question is to determine if preventive maintenance is applicable, and if so, how often should it be scheduled. Referring to Figure 6.4, failures can be grouped into three categories based on the behavior of the failure rate. **Infant mortality** failures are characterized by a decreasing failure rate. Recall from Chapter 3, that the hazard function (failure rate) of the Weibull distribution is decreasing if the shape parameter, β, is less than 1. **Random**[*] failures exhibit a constant failure rate; the shape parameter of the Weibull distribution is equal to 1. **Wear-out** failures have an increasing failure rate; the shape parameter of the Weibull distribution is greater than 1.

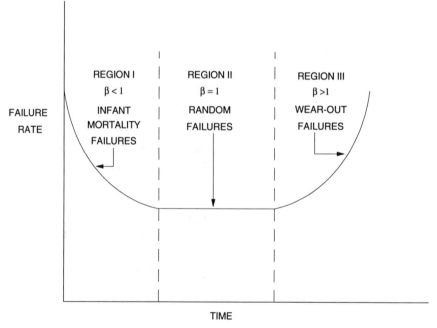

Figure 6.4. The bathtub curve.

---

[*] This term can be confusing, since all failures occur randomly. This portion of the bathtub curve is also referred to as the "useful life". This term is also confusing since many products exhibit a decreasing or increasing failure fate for their entire life.

Infant mortality failures are premature failures that can often be prevented by management. If infant mortality failures cannot be prevented, a burn-in procedure can be implemented to eliminate the failures before the product is shipped. Preventive maintenance is not applicable for an item with a decreasing failure rate. Performing preventive maintenance restores the system to its initial state which has a higher failure rate; preventive maintenance increases the number of failures.

Some causes of infant mortality failures are:

- Improper use
- Inadequate materials
- Over-stressed components
- Improper setup
- Improper installation
- Poor quality control
- Power surges
- Handling damage

Random failures cannot be prevented with preventive maintenance. The failure rate is constant, so preventive maintenance has no affect on failures. Reliability can be increased by redesigning the item, or in some cases, by implementing an inspection program.

Wear-out failures can be prevented with preventive maintenance. The failure rate is increasing with time, so preventive maintenance restores the system to a state with a lower failure rate. The question is how often should preventive maintenance be scheduled.

The time to fail for an item is variable, and can be represented by a probability distribution, $f(x)$. Referring to Figure 6.5, the cost of failures per unit time decreases as preventive maintenance is done more often, but the cost of preventive maintenance per unit time increases. There exists a point where the total cost of failures and preventive maintenance per unit time is at a minimum; the optimum schedule for preventive maintenance.

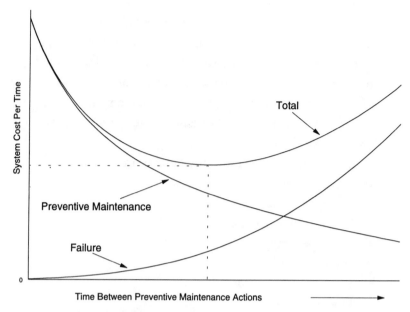

Figure 6.5. Optimum schedule for preventive maintenance.

The optimum time between maintenance actions is found by minimizing the total cost per unit time.

$$C_T = \frac{C_p \int_T^\infty f(t)dt + C_f \int_0^T f(t)dt}{T \int_T^\infty f(t)dt + \int_0^T t f(t)dt} \tag{6.13}$$

where: C_p is the cost of preventive maintenance,
   C_f is the cost of a failure, and
   T is the time between preventive maintenance actions.

Minimizing Equation 6.13 is tedious, and numerical routines are usually required. Dodson (1994), developed a tabular solution for this problem given the following assumptions.

1. The time to fail follows a Weibull distribution.
2. Preventive maintenance is performed on an item at time T, at a cost of C_p.
3. If the item fails before time = T, a failure cost of C_f is incurred.

4. Each time preventive maintenance is performed, the item is returned to its initial state; that is, the item is "as good as new."

The optimum time between preventive maintenance actions is

$$T = m\theta + \delta \tag{6.14}$$

where: m is a function of the ratio of the failure cost to the preventive maintenance cost, and the value of the shape parameter, and is given in Table 6.1.

θ is the scale parameter of the Weibull distribution, and

δ is the location parameter of the Weibull distribution.

Table 6.1. Values of m.

C_f/C_p	ß							
	1.5	2.0	2.5	3.0	4.0	5.0	7.0	10.0
2.0	2.229	1.091	0.883	0.810	0.766	0.761	0.775	0.803
2.2	1.830	0.981	0.816	0.760	0.731	0.733	0.755	0.788
2.4	1.579	0.899	0.764	0.720	0.702	0.711	0.738	0.777
2.6	1.401	0.834	0.722	0.688	0.679	0.692	0.725	0.766
2.8	1.265	0.782	0.687	0.660	0.659	0.675	0.713	0.758
3.0	1.158	0.738	0.657	0.637	0.642	0.661	0.702	0.749
3.3	1.033	0.684	0.620	0.607	0.619	0.642	0.687	0.739
3.6	0.937	0.641	0.589	0.582	0.600	0.627	0.676	0.730
4.0	0.839	0.594	0.555	0.554	0.579	0.609	0.662	0.719
4.5	0.746	0.547	0.521	0.526	0.557	0.591	0.648	0.708
5	0.676	0.511	0.493	0.503	0.538	0.575	0.635	0.699
6	0.574	0.455	0.450	0.466	0.509	0.550	0.615	0.683
7	0.503	0.414	0.418	0.438	0.486	0.530	0.600	0.671
8	0.451	0.382	0.392	0.416	0.468	0.514	0.587	0.661
9	0.411	0.358	0.372	0.398	0.452	0.500	0.575	0.652
10	0.378	0.337	0.355	0.382	0.439	0.488	0.566	0.645
12	0.329	0.304	0.327	0.357	0.417	0.469	0.550	0.632
14	0.293	0.279	0.306	0.338	0.400	0.454	0.537	0.621
16	0.266	0.260	0.288	0.323	0.386	0.441	0.526	0.613
18	0.244	0.244	0.274	0.309	0.374	0.430	0.517	0.605
20	0.226	0.230	0.263	0.298	0.364	0.421	0.508	0.598

Continued on next page...

Table 6.1—*continued...*

C_f/C_p	ß							
	1.5	2.0	2.5	3.0	4.0	5.0	7.0	10.0
25	0.193	0.205	0.239	0.275	0.343	0.402	0.492	0.584
30	0.170	0.186	0.222	0.258	0.328	0.387	0.478	0.573
35	0.152	0.172	0.207	0.245	0.315	0.374	0.468	0.564
40	0.139	0.160	0.197	0.234	0.304	0.364	0.459	0.557
45	0.128	0.151	0.187	0.225	0.295	0.356	0.451	0.550
50	0.119	0.143	0.179	0.217	0.288	0.348	0.444	0.544
60	0.105	0.130	0.167	0.204	0.274	0.335	0.432	0.534
70	0.095	0.120	0.157	0.193	0.264	0.325	0.422	0.526
80	0.087	0.112	0.148	0.185	0.255	0.316	0.415	0.518
90	0.080	0.106	0.141	0.177	0.248	0.309	0.407	0.513
100	0.074	0.101	0.135	0.172	0.241	0.303	0.402	0.507
150	0.057	0.082	0.115	0.150	0.217	0.278	0.379	0.487
200	0.047	0.071	0.103	0.136	0.203	0.263	0.363	0.472
300	0.035	0.058	0.087	0.119	0.182	0.243	0.343	0.454
500	0.025	0.045	0.071	0.100	0.161	0.219	0.319	0.431
1000	0.016	0.032	0.054	0.079	0.135	0.190	0.288	0.403

Example 6.6

The cost of failure for an item is $1,000. The cost of preventive maintenance for this item is $25. The following Weibull distribution parameters were determined from time to fail data: $\beta = 2.5$, $\theta = 181$ days, $\delta = 0$. How often should preventive maintenance be done?

Solution

The ratio of failure cost to PM cost is

$$\frac{C_f}{C_p} = \frac{1000}{25} = 40$$

Entering Table 6.1 with this ratio and a shape parameter of 2.5, give 0.197 for the value of m.

A PM should be done every

$$T = (0.197)(181) + 0 = 35.657 \text{ days}$$

This is shown graphically in Figure 6.6.

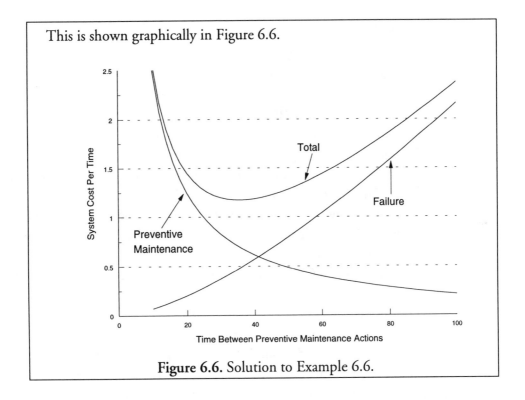

Figure 6.6. Solution to Example 6.6.

Example 6.7

Repeat Example 6.6 with the following Weibull distribution parameters: $\beta = 0.8$, $\theta = 181$ days, $\delta = 0$.

Solution

When the shape parameter of the Weibull distribution is less than or equal to 1.0, the optimum solution is to do no preventive maintenance.

Dodson and Kirkland (1994) have developed a software package, "The Reliability and Maintenance Analyst," that determines optimum preventive maintenance schedules as well as optimum inspection schedules. This package also determines the parameters of the Weibull distribution. "The Reliability and Maintenance Analyst" can be ordered from:

Applied Reliability Concepts & Training, Inc.
3933 Hwy 61 N
Boonville, Indiana 47601
812-897-0271

6.3 Designing for maintainability

Maintenance may be divided into the following tasks:

1. **Disassembly**—Equipment disassembly to the extent necessary, to gain access to the item that is to be replaced. How difficult is it to access the failed part? How much time does it take?

2. **Interchange**—Removing the defective item and installing the replacement. How difficult is it to exchange the defective part? How much time does it take?

3. **Reassembly**—Closing and reassembly of the equipment after the replacement has been made. Again difficulty and time should be a consideration.

Considering that the ease of maintenance may be measured in terms of man-hours, material, and money. Savings are attributable to the fact that designing for ease of maintenance is considered to be a design enhancement because it provides for the recognition and elimination of areas of poor maintainability during the early stages of the design life cycle. Otherwise, this area of poor maintainability would only become apparent during demonstration testing or actual use. After which time, correction of design deficiencies would be costly and would unduly delay schedules and missions. The ease with which corrective action may be taken is the key to designing for maintainability.

Moss (1985) gives eight guidelines that should be considered when designing for maintainability. Following these guidelines will help produce a design that is easily repaired, thus increasing maintainability and availability.

1. **Standardization**—Ensure compatibility among mating parts, and minimize the number of different parts in the system. Instead of using a 4mm bolt in one area and a 5mm bolt in another area, use a 5mm bolt in both areas. This will reduce spare parts requirements.

2. **Modularization**—Enforce conformance of assembly configurations to standards based on modular units with standard sizes, shapes, and interface locations. This allows use of standardized assembly and disassembly procedures.

3. **Functional packaging**—Expedite repair of faulty systems by containing all components of an item performing a function in a package. Replacing the faulty package repairs the unit.

4. **Interchangeability**—Control dimensional and functional tolerances to assure that items can be replaced in the field without physical rework.

5. **Accessibility**—Control spatial arrangements to allow accessibility. Items should be arranged to allow room for a worker to be comfortable when making repairs. All items should be accessible. Un-failed items should not have to be removed to gain access to a failed item.

6. **Malfunction annunciation**—Provide a means of notifying the operator when a malfunction is present. The oil pressure and temperature gauges on an automobile are examples.

7. **Fault isolation**—Assure that a malfunction can be traced. A simple method is to provide connectors that can be connected to external test equipment to determine if a component is operating properly. Often built-in diagnostics are provided with a system.

8. **Identification**—Provide a method for unique identification of all components as well as a method for recording preventive and corrective maintenance.

6.4 System effectiveness

The Weapons System Effectiveness Industry Advisory Committee (WSEIAC) developed a performance measurement for repairable systems that incorporates availability, capability and reliability. The measurement is **system effectiveness**. In order for a system to be effective, the system must be available when called on, the system must have the capability to complete the stated task, and the system must achieve the mission (i.e. be reliable).

The ARINC Research Corporation has also developed a measure of system effectiveness based on mission reliability, operational readiness and design adequacy. This relationship is shown in Figure 6.7.

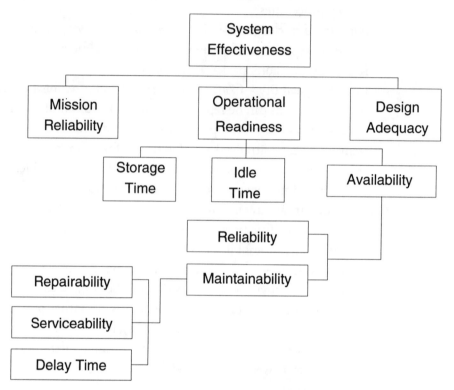

Figure 6.7. System effectiveness.

System effectiveness can be quantified as

$$SE = (MR)(OR)(DA) \tag{6.15}$$

    where: MR is mission reliability,
                OR is operational readiness, and
                DA is design adequacy.

Example 6.8

A missile system not originally designed to intercept Scud missiles has been employed to do so. Assuming this missile's design adequacy for intercepting Scud missiles is 0.9. Determine the system effectiveness if operational readiness is 0.98 and mission reliability is 0.87.

Solution

System effectiveness is

$$SE = (0.87)(0.98)(0.9) = 0.7673$$

6.5 Exercises

1. Describe the 6 components of maintainability and their relationship.
2. Describe the differences in inherent availability, achieved availability, and operational availability.
3. Given the time to repair follows a Weibull distribution with a shape parameter of 4, a scale parameter of 130 and a location parameter of 10, graph maintainability as a function of time.
4. For the system described in Exercise 2, what is the maintainability at time = 5, time = 25, time = 200?
5. Explain why availability at time = 0 is equal to 1.0.
6. An item has a constant failure rate of 50, and a constant repair rate of 22, what is the steady-state availability?
7. For the system in Exercise 5, graph availability as a function of time.
8. For the system in Exercise 5, determine the uptime for the interval (0,5).
9. For the system in Exercise 5, plot uptime as a function of time.
10. Three components in series have mean times to fail of 50, 60, and 70 respectively. The mean repair times are 30, 40, and 50 respectively. What is the steady-state availability, assuming all non-failed components remain operating during system downtime?
11. Repeat Exercise 9 assuming the 3 components are in parallel.
12. Repeat Exercise 9 assuming all components cease operating during system downtime.
13. Repeat Exercise 9 assuming all components cease operating during system downtime, and the 3 components are in parallel.
14. Explain what is meant by infant mortality failures.
15. Explain what is meant by wear-out failures.
16. A component has a time to fail that follows a Weibull distribution with a shape parameter of 3.5 and a scale parameter of 67. The component can be replaced at a cost of $200; but if the component fails, the cost is $20,000. How often should the component be replaced?
17. Repeat Exercise 15 with Weibull parameters of $\beta = 0.89$ and $\theta = 190$.

18. What is the required operational readiness if a system effectiveness of 0.997 is required, and mission reliability is 0.999, and design adequacy is 0.9999?

6.6 References

Dhillon, B. S. 1985. *Quality Control, Reliability, and Engineering Design*. New York: Marcel Dekker.

Dodson, Bryan, and Jack Kirkland. 1994. *The Reliability & Maintenance Analyst*. Auburn Hills, MI: Espinoza Consulting.

Dodson, Bryan. 1994. Determining the optimum schedule for preventive maintenance. *Quality Engineering* 6(4):667–679.

Dodson, Bryan. 1994. Using statistics to schedule maintenance. In *Proceedings of the 2nd Annual Reliability and Maintainability Symposium*. Dallas, TX.

Dodson, Bryan. 1993. Using the Weibull distribution to schedule preventive maintenance. In *Proceedings of the 31st Annual Reliability Engineering and Management Institute*. Tucson, AZ.

Dodson, Bryan. 1993. Optimizing schedules for equipment monitoring. In *Proceedings of the 1993 CSI User Conference*. Louisville, KY.

Dodson, B. L., and M. D. Mulcahy. 1992. *Certified Reliability Engineer Examination Study Guide*. Tucson, AZ: Quality Publishing.

Dovich, R. A. 1990. *Reliability Statistics*. Milwaukee, WI: ASQC–Quality Press.

Ireson, G. W., and C. F. Coombs. 1988. *Handbook of Reliability Engineering and Management*. New York: McGraw-Hill.

Kapur, K. C., and L. R. Lamberson. 1977. *Reliability in Engineering Design*. New York: John Wiley & Sons.

Krishnamoorthi, K. S. 1992. *Reliability Methods for Engineers*. Milwaukee, WI: ASQC–Quality Press.

Lewis, E. E. 1987. *Introduction To Reliability Engineering*. New York: John Wiley & Sons.

Moss, M. A. 1985. *Designing for Minimal Maintenance Expense.* New York: Marcel Dekker.

O'Conner, P. D. T. 1993. *Practical Reliability Engineering.* New York: John Wiley & Sons.

US Department of Defense. *MIL-HDBK-472: Maintainability Prediction.* Philadelphia: Naval Publications and Forms Center.

US Department of Defense. *MIL-STD-470: Maintainability Program for Systems and Equipment.* Philadelphia: Naval Publications and Forms Center.

US Department of Defense. *MIL-STD-471: Maintainability Verification, Demonstration and Evaluation* Philadelphia: Naval Publications and Forms Center.

♦ ♦ ♦
CHAPTER

7

Failure Mode, Effects and Criticality Analysis

Failure Mode, Effects and Criticality Analysis (FMECA) is a powerful design analysis tool that is used to increase system reliability. It can be applied during the initial design phase or to existing equipment. To be more effective, the FMECA should relate to the nature of the design process itself. In either case, it considers overall design, operating and service problems, while at the same time addressing process and safety problems.

If used as a design tool, the benefit of FMECA depends upon the timeliness in which information is communicated in the early design phase. Timeliness is probably the most important factor in differentiating between effective and ineffective implementation of the FMECA. The efforts and sophistication of the approach used much depends on the requirements of each individual program. In any case, the FMECA should contribute to the overall program decision.

7.1 Criticality analysis

The objective of an FMECA is to identify all failure modes in a system design. Its purpose is to identify all catastrophic and critical failure probabilities so they can be minimized as early as possible. Therefore, the FMECA should be started as soon as preliminary design information is available and extended as more information becomes available in suspected problem areas.

The effects of all failure modes are not equal with respect to the total impact on the system concerning safety and overall system performance. The designer, faced with this dilemma, needed a tool that would rank the significance of each potential failure for each component in the system's design alternatives. Because of the need for such justification, the criticality analysis function was added to the Failure Mode and Effects Analysis (FMEA) process, thus creating Failure Mode, Effects and Criticality Analysis (FMECA).

This tool has been used extensively by the military in the last three decades. In recent years, more commercial industries have been requiring the FMECA to evaluate new designs and even more recently to improve the reliability of existing equipment. Military Standard 1629 is a good reference for Failure Mode, Effects and Criticality Analysis.

7.1.1 The qualitative approach to FMECA

This approach should be used when specific failure rate data is not available. Failure modes identified by the FMECA process are assessed by their probability of occurrence. To establish qualitative measures of occurrence, severity and detection, criteria must be established that subjectively relates to the overall effect on the process. Examples are offered in Tables 7.1, 7.2, and 7.3, to serve as guides in establishing qualitative measures. The product of the measures of occurrence, severity and detection is called the Risk Priority Number (RPN). Tables 7.1, 7.2, and 7.3 are for example only. The numbers or criteria assigned to any particular ranking system are at the discretion of the user. Detailed instructions on how to use this criterion on the FMECA form is explained in Section 7.1.4.

7.1.2 FMECA quantitative approach

Method 102 outlined in MIL-STD-1629 is the quantitative approach used for the FMECA process. Figure 7.1 is the worksheet used for this method.

Table 7.1. Occurrence probabilities.

Rank	Occurrence Criteria	Occurrence Rates (cycles, hrs, etc.)
1	Unlikely. Unreasonable to expect this failure mode to occur.	—
2	Isolated. Based on similar designs having a low number of failures.	1/10,000
3	Sporadic. Based on similar designs that have experienced occasional failures.	1/1,000
4	Conceivable. Based on similar designs that have caused problems.	1/100
5	Recurrent. Certain that failures will ensue.	1/10

NOTE: The ranking criteria selected must be consistent throughout the FMECA.

Table 7.2. Severity Probabilities.

Rank	Severity Criteria
1	Minor. No noticeable effect. Unable to realize that a failure has occurred.
2	Marginal. Annoying. No system degradation.
3	Moderate. Causing dissatisfaction. Some system degradation.
4	Critical. Causing a high degree of dissatisfaction. Loss of system function.
5	Catastrophic. A failure which may cause death or injury. Extended repair outages.

NOTE: The ranking criteria selected must be consistent throughout the FMECA.

The failure mode and criticality number (C_m) is the portion of the criticality number for the item due to a particular failure mode. This criticality number replaces the RPN number used in the qualitative method described in the previous section. The C_m for a failure mode is determined by the expression

$$C_m = \beta \alpha \lambda_p t \qquad (7.1)$$

where: β = conditional probability of loss of function,

α = failure mode ratio,

λ_p = part failure rate, and

t = duration or operating time.

Table 7.3. Detection probabilities.

Rank	Detection Criteria	Probability
1	Very High probability of detecting the failure before it occurs. Almost always preceded by a warning.	80%–100%
2	High probability of detecting the failure before it occurs. Preceded by a warning most of the time.	60%–80%
3	Moderate probability of detecting the failure before it occurs. About a 50% chance of getting a warning.	40%–60%
4	Low probability of detecting the failure before it occurs. Always comes with little or no warning.	20%–40%
5	Remote probability of detecting the failure before it occurs. Always without a warning.	0%–20%

NOTE: The ranking criteria selected must be consistent throughout the FMECA.

The β values represent the analyst's judgment as to the conditional probability that the loss will occur and should be quantified in general accordance with the following:

Failure effect	Probability of loss of function
Actual loss	$\beta=1$
Probable loss	$0.10<\beta<1.00$
Possible loss	$0<\beta<0.10$
No effect	$\beta=0$

The failure mode ratio, α, is the probability that the part or item will fail. If all potential failure modes of a particular part or item are listed, the sum of the α values for that part or item will equal one. Individual failure mode multipliers may be derived from failure rate source data or from test and operational data. If failure mode data are not available, the α values should represent the analyst's judgment based upon an analysis of the item's functions.

Part failure rates, λ_p, are derived from appropriate reliability prediction methods using mean-time-between-failure (MTBF) data or possibly other data obtained from handbooks or reference material. Manufacturers often supply failure data; however, it is important that the environment the item will be subjected to is similar to the environment the manufacturer used when obtaining the failure data.

The operating time, t, is usually expressed in hours or the number of operating cycles of the item being analyzed.

The α and β values are often subjective, thus making the supposed quantitative method somewhat qualitative. All things considered, it is generally understood that the FMECA process is a qualitative method of analysis.

System _____

Indenture Level _____

Reference Drawing _____

Mission _____

Date _____

Sheet _____ of _____

Compiled by _____

Approved by _____

ID #	Item Identification	Function	Failure Modes & Causes	Mission Operational Mode	Severity Class	Failure Probability & data Source	Failure Effect Probability	Failure Mode Ratio	Failure Rate	Operating Time	Failure Mode Criticality	Item Criticality	Remarks

Figure 7.1. MIL-STD-1629 worksheet for method 102.

7.1.3 FMECA process

The process outlined here demonstrates a method, often used throughout industry today, that incorporates the basic FMECA and a qualitative Criticality Analysis on the same form. Exact forms, as defined in MIL-STD 1629, are usually modified by different users to fit individual conditions and standards.

The FMECA process is a combination of group discussions, team meetings, and individual studies. The meetings are typically led by the design engineer or an expert in Failure Mode, Effects and Criticality Analysis.

Entire systems are much too complex to be covered by one FMECA. The system should be defined and separated into sub-systems, also known as the infrastructure, early in the process. It should be a consensus as to how and why the system is separated, since addressing a single part is usually not an efficient use of resources. The FMECA should be done at some major level. For example, for an automobile you might list the *drive train, frame, body, and support equipment* separately.

The team is led into discussion about the individual functions of each sub-system and how they interact with the overall system. At this time, team members should be supplied with pertinent technical data including layouts, functional descriptions, prints, etc., of the system being analyzed. After the initial discussions and examination, the infrastructure is separated into infrastructure sub-systems. For example, an automobile drive train might be divided into the engine, the transmission, the drive gearing, and support equipment. This should be done for each infrastructure.

At this time, the engineer or team leader prompts the team to identify the process or machine functions. The functions of each infrastructure sub-system is then discussed, and the data is input on the FMECA form. After all functions are established, *FAILURE MODES, EFFECTS, CAUSES, PROBABILITIES, and RECOMMENDED CORRECTIVE ACTIONS* are then input on the form.

7.1.4. Steps for completing the form

Refer to Figure 7.2 for the remainder of this section.

INFRASTRUCTURE:
PROJECT ENGINEER:
DATE:

SYSTEM:					
COMPANY/LOCATION:					
OUTSIDE SUPPLIER(S):					

INFRASTRUCTURE SUB-SYSTEM	SUB-SYSTEM FUNCTION	FAILURE MODE	EFFECTS OF FAILURE	CAUSE(S) OF FAILURE	OCC	SEV	DET	RPN	RECOMMENDED CORRECTIVE ACTION & STATUS
WHAT DOES IT DO?	WHAT FUNCTION CAN BE LOST?	HOW COULD IT FAIL TO PERFORM THIS FUNCTION? 1. 2. 3.	WHAT HAPPENS IF IT FAILS?	WHAT CAUSES IT TO FAIL?	LIKELIHOOD OF OCCURRENCE	CONSEQUENCE SERIOUSNESS OF EVENT	PROBABILITY OF NON-DETECTION EARLY	OCC × SEV × DET	HOW CAN THIS FAILURE BE PREVENTED?

Figure 7.2. Sample FMECA form for existing equipment.

First Column—Infrastructure sub-system

What does this sub-system do? Describe briefly what the equipment is designed to do. Be as concise in the description as possible. For example, hold temperature below 200° F during continuous operation.

Second Column—Sub-system function

What function is lost if the sub-system fails? For example, temperature regulation is lost.

Third Column—Failure mode

Anticipation of failures is the goal. The question here is how could it fail, not will it fail. Try to determine all possibilities for the system failing to meet objectives. Some distinctive failure modes are:

Over/undersize	Cracked	Breaks
Torn or Split	Open	Mis-aligned
Rough	Out-of-balance	Pitting
Eccentric	Leaking	Deformed

NOTE: Try to be specific. For example, say, "gas line leaking and deformed" instead of "gas line fails." Always find a word to replace "fails or failed."

Fourth Column—Effects of failure

Describe what will happen as a result of each failure mode. Will the equipment be totally inoperative, inefficient, inaccurate, etc.?

Fifth Column—Cause of failure

Again, try to anticipate the cause of the failure mode described. Ask what might cause this particular failure mode. Fault-tree analysis is sometimes used at this point to determine root causes (refer to Section 7.3). If time does not permit the use of a fault tree, list all conceivable causes for each failure mode. Examples of causes might be:

Worn or broken tooling	Improper part location
Worn bearings	Overload
Poor handling	Improper weld
Contamination	Interference
Inefficient cooling	Over pressure
Heat treat shrinkage	Inadequate lubrication

NOTE: In columns 7, 8, and 9, it is important to remember that the ratings apply to the failure mode and not to the cause of the failure.

Sixth Column—Occurrence

Estimate the likelihood that the failure will occur using a previously set evaluation scale. Table 7.1 (Section 7.1) gives an example of an evaluation scale for the likelihood of a failure. The lowest number of the scale must indicate the lowest probability of occurrence, and the highest number must indicate the highest probability of occurrence.

Seventh Column—Severity

Estimate the consequences of the failure using a predetermined scale with the lowest number of the scale indicating minor concerns and the highest number indicating major consequences. Table 7.2 (Section 7.1) gives an example of an evaluation scale for the consequences of a failure.

Eighth Column—Detection

Estimate the ability to predict the failure. Table 7.3 (Section 7.1) gives an example of an evaluation scale for the ability to predict a failure. Use a predetermined scale with the lowest number indicating a very high probability that the failure mode will be detected before reaching the customer.

Ninth Column—RPN

Estimate the Risk Priority Number (RPN). The product of the occurrence, severity, and detection provides a relative priority to each failure mode. From this number critical summaries can be developed for prioritizing follow-up actions.

Tenth Column—Recommended corrective action & status

Corrective actions are most usually found to be design changes, either to the equipment or the process. Changes should be focused on reducing failure occurrences, reducing the consequences of failures, and increasing the ability to predict failures. Remember the idea is to reduce failures, not just detect them.

7.1.5. FMECA follow-up report

Follow-up is critical to the FMECA's success. The basic recommendations that the FMECA and the follow-up provide should set a solid foundation for corrective action.

A good tool to use for the follow-up report is a matrix. The first thing to do is establish the matrix criteria (see Table 7.4). Keep in mind that this information will be used to present recommendations to management for approval. The end result should provide answers to all major concerns, such as, why are these problems being worked on, how much will this project cost, what is the time frame, etc.?

Table 7.4. Sample matrix report criteria.

Equipment	Difficulty	% Solved	Cost ($)	Time Required	Actions
Failure mode & rank #	1= Very easy 2 = Easy 3 = Medium 4 = Hard 5 = Very hard	Percent of total ranked order	A = 0 B = Very low C = Low D = Medium E = High	1 = 1–5 units 2 = 6–10 units 3 = 11–15 units 4 = 15–20 units 5 = 21–30 units 6 = 31–50 units	Recommended actions

The next step is to compile the RPNs from the highest number to the lowest (see Table 7.5). This example shows that the number one problem identified by the FMECA is the conveyor system's guide rollers breaking. Also note that the redesigning of these rollers will eliminate three other failure modes; guide rollers seizing, tracking bars bending and bent track rips belt.

Now total the RPN numbers for a number representing 100% of the problems in the sub-system. In the example in Table 7.5, this number is 520.

Table 7.5. Ranked order chart.

Rank	RPN	Component	Failure mode
1	125	Conveyor system	Guide rollers break
2	100	Drying chamber	Plugged drains
3	90	Air compressor valves	Corrosion
4	80	Ventilation	Louvers stick
5	60	Conveyor system	Guide rollers seize
6	40	Conveyor system	Tracking bars bend
7	20	Conveyor system	Bent track rips belt
8	5	Drying chamber	High humidity

If the RPNs for just the CONVEYOR SYSTEM are totaled, the result is 245. Accepting that 245 is 47% of 520, with 520 representing at, or near, 100% of the total population of failure modes, it can be reasonably said that by taking actions to eliminate the cause of the top failure mode, 47% of the overall problem can be solved. This is shown on the matrix in Table 7.6. The cost, complexity, time, etc., of any potential changes should be discussed as a team and a consensus drawn. Table 7.7 is an example of how a safety concern of the FMECA process could be handled on a matrix.

Table 7.6. Completed sample matrix for equipment.

Equipment	Difficulty	% Solved	Cost ($)	Time Required	Actions
Conveyor System; Rank = 1; RPN = 125; Other ranked items effected 5,6, & 7	Hard	47%	Low	Category 6, 45 days	Installed self-lubricating double-guide rollers. Redesigned track bars. Redesigned retainers. Redesigned pins.

NOTE: This Table is based on Tables 7.1, 7.2, and 7.3, where 5 is the highest possible value in ranking criteria. Thus, 125 would be the highest possible RPN (5x5x5).

Table 7.7. Sample matrix report criteria.

Equipment	Difficulty	% Solved	Cost ($)	Time Required	Actions
Inline plugs	Hard	50%	Very low	5 weeks	Installed inline plugs in discharge

7.1.6. What it takes to do a successful FMECA

The keys to a successful FMECA are the same when applied to the initial design or to existing designs. Management support and the diversity of the team are the most important considerations, followed by training for the facilitator and the team members.

Steps must be taken to assure management's support for the project from beginning to end. First, management must understand the benefits of the FMECA. After completing the FMECA, a quantifying report reflecting the total impact of the FMECA's suggested corrective actions and implementation plans should be presented to management.

A good FMECA team will include personnel that are directly involved with the process to be analyzed. Examples include, but certainly not limited to: electrical and mechanical maintenance technicians, machine operators, technical specialists, design engineers, and even a representative from the equipment supplier if possible.

The FMECA facilitator should be trained to ask appropriate key questions and be prepared to probe the team for answers to describe the equipment's functions, failure modes and their effects. A good facilitator should also be able to assist the team with establishing criteria for the equipment's ranking indexes and organize information as it comes from the team members.

Some time should be allotted for new FMECA team members to become familiar with the FMECA process prior to beginning the actual FMECA. The team should have a good understanding of the purpose and benefits of the FMECA as well as an understanding of the team's objectives. If time allows, training should include an actual FMECA on some less complex piece of equipment such as a flashlight or cigarette lighter. On the basis of past experiences, this training can be accomplished in about four hours.

The use of a computer with the ability to project the screen during the FMECA team meetings is highly recommended. Software containing a standard FMECA blank form should be filled in as data is received from the team members. A copy of the form should be distributed after each meeting to enable the team to review the data and recommend any changes at the next meeting.

Although the use of the computer and software are not an absolute necessity for the successful FMECA, this practice is not only a time-saver, but helps keep the team's ideas organized and on track.

7.2 Environmental requirements and influence

When the FMECA team members are properly selected, the FMECA process will address all problems concerning design, manufacturing, process, safety and environment. The consequences of these problems are addressed during the study of the Failure Mode during the FMECA. Preventive measures for failures where an individual's well-being in the workplace is concerned should always be given top priority. According to John Moubray (1991), "A failure mode has safety consequences if it causes a loss of function or other damage which could hurt or kill someone."

The overall design must consider how the environment influences the system during testing, storage, installing and operating. When considering the failure mode effects, think about the impact on society in general if the failure happened. Society may, in some cases, be considered as a customer because if the product is not accepted due to environmental effects, it may not be successful. "A failure mode has environmental consequences if it causes a loss of function or other damage which could lead to the breach of any known environmental standard or regulation," (Moubray, 1991).

7.3 Differences between part function, part failure mechanism, failure effect, failure detection, and failure mode

The definitions which follow form the fundamentals of FMECAs. These definitions will enable the reader to understand the differences between Part Function, Part Failure Mechanism, Failure Effect, Failure Detection, and Failure Modes. These definitions were taken from MIL-STD-1629.

1. **Failure Mode and Effects Analysis (FMEA)**—A procedure by which each potential failure mode in a system is analyzed to determine the results, or effects thereof, on the system and to classify each potential failure mode according to its severity.

2. **Failure mode**—The manner by which a failure is observed. Generally describes the way the failure occurs and its impact on equipment operation.

3. **Failure effect**—The consequence(s) a failure mode has on the operation, function, or status of an item. Failure effects are usually classified according to how the entire system is impacted.

4. **Failure cause**—The physical or chemical process, design defects, part misapplication, quality defects, or other processes that are the basic reason for failure or which initiate the physical process by which deterioration proceeds to failure.

5. **Environments**—The conditions, circumstances, influences, stresses and combinations thereof, surrounding and affecting systems or equipment during storage, handling, transportation, testing, installation, and use in standby status and operations.

6. **Detection mechanism**—The means or methods by which a failure can be discovered by an operator under normal system operation or can be discovered by the maintenance crew by some diagnostic action.

7. **Severity**—The consequences of a failure as a result of a particular failure mode. Severity considers the worst potential consequence of a failure, determined by the degree of injury, property damage, or system damage that could ultimately occur.

8. **Criticality**—A relative measure of the consequences of a failure mode and its frequency of occurrence.

9. **Criticality analysis (CA)**—A procedure by which each potential failure mode is ranked according to the combined influence of severity and probability of occurrence.

10. **FMECA-Maintainability information**—A procedure by which each potential failure is analyzed to determine how the failure is detected and the actions to be taken to repair the failure.

11. **Single failure point**—The failure of an item that would result in failure of the system and is not compensated for by redundancy or alternative operational procedure.

12. **Undetectable failure**—A postulated failure mode in the FMEA for which there is no failure detection method by which the operator is made aware of the failure.

13. **FMECA planning**—Planning the FMECA work involves the contractor's procedures for implementing their specified requirements. Planning should include updating to reflect design changes and analysis results. Worksheet formats, ground rules, assumptions, identification of the level of analysis, failure definitions, and identification of coincident use of the FMECA by the contractor and other organizational elements should also be considered.

14. **Ground rules and assumptions**—The ground rules identify the FMECA approach (e.g., hardware, functional or combination), the lowest level to be analyzed, and include statements of what might constitute a failure in terms of performance criteria. Every effort should be made to identify and record all ground rules and analysis assumptions prior to initiation of the analysis; however, ground rules and analysis assumptions may be adjusted as requirements change.

15. **Analysis approach**—Variations in design complexity and available data will generally dictate the analysis approach to be used. There are two primary approaches for the FMECA. One is the hardware approach that lists individual hardware items and analyzes their possible failure modes. The other is the functional approach that

recognizes that every item is designed to perform a number of outputs. The outputs are listed and their failures analyzed. For more complex systems, a combination of the functional and hardware approaches may be considered.

16. **Hardware approach**—The hardware approach is normally used when hardware items can be uniquely identified from schematics, drawings, and other engineering and design data. This approach is recommended for use in a part level up approach often referred to as the bottom-up approach.

17. **Functional approach**—The functional approach is normally used when hardware items cannot be uniquely identified or when system complexity requires analysis from the top down.

18. **Level of analysis**—The level of analysis applies to the system hardware or functional level at which failures are postulated. In other words, how the system being analyzed is segregated. (e.g., a section of the system, component, sub-component, etc.)

19. **Failure definition**—This is a general statement of what constitutes a failure of the item in terms of performance parameters and allowable limits for each specified output.

20. **Trade-off study reports**—These reports should identify areas of marginal and state-of-the-art design and explain any design compromises and operating restraints agreed upon. This information will aid in determining the possible and most probable failure modes and causes in the system.

21. **Design data and drawings**—Design data and drawings identify each item and the item configuration that perform each of the system functions. System design data and drawings will usually describe the system's internal and interface functions beginning at system level and progressing to the lowest indenture level of the system. Design data will usually include either functional block diagrams or schematics that will facilitate construction of reliability block diagrams.

22. **Block diagrams**—Block diagrams that illustrate the operation, interrelationships, and interdependencies of the functions of a system are

required to show the sequence and the series dependence or independence of functions and operations. Block diagrams may be constructed in conjunction with, or after defining the system and shall present the system breakdown of its major functions. More than one block diagram is sometimes required to represent alternative modes of operation, depending upon the definition established for the system.

23. **Functional block diagrams**—Functional block diagrams illustrate the operation and interrelationships between functional entities of a system as defined in engineering data and schematics. An example of a functional block diagram, taken from MIL-STD-1629, is shown in Figure 7.9.

24. **Reliability block diagrams**—Reliability block diagrams define the series dependence, or independence, of all functions of a system or functional group for each life-cycle event. An example of a reliability block diagram, taken from MIL-STD-1629, is shown in Figure 7.10.

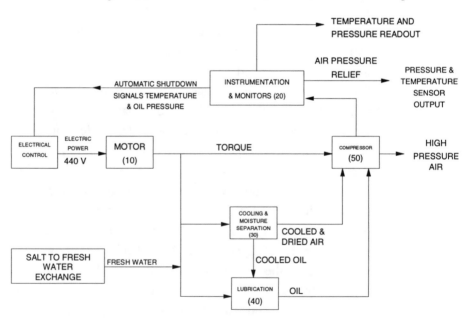

Figure 7.9. Functional block diagram.

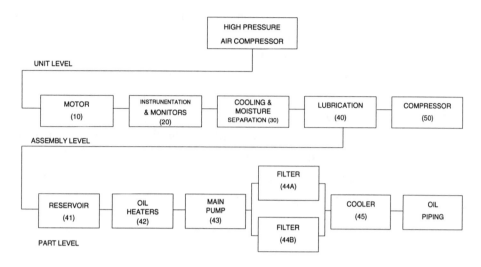

Figure 7.10. Reliability block diagram.

25. **Severity classification**—This classification is assigned to provide a qualitative measure of the worst potential consequences resulting from design error or item failure. Classifications should be assigned to each identified failure mode and each item analyzed in accordance with the loss statements below. It may not be possible to identify an item or a failure mode according to the loss statements in the four categories below, but similar loss statements based on various inputs and outputs can be developed and included in the ground rules for the FMECA activity. Severity classification categories that are consistent with MIL-STD-882 are defined as follows:

- **Category I–Catastrophic**—A failure that may cause injury or death.
- **Category II–Critical**—A failure which may cause severe injury, major property damage, or major system damage that will result in major downtime or production loss.
- **Category III–Marginal**—A failure which may cause minor injury, minor property damage, or minor system damage which will result in delay or loss of system availability or degradation.

- **Category IV–Minor**—A failure not serious enough to cause injury, property damage or system damage, but will result in unscheduled maintenance or repair.

These categories can be attached to a cost or any other factor, but when used in the established criteria, should be consistent throughout the analysis.

26. **FMECA report**—The results of the FMECA and other related analyses should be included in a report that identifies the level of the analysis, documents the data sources and techniques used in performing the analysis, and gives the system definition.

7.4 Exercises

1. On the FMECA form shown in Figure 7.3 (following page), list five possible failure modes for the conveyor.

2. For each failure mode listed in Exercise 1, input two failure effects in the example FMECA form.

3. For each failure mode listed in Exercise 1, list two failure causes.

4. Calculate the RPN for each failure mode in Exercise 1, given

    Failure mode 1—OCC=4; SEV=5; DET=1
    Failure mode 2—OCC=2; SEV=3; DET=3
    Failure mode 3—OCC=3; SEV=3; DET=5
    Failure mode 4—OCC=3; SEV=5; DET=5
    Failure mode 5—OCC=3; SEV=3; DET=4

5. Input recommended actions for the item with the highest RPN in Exercise 4. What portion of the "total" problem does this item represent?

6. What does the failure mode and criticality number (Cm) replace in the most common qualitative methods?
    a. Severity number
    b. Risk Priority Number
    c. Failure Effects Number
    d. Failure Mode Number

7. The objective of an FMECA is to
    a. Identify all failure modes
    b. Identify failure probabilities
    c. Increase product reliability
    d. All of the above

8. A good reference for FMECA is
    a. MIL-STD-781
    b. MIL-STD-414
    c. MIL-STD-1629
    d. MIL-HDBK-217

SYSTEM: Tipple Coal Mine									INFRASTRUCTURE: Separators	
COMPANY/LOCATION: Black Star Coal of America									PROJECT ENGINEER:	
OUTSIDE SUPPLIER(S):									DATE:	
INFRASTRUCTURE SUB-SYSTEM	SUB-SYSTEM FUNCTION	FAILURE MODE	EFFECTS OF FAILURE	CAUSE(S) OF FAILURE	OCC	SEV	DET	RPN	RECOMMENDED CORRECTIVE ACTION & STATUS	
Conveyor A	Transport coal from Hopper #1 to Hopper #2 at 100 fpm ± 10 fpm at a maximum handling capacity of 50 tons ± 5 tons.									

Figure 7.3. Example problem FMECA form.

9. FMECA team meetings are typically led by a
   a. Consultant
   b. Engineer
   c. Facilitator
   d. Contractor

10. When identifying failure causes it is sometimes necessary to use
   a. Root cause analysis
   b. Fault tree analysis
   c. Historical data
   d. Failure test data

11. The FMECA process will address all problems concerning
   a. Design
   b. Process
   c. Safety
   d. All of the above

12. A failure is thought to have environmental consequences if it
   a. Causes a safety problem in the workplace
   b. Causes a hazard in the community
   c. Breaches any environmental standard or regulation
   d. All of the above

13. The FMECA eliminates failure modes in the design phase focusing attention on
   a. Engineering standards
   b. Company policies
   c. Critical parts
   d. Unreliable parts

14. FMECA classifies each failure mode according to
   a. Probability
   b. Criticality
   c. Severity
   d. Unreliability

15.   The means or methods in which an operator detects a failure is called the
   a. Alert mechanism
   b. Alarm mechanism
   c. Detection mechanism
   d. Reliable mechanism
16. A relative measure of the consequences of a failure mode and its frequency is called the
   a. Severity
   b. Frequency
   c. Relative measure
   d. Criticality
17. Outside influences, stresses, circumstances and/or a combination thereof, effecting systems relates to the
   a. Designer
   b. Environment
   c. Operator
   d. None of the above

7.5 References

Dodson, B. L., and M. D. Mulcahy. 1992. *Certified Reliability Engineer Examination Study Guide.* Tucson, AZ: Quality Publishing.

Ireson, G. W., and C. F.Coombs. 1988. *Handbook of Reliability Engineering and Management.* New York: McGraw-Hill.

Kececioglu, D. 1991. *Reliability Engineering Handbook, Volume 2.* Englewood Cliffs, NJ: Prentice Hall.

Lewis, E. E. 1987. *Introduction To Reliability Engineering.* New York: John Wiley & Sons.

Moubray, John. 1991. *Reliability-Centered Maintenance.* Oxford: Butterworth-Heinemann.

Sundarajan, C. 1991. *Guide To Reliability Engineering: Data, Analysis, Applications, Implementation, And Management.* New York: Van Nostrand Reinhold.

US Department of Defense. 1980. *MIL-STD-1629: Procedures for Performing a Failure Mode, Effects and Criticality Analysis.* Philadelphia: Naval Publications and Forms Center.

Part Selection and Derating

Conducting an aggressive parts control and application program increases the probability of achieving and maintaining inherent equipment reliability, and minimizes parts proliferation, logistics support costs, and system life cycle costs. The added investment required for a vigorous program which controls parts selection and application can be offset by reduced system life cycle costs for reparable systems and by overall system effectiveness for non-reparable systems. In some cases the use of higher quality parts can even lower item acquisition cost through reduction in the amount of assembly line rework as well as eliminate additional costs for drawings and test data required when using non-standard parts.

Failure rates of parts are correlated to the stress and strength relationship of the design parameters. Using parts that are rated to withstand stresses above the design strength parameters is called **derating**. Derating parts will ultimately increase reliability by decreasing their failure rates.

This chapter explains techniques for use in reliability tests performed during the integrated test programs specified in MIL-STD-785 and MIL-HDBK-781. Prediction methods are covered in detail in MIL-HDBK-217 (failure rate data on electrical parts) and RADC-TR-85-194 (failure rate data on mechanical and electromechanical parts).

8.1 Evaluation of parts for reliability

Parts and components are the basic items comprising higher level assemblies, which in turn ultimately constitute the system, where the "system" may be a radio, an automobile, or an airplane. Significant contributions toward system optimization can be realized by applying attention and resources to parts application, selection, and control starting early in the design phase and continuing throughout the life of the system.

An effective parts program requires the use of knowledgeable parts engineers by supporting activities. Logisticians should always be consulted for their inputs, because they will be required to support the system operationally. The investment in parts programs generally pays handsome dividends in terms of reduced operational costs and improved system operation effectiveness.

8.1.1 Application and specification

The decision as to the depth and extent of the parts program designed for a particular item acquisition should be made based on considerations of factors such as: operation criticality, parts essentiality (to assure successful operation and reduced frequency of maintenance), the maintenance concept, production quantity, parts availability, amount or degree of new design, and parts standardization status. A comprehensive parts program (MIL-STD-965) can be just as essential for a relatively simple device (e.g., radio) with a large projected inventory as for a single, complex device (e.g., space shuttle).

A comprehensive parts program will consist of the following elements:
  a. Parts standardization
  b. Parts application (derating) guidelines
  c. Parts testing, screening, or validation
  d. Government/Industry Data Exchange Program (GIDEP) participation as applicable (MIL-STD-1556)

If such a program is implemented, it is imperative that qualified personnel are assigned, because the dynamic nature of parts and component technology can quickly render existing knowledge and experience obsolete.

8.1.2 Program basic objectives

The basic objective of the parts program is to control the selection and use of standard and nonstandard parts. Occasionally, depending on the system, it becomes necessary to propose the use of a nonstandard part. Proposals for use of nonstandard parts should be made and accepted only after other options that use standard parts have been investigated. Before choosing an application, a judgment should be made on whether the part in question meets enough of the criteria to make it a standard part.

Parts programs should be initiated early in design and continued throughout the life of the system. Before the beginning of full-scale development, the procuring activity should clearly describe the part quality level preference order for use in the system. In addition, the procuring activity should identify prohibited part types. For certain applications, special tests of standard parts may have to be used to obtain acceptable parts which are then unique and must be identified as such. It is most important to emphasize, however, that special testing, identification, and selection inhibits standardization, since those processes produce a nonstandard part that may not be readily available to support the system through its life.

8.1.3 Program activities

Parts program activities are interrelated with analyses performed by other disciplines such as safety, quality engineering, maintainability, survivability and vulnerability. In some cases, upgraded or unique parts are needed to meet system requirements. In other cases, standard or readily available parts can be used to minimize life cycle costs and ensure supportability.

8.2 Reliability testing for parts

The reliability test program should serve three objectives in the following priorities:

1. Disclose deficiencies in item design, materiel and workmanship
2. Provide measured reliability data as input for estimates of operational readiness, mission success, maintenance manpower cost, and logistics support cost

3. Determine compliance with quantitative reliability requirements

Cost and schedule investment in reliability testing should conform to these priorities to ensure that the overall reliability program is both effective and efficient. Four types of reliability testing described in MIL-STD-785 are:

1. Environmental Stress Screening (ESS—task 301)
   a. A test, or a series of tests, specifically designed to disclose weak parts and workmanship defects.
   b. It should be applied to parts or equipment, as appropriate and cost-effective, to remove defects that would otherwise cause failures during higher-level testing or early field service.

2. Reliability Development/Growth Test (RDGT—task 302)
   a. A planned, pre-qualification, test-analyze-and-fix process, in which parts or equipment are tested under actual, simulated, or accelerated environments to disclose design deficiencies and defects.
   b. This testing is intended to provide a basis for early incorporation of corrective actions, and verification of their effectiveness, thereby promoting reliability growth.

3. Reliability Qualification Test (RQT—task 303)
   a. A test intended to provide assurance that minimum acceptable reliability requirements have been met before items are committed to production.
   b. The test must be operationally realistic, and must provide estimates of demonstrated reliability.

4. Production Reliability Acceptance Test (PRAT—task 304)
   a. A test that is intended to simulate in-service evaluation of the delivered item or production lot.
   b. The statistical test plan must define criteria for compliance which limit the probability that the item tested, and the lot it represents, may have a true reliability less than the minimum acceptable reliability, and these criteria must be tailored for cost and schedule efficiency.

ESS and RDGT are reliability engineering tests. Program plans should emphasize early investment in these tests to avoid subsequent cost and schedule delays. Reliability qualification tests (RQT and PRAT) are reliability accounting tests. They should be tailored for effectiveness and efficiency (maximum return on cost and schedule investment) in terms of the management information they provide. A properly balanced reliability program will emphasize ESS and RDGT, and limit, but not eliminate, RQT and PRAT. However, be reminded that testing does not improve reliability. Only corrective actions that prevent the recurrence of failures in the operational inventory actually improve reliability.

8.2.1 Integrated testing

Performance, reliability and environmental stress testing should be combined, and environmental stress types should be combined insofar as practical. These tests should be drawn together into an integrated, effective and efficient test program. For example, mechanical, hydraulic, pneumatic and electrical equipment is usually subjected to three qualification tests: performance, environmental, and endurance (durability). The integration of these separate tests into a more comprehensive reliability test program can avoid costly duplication and ensure that deficiencies are not overlooked as they often are in the fragmented approach.

8.2.2 The performance test

Performance tests should be conducted as soon as items are fabricated. They should be brief, and should provide the immediate basis for correction of any deficiencies they disclose. However, an item that has passed its performance test must not be considered compliant until it has shown that it will perform reliability under realistic conditions.

8.2.3 The environmental test

Environmental tests such as those described in MIL-STD-810 should be considered an early portion of RDGT. They must be conducted early in development, to ensure that time and resources are available to correct the deficiencies they disclose, and the corrections must be verified under stress. Such information must be included in the Failure Reporting, Analysis and Corrective Action System (FRACAS), reviewed in Chapter 2, as an integral aspect of the reliability program.

8.2.4 The endurance test

Endurance (durability) testing usually consists of a normal test, an overload test, and a mission profile cycling test that duplicates or approximates the conditions expected in service. Failures must be evaluated, and corrective actions must be incorporated in the test items. The test must then be rerun or completed and an additional run conducted to show the problems have been corrected. This information must also be included in the FRACAS. An integrated test program will combine reliability testing and durability testing.

8.2.5 Test realism

A test is realistic to the degree that test conditions and procedures simulate the operational life, mission, and environmental profile of a production item. Realistic testing can disclose deficiencies and defects that otherwise would be discovered only after an item is put into service, and it can reduce the disparity between laboratory and operational reliability values. Therefore, test realism should be a primary consideration in every reliability test. A test that only discloses a small fraction of the operational failures it is supposed to disclose is a waste of time and resources. Conversely, a test that induces failures that will not occur in service forces unnecessary expenditures of time and resources to correct those failures. Finally, the degree to which any reliability test must simulate field service depends on the purpose of the test.

Low test realism is often due to omission of a relevant stress, or incomplete definition of a type of stress. For example, failures that are caused by vibrations are seldom found by tests that apply no vibration, or by tests that ignore the relevant combinations of vibration frequency, amplitude and duration of exposure. Establishment of realistic test conditions and procedures requires a knowledge of the life profile from factory to final expenditure, to include the micro-environments an item will experience during each phase of its life profile, based on measurement of the actual stresses experienced by similar items.

It is appropriate to apply stress levels greater that those expected in service, if the purpose of the test is to disclose deficiencies, and if test conditions do not induce failures that will not occur in service. On the other hand, both over-stress and under-stress make reliability estimates inaccurate and distort test results used to determine compliance. Therefore, over-stress (and step-stress) testing may be applied during ESS and the early portion of RDGT, but the final portion of RDGT, and both RQT and PRAT, should simulate the operational life profile insofar as it is practical and cost-effective.

Precise simulation of the operational life profile would expose each item and each part of each item to the exact stress types, levels, and durations they would experience in service. Such idealistic testing is seldom practical or cost-effective. Some stress types cannot be combined in the same test facility, and some may cost more to reproduce in the laboratory than they are worth in terms of the failures they cause in service. Stress types may be applied in series for ESS and the early portion of PRAT. Total test time may be compressed by reducing the amount of time spent in simulating less stressful phases of the life profile. Over-stress is a valid way to accelerate the discovery of deficiencies and defects, but it is not a valid means of compressing test time when reliability is to be measured. MIL-STD-781 contains guidance for realistic combined-stress, life, mission, and profile reliability testing.

8.3 Vendor evaluation of part reliability

Vendors should be required to provide methods and procedures for control and testing of all reliability critical items. Reliability critical items are those items whose failure can significantly affect system safety, availability, mission success, or total maintenance support cost. Critical items should include, but not be limited to, those identified by reliability analysis and Failure Mode, Effects and Criticality Analysis (FMECA), reviewed in Chapter 7. High-value items should always be considered reliability critical for life cycle cost. When reliability critical items are specified, the vendor's procedures should include engineering support of the item during development or field testing, which include provisions for confirming failures that may occur, expediting failure cause determination, and determining and incorporating, or verifying, the necessary corrective action.

8.4 Derating principles

The strength of an item is a relative measure of the stress that can be applied to the item. The failure rate of an item increases as nominal stress approaches and exceeds the nominal strength. Failure rates generally decrease when stresses are reduced to levels below designed strengths. Derating may thus be defined as a method of assuring that stresses, either environmental or operational, are applied below rated values to enhance reliability by decreasing failure rates. For example, a capacitor rated at 400V assigned to a 200V application, or a structural load calculated at 25 tons, designed to support 125 tons.

MIL-STD-721 defines derating as:

a. Using an item in such a way that applied stresses are below rated values, or

b. The lowering of the rating of an item in one stress field to allow an increase in another stress field.

The effect of failure rates on increased temperatures is an effect called the Arrhenius model. This model is covered in detail in Chapter 5. It was developed by the USAF and published in MIL-HDBK-217. The model is used for predicting failure rates for electronic systems and is based on the Arrhenius equation. There is a "rule of thumb" for the Arrhenius effect which states that for every 10°C increase in temperature, the chemical reactions for electronic and electrical components double (Dovich, 1990). The following examples show this "rule of thumb" to be unreliable in some cases and should be used with caution.

Example 8.1

A MIL-C-81 capacitor, variable, ceramic, has a failure rate of 0.072 per 10^6 hours at a 50% stress level, at 50°C (T=125°C Max Rated). Using the table in Figure 8.1; what is the failure rate at 60°C with the same stress level?

Solution

Following down the left column under T_A(°C) to 50, and moving right to the point where 0.5 is intersected, a failure rate of 0.072 per 10^6 hours is found. Across from 60 the failure rate is found to be to be 0.077 per 10^6 hours. (NOTE: A 10° increase in temperature resulted in a failure rate increase of only 7%—not near double.)

Example 8.2

Referring to Figure 8.1, holding the temperature constant at 50°C, what would the failure rate be at a stress level of 30%?

Solution

Following down the left column under (T_A(°C)) to 50, and moving right to the point where 0.3 is intersected, a failure rate to be 0.018 per 10^6 hours is found. (NOTE: The failure rate has decreased by 400% by lowering the stress level by 20%. Lowering the temperature by 10°C (17%) resulted in only 7% decrease in failure rate.)

Base Failure Rate - λ_b
(T = 125°C Max Rated)
(MIL-C-81 Styles CV 35, 36)

T_A (°C)	Stress				
	.1	.3	.5	.7	.9
0	.0028	.015	.061	.16	.35
10	.0028	.015	.062	.17	.35
20	.0029	.016	.064	.17	.36
30	.0030	.016	.066	.18	.37
40	.0031	.017	.068	.18	.39
50	.0033	.018	.072	.19	.41
60	.0035	.019	.077	.21	.44
70	.0038	.021	.084	.23	.48
80	.0043	.023	.095	.25	.54
90	.0050	.027	.11	.30	.63
100	.0062	.033	.14	.36	.76
110	.0079	.043	.17	.47	.98
120	.011	.059	.24	.64	1.4

$$\lambda_b = .00224\left[\left(\frac{S}{.17}\right)^3 + 1\right]\exp\left(1.59\left(\frac{T+273}{398}\right)^{10.1}\right)$$

T = Ambient Temperature (°C)
S = Ratio of Operating to Rated Voltage

Operating voltage is the sum of applied D.C. voltage and peak A.C. voltage.

Figure 8.1. Specification tables (from MIL-HDBK-217F, p. 10-27).

8.4.1 Application method

Parts application criteria should be developed as part of the equipment designer standards and should be adhered to because of fact that dramatically increasing failure rates can decrease reliability with exposure to increased stress levels. MIL-P-11268 and MIL-E-5400 may be referenced for establishing the parts application criteria.

Deviations to the parts application criteria should be granted only after evaluating the actual part stress conditions. This practice is to assure that the rated value of the part used is equal to, or greater than, the expected stress. Design alternatives, trade-offs, impact on circuit and overall system reliability may then be assessed.

8.4.2 Technique based on part failure rates

Reliability predictions should be accomplished at the lowest equipment level that the preliminary design and configuration analyses permit. While electronic part failure rate prediction techniques are available in the current edition of MIL-HDBK-217, techniques for predicting failure rates for mechanical and electromechanical devices, are not so readily available. Therefore dialogue between reliability and design engineers is important to ensure that mission and environmental impacts on device performance are accounted. In either the electronic or the non-electronic cases, the part or component failure rates are the basic building blocks for accomplishing higher level predictions.

Equipment level predictions using part failure rates:

1. Provide a basis for identifying design, part selection, application and environmental problem areas
2. Provide early indication of capability to meet the reliability test requirements
3. Are essential inputs to system and subsystem level predictions

Reliability predictions at any equipment level become inputs to higher level predictions. The better the predictions, in terms of reduced uncertainty, the more justifiable are the reliability and design decisions resulting therefrom, whether the decision is to maintain the status quo or to take action to improve hardware reliability.

8.5 Summary

The fundamental reason for early predictions based on parts failure rates is to precipitate appropriate action during development, when it is most tolerable from a program standpoint and most effective from the basic reliability and mission reliability viewpoints. Early review of reliability predictions at lowest equipment levels can identify parts or components that have inadequate margins between parts strength and expected applied stresses. In addition, the earlier the review is performed, generally the greater is the range of acceptable options for improving the predictions and the equipment through derating techniques.

Whenever predictions fall short of allocated reliability requirements, alternatives such as the following should be considered:

- identify suitable substitutes
- re-allocate reliability
- improve selected parts and components
- modify to decrease severity of environments (apply derating techniques)

Some alternatives are more feasible and acceptable than others at given points in development, but all are easier and less expensive to accomplish earlier that later.

8.6 Exercises

1. Describe the benefits of part standardization.
2. Explain some principal functions of a parts control, selection, and integration program.
3. Using the table below, what stress level would cause the greatest failure rate increase if the temperature was raised from 70° to 100°?
   a. .1
   b. .3
   c. .5
   d. .7
   e. .9

			Stress		
T_A(°C)	.1	.3	.5	.7	.9
0	.0028	.015	.061	.16	.35
10	.0028	.015	.061	.16	.35
20	.0029	.016	.064	.17	.35
30	.0030	.016	.066	.18	.37
40	.0031	.017	.068	.18	.39
50	.0033	.018	.072	.19	.141
60	.0035	.019	.077	.21	.44
70	.0038	.021	.084	.23	.48
80	.0043	.023	.095	.25	.54
90	.0050	.027	.11	.30	.63
100	.0062	.033	.14	.36	.76
110	.0079	.043	.17	.47	.98
120	.011	.059	.24	.64	1.4

Extract from MIL-HDBK-217

4. Using the table from Exercise 3, which of the following would have the most positive effect on the item's failure rates?
   a. At 100°C, 50% stress; lower temp to 50°
   b. At 120°C, 50% stress; lower temp to 50°
   c. At 100°C, 50% stress; lower stress to 30%
   d. At 120°C, 50% stress; lower stress to 30%

5. The basic objective of a parts program is to
   a. control the selection and use of standard and nonstandard parts
   b. assure that parts are available when needed
   c. control and maintain cost effective inventories
   d. eliminate unreliable parts

6 A reliability test program should
   a. disclose deficiencies in item design, materiel and workmanship
   b. provide measured reliability data as input for estimates of operational readiness, mission success, maintenance manpower cost, and logistics support cost
   c. determine compliance with quantitative reliability requirements
   d. all of the above

7. The Reliability Qualification Test (RQT) is designed primarily to
   a. disclose weak parts
   b. simulate in-service evaluations of the delivered item
   c. assure that minimum acceptable reliability requirements have been met
   d. disclose design deficiencies under simulated conditions

8. Which of the following are considered reliability engineering tests?
   a. Reliability Qualification Test
   b. Production Reliability Acceptance Test
   c. Reliability Development/Growth Test
   d. all of the above
   e. a and c above

9. Applying stresses to an item below the designed strength will
   a. increase reliability
   b. increase the failure rate
   c. decrease the failure rate
   d. a and c above

10. The effects of failure rates on increased temperatures is called the
    a. Thermal Model
    b. Full Scale Model
    c. Arrhenius Model
    d. Derating effects
11. Which of the following has the greatest impact on failure rates?
    a. stress/strength correlation
    b. stress/temperature correlation
    c. actual/simulated correlation
    d. standard/nonstandard parts
12. A test that is primarily done to disclose weak parts is the
    a. Reliability Development/Growth Test
    b. Reliability Qualification Test
    c. Production Reliability Acceptance Test
    d. Environmental Stress Screening Test

8.7 References

Dovich, Robert A. 1990. *Reliability Statistics.* Milwaukee, WI: ASQC–Quality Press.

Rome Air Development Center (RADC). 1985. *RADC-TR-85-194: RADC Non-electronic Reliability Notebook.* Document #AD A163900. Springfield, VA: National Technical Information Service.

US Department of Defense. *MIL-E-5400: General Specification for Electronic Equipment, Airborne.* Philadelphia: Naval Publications and Forms Center.

US Department of Defense. *MIL-HDBK-217: Reliability Prediction of Electronic Equipment.* Philadelphia: Naval Publications and Forms Center.

US Department of Defense. *MIL-P-11268: Parts, Materials, and Processes Used in Electronic Equipment.* Philadelphia: Naval Publications and Forms Center.

US Department of Defense. *MIL-STD-781: Reliability Testing for Engineering Development, Qualification, and Production.* Philadelphia: Naval Publications and Forms Center.

US Department of Defense. *MIL-STD-785: Reliability Program for Systems and Equipment Development and Production.* Philadelphia: Naval Publications and Forms Center.

US Department of Defense. *MIL-STD-810: Environmental Test Methods and Engineering Guidelines.* Philadelphia: Naval Publications and Forms Center.

US Department of Defense. *MIL-STD-965: Parts Control Program.* Philadelphia: Naval Publications and Forms Center.

CHAPTER

9

Reliability Design and Management Control

A major problem that confronts all organizations responsible for a reliability program is the selection of tasks which can materially aid in attaining program reliability requirements. Today's schedule and funding constraints mandate a cost-effective selection based on identified program needs. The considerations presented herein are intended to provide the rationale for this selection. They are also intended to jog the memory for "lessons learned" to provoke questions that must be answered and to encourage dialogue with other engineers, operations and support personnel so that answers to questions and solutions to problems may be found.

This chapter is based on Appendix A of MIL-STD-785, which provides guidance for the selection of tasks to fit the needs of any reliability program. MIL-STD-785 states, in the statement of purpose of this appendix, that it may be used to tailor reliability requirements in the most cost effective manner that meets established program objectives.

9.1 Reliability program management principles

Table 9.1 provides general guidance in summary form, of "when and what" to include in a proposal to establish an acceptable and cost effective reliability program. This table can be used to initially identify the elements that are

Table 9.1 Application matrix.

TASK	TITLE	TASK TYPE	PROGRAM PHASE			
			CONCEPT	VALID	FSED	PROD
101	RELIABILITY PROGRAM PLAN	MGT	S	S	G	G
102	MONITOR/CONTROL OF SUB-CONTRACTORS AND SUPPLIERS	MGT	S	S	G	G
103	PROGRAM REVIEWS	MGT	S	S	G	G
104	FAILURE REPORTING, ANALYSIS, AND CORRECTIVE ACTION SYSTEM (FRACAS)	ENG	NA	S	G	G
105	FAILURE REVIEW BOARD (FRB)	MGT	NA	S	G	G
201	RELIABILITY MODELING	ENG	S	S	G	GC
202	RELIABILITY ALLOCATIONS	ACC	S	S	G	GC
203	RELIABILITY PREDICTIONS	ACC	S	S	G	GC
204	FAILURE MODES, EFFECTS, AND CRITICALITY ANALYSIS (FMECA)	ENG	S	S	G	GC
205	SNEAK CIRCUIT ANALYSIS (SCA)	ENG	NA	NA	G	GC
206	ELECTRONIC PARTS/CIRCUITS TOLERANCE ANALYSIS	ENG	NA	NA	G	GC
207	PARTS PROGRAM	ENG	S	S	G	G
208	RELIABILITY CRITICAL ITEMS	MGT	S	S	G	G
209	EFFECTS OF FUNCTIONAL TESTING, STORAGE, HANDLING, PACKAGING, TRANSPORTATION, AND MAINTENANCE	ENG	NA	S	G	GC
301	ENVIRONMENTAL STRESS SCREENING (ESS)	ENG	NA	S	G	G
302	RELIABILITY DEVELOPMENT /GROWTH TESTING	ENG	NA	S	G	NA
303	RELIABILITY QUALIFICATION TEST PROGRAM (RGT)	ACC	NA	S	G	G
304	PRODUCTION RELIABILITY ACCEPTANCE TEST PROGRAM (PRAT)	ACC	NA	NA	S	G

CODE DEFINITIONS

TASK TYPE:
  ACC—RELIABILITY ACCOUNTING
  ENG—RELIABILITY ENGINEERING
  MGT—MANAGEMENT

PROGRAM PHASE:
  S—SELECTIVELY APPLICABLE
  G—GENERALLY APPLICABLE
  GC—GENERALLY APPLICABLE TO DESIGN CHANGES ONLY

Source: MIL-STD-785, APPENDIX A.

typically included in an effective reliability program for the particular acquisition phase involved. The problem of prioritizing or establishing a base line group from all the tasks in this table cannot be solved unless variables like system complexity, program phase, availability of funds, schedule, etc., are known. The reliability program plan (Task 101) should always be considered for determining the need for this task. However, individual tasks may be cited without requiring a reliability program plan. Sections 9.1.1 through 9.1.10 contain summaries, based on MIL-STD-785, for each task listed in Table 9.1. These summaries may be used to determine which tasks are appropriate to include in the program.

9.1.1 Task 101

The reliability program plan is a tool to assist in managing an effective reliability program and to evaluate the approach to, understanding of, and execution of reliability tasks. It ensures that procedures for implementing and controlling reliability tasks are adequate, and structured to ensure that appropriate attention will be focused on reliability activities.

The plan should include, but not be limited to, the following:

1. A description of how the program will be conducted, how each task will be performed and procedures to evaluate status and control of each task (Task 101).
2. The description of interrelationships of reliability tasks and how they will interface with other system-oriented tasks. This description includes schedules with estimated start and completion points for each task (Task 104, 204, 208, etc.).
3. The identification of known reliability problems and proposed solutions or the proposed plan to solve the problems (Task 105).
4. The designation of reliability milestones (design and test—Task 201, 202, 203, etc.).
5. Identification of key personnel for managing the reliability program. Include a description of the management structure, the interrelationship between line, service, staff etc. (Task 101).

6. A statement of what source of design guidelines or design review checklist will be utilized. Include a description of how reliability contributes to the total design, and the level of authority and constraints on this engineering discipline (Task 103).

7. Identification of inputs that the contractor needs. Inputs should include measured basic reliability and mission reliability values, measured environmental stresses, typical failure modes, and critical failure modes (Task 102).

9.1.2 Task 102

Continual visibility of subcontractor activities is essential so that timely and appropriate management action can be taken as the need arises. It is prudent to include contractual provisions that permit the procuring activity to participate, at its discretion, in appropriate formal prime or subcontractor meetings. Information gained at these meetings can provide a basis for follow-up action necessary to maintain adequate visibility of subcontractors' progress.

Active participation in the closed-loop Failure Analysis, Reporting and Corrective Action System (FRACAS—Chapter 2) should be required of all equipment contractors. The information about unplanned events which this system can provide is a major factor in assessing and maintaining reliability program effectiveness. It is reasonable to assume that equipment failures will occur during service evaluation testing. During this testing it is very important to determine as rapidly as possible the cause of such failures, the need for corrective action, and the specific action to be taken. For this reason support of these tests is advisable, and should be considered for inclusion in program requirements.

9.1.3 Task 103

Design reviews are an important management and technical tool for the reliability organization. Typically, reviews are held to evaluate the progress, consistency and technical adequacy of a selected design and test approach. Formal review and assessment of reliability requirements should be conducted at major program points, identified as system program reviews. The reviews should be held at least quarterly, although the time can be extended as the program progresses. Representative discussion items include all reliability analyses, failure analysis, test schedules and progress, problems related to vendor and contractor reliability programs, parts and design problems. As the program develops, reliability progress is assessed by the use of additional program reviews as necessary.

These reviews identify and discuss all pertinent aspects of the reliability program. MIL-STD-785 classifies design reviews into the following four categories:

Preliminary Design Review—Conducted prior to initial design. According to Dhillon (1985), the purpose of this type of design review is to examine each requirement for such things as completeness, validity, and accuracy. An integral part of this review is the updating of the reliability status, which includes:

　a.　Reliability modeling
　b.　Reliability apportionment
　c.　Reliability predictions
　d.　FMECA
　e.　Reliability content of specification
　f.　Design guideline criteria
　g.　Other tasks as identified

Test Readiness Review—Conducted primarily to assure appropriate test methods are in place for establishing reliability prediction. Discussions here include, but are not limited to, the following:

　a.　Reliability analyses status, primarily prediction
　b.　Test schedules, profiles, plans, failure definitions, and reporting format
　c.　Failure reporting and corrective action implementation

Critical Design Review—Conducted during the final design stages. During this review a considerable amount of data should be available for the design team (i.e. test results, reports from earlier reviews and other predictive information). Topics for discussion during this review should include, but are not limited to:

a. Reliability content of specifications
b. Reliability prediction and analyses
c. Parts program status
d. Reliability critical items program
e. Other problems affecting reliability
f. Failure Mode, Effects and Criticality Analysis
g. Identification of circuit reference designators whose stress levels exceed the recommended parts application criteria

Production Readiness Review—Conducted to determine if the product is production ready. Discussions will include:

a. Results of the applicable reliability qualification tests
b. Results of the applicable reliability growth testing

In addition to more detailed coverage of those items discussed at the preliminary and critical reviews, formal program reviews should address progress on all reliability tasks specified. All reviews provide an opportunity to review and assign action items and to explore other areas of concern. A mutually acceptable agenda should be generated to ensure that all reliability open items are covered and that all participants are prepared for meaningful discussions.

9.1.4 Tasks 104–105

The purpose of Task 104 is to establish a closed loop failure reporting system, procedures for analysis of failures to determine cause, and documentation for recording corrective action taken. The purpose of Task 105 is to review failure trends and corrective action status, and to assure that adequate corrective actions are taken in a timely manner and recorded during the development and production phases of the program. Details of these tasks are found in Chapter 2.

9.1.5 Tasks 201–202–203

The purpose of Task 201 is to develop a reliability model for making numerical apportionments and estimates to evaluate system equipment reliability. The purpose of Task 202 is to assure that once quantitative system requirements have been determined, they are allocated or apportioned to lower levels. The purpose of Task 203 is to estimate the basic reliability and mission reliability of the system equipment and to make a determination of whether these reliability requirements can be achieved with the proposed design. Details of these tasks are found in Chapters 3 and 4.

9.1.6 Tasks 204–205–206

The purpose of Task 204 is to identify potential design weaknesses through systematic, documented consideration of all likely ways in which a component or equipment can fail, and causes for each failure mode and the effects of each failure. The purpose of Task 205 is to identify latent paths which cause occurrence of unwanted functions or inhibit desired functions, assuming all components are functioning properly. The purpose of Task 206 is to examine the effects of parts electrical tolerances and parasitic parameters over the range of specified operating temperatures. Details of these tasks are found in Chapter 7.

9.1.7 Tasks 207–208–209

The purpose of Task 207 is to control the selection and use of standard and nonstandard parts. The purpose of Task 208 is to identify and control those items which require "special attention" because of complexity, application of advanced state-of-the-art techniques, and the impact of potential failure on safety, readiness, mission success, and demand for maintenance support. The purpose of Task 209 is to determine the effects of storage, handling, packaging, transportation, maintenance, and repeated exposure to functional testing on hardware reliability. Details of these tasks are found in Chapter 8.

9.1.8 Tasks 301

The purpose of Task 301 is to establish and implement environmental stress screening procedures so that early failures due to weak parts, workmanship defects, and other non-conformance anomalies can be identified and removed from the equipment. Details of this task are found in Chapters 5 and 8.

9.1.9 Task 302

The purpose of Task 302 is to conduct pre-qualification testing to provide a basis for resolving the majority of reliability problems early in the development phase, and for incorporating corrective action to preclude recurrence, prior to the start of production. Details of this task are found in Chapters 5 and 8.

9.1.10 Tasks 303–304

The purpose of Task 303 is to determine that the specified reliability requirements have been achieved. The purpose of Task 304 is to assure that the reliability of the hardware is not degraded as the result of changes in tooling, processes, work flow, design, parts quality, or other characteristics identified by procurement. Details of these tasks are found in Chapters 5 and 8.

9.2 Design review teams

There are two key people on a typical design review team: the design engineer, responsible for the preparation of the design; and the reliability engineer, responsible for assuring the specified reliability requirements. Other members, dependent upon the complexity of the design, should include representatives from procurement, manufacturing, production, sales, etc. The purpose of the design review team is to increase reliability and improve design characteristics with minimum costs. There are two criteria that must be met for a successful design review team to be effective: it must be multi-disiplined and authoritative. If a review team is wanted only for advisory purposes, then hiring consultants would be the best alternative. The main thing to remember is that the design review should not be attempted by only one or two people and must be multi-disiplined as well as authoritative to be effective.

9.3 Follow-up and corrective-action

From time to time during the program, transitions from one phase to another have to be made. In addition, there may be other occasions within phases when changes in the program are required. As transition or other change points approach, those responsible for monitoring and achieving system reliability must evaluate the needs for the reliability program and determine its structure if it is needed. A checklist is sometimes used for monitoring the system to assure that all bases are covered throughout the reliability program. Table 9.2 provides a general checklist example that may be used as a guide for evaluating a reliability program. This checklist includes categories for reliability modeling and allocation, which are sometimes delivered as part of a prediction report. O'Connor (1989), offers a word of caution when using checklists: "Relying upon the use of checklists may result in little preparatory work and can become a substitute for thinking." According to O'Connor, there are three golden rules for the use of checklists:

1. Don't use them during the formal review meetings, only in the design office.
2. Avoid vague questions, such as, "Are the grease points accessible?" "What access is provided for lubrication?" is a better question. Try to ask for a more detailed response—avoid "Yes" or "No" answers.
3. Make sure they are pertinent to the design and up to date.

While most tasks can be performed at varying levels of detail, it is important to ensure that only essential tasks are specified, to avoid wasting resources. What has, or what will have been, achieved should be critically appraised at given milestones. For example, as the transition between Full Scale Engineering Development Phase (FSED*) and Production Phase (PROD†) approaches, judgments regarding reliability tasks during production must be made. In some instances, only minimal testing will be required, while in other instances, a substantial number of FSED tasks will need to be continued. Other cases may call for a reliability growth program or a phase-unique task such as Production Reliability Acceptance Test (PRAT‡). The FSED–PROD transition point was chosen for illustrative purposes; similar reasoning

---

* <u>Full-scale engineering development phase</u>: The period when the system and the principal items necessary for its support are designed, fabricated, tested and evaluated.

† <u>Production phase</u>: The period from production approval until the last system is delivered and accepted.

‡ <u>Production Reliability Acceptance Test</u>: A task assuring that the reliability of the hardware is not degraded as the result of changes in tooling, processes, design, parts quality, or other characteristics.

applies whenever program change points occur or are anticipated. The purpose here is to emphasize that the reliability manager should assess and project

Table 9.2 Reliability Analysis Checklist

Major Concerns	Comments
MODELS	
Are all functional elements included in the reliability block model?	System design drawings must be reviewed to be sure that the reliability model agrees with the hardware.
Are all modes of operation considered in the math model?	Duty cycles, alternate paths, degraded conditions and redundant units must be defined and modeled.
Do the math model results show that the design achieves the reliability requirement?	Unit failure rates and redundancy equations are used from the detailed part predictions in the system math model (See MIL-STD-756, Reliability Prediction and Modeling).
ALLOCATION	
Are system reliability requirements allocated (subdivided) to useful levels?	Useful levels are defined as: equipment for subcontractors, assemblies for sub-subcontractors, circuit boards for designers.
Does the allocation process consider complexity, design flexibility, and safety margins?	Conservative values are needed to prevent reallocation at every design change.
PREDICTION	
Does the sum of the parts equal the value of the module or unit?	Many predictions neglect to include all the parts producing optimistic results (check for solder connections, connectors, circuit boards).
Are environmental conditions and part quality representative of the requirements?	Optimistic quality levels and favorable environmental conditions are often assumed causing optimistic results.
Are the circuit and part temperatures defined and do they represent the design?	Temperature is the biggest driver of part failure rates; low temperature assumptions will cause optimistic results.
Are equipment, assembly, subassembly and part reliability drivers identified?	Identification is needed so that corrective actions for reliability Improvement can be considered.
Are alternate (Non-MIL-HDBK-217) failure rates highlighted along with the rationale for their use?	Use of alternate failure rates, if deemed necessary, require submission of backup data to provide credence in the values.
Is the level of detail for the part failure rate models sufficient to reconstruct the result?	Each component type should be sampled and failure rates completely reconstructed for accuracy.
Are critical components such as VHSIC, Monolithic Microwave Integrated Circuits (MMIC), Application Specific Integrated Circuits (ASIC) or Hybrids highlighted?	Prediction methods for advanced technology parts should be carefully evaluated for impact on the module and system.

Source: MIL-HDBK-217

accomplishments, determine what still needs to be accomplished to achieve reliability requirements, and then tailor a program to meet those requirements. MIL-STD-785 notes that "Tailoring" should not be interpreted as a license to specify a zero reliability program. Necessity and sufficiency are the key criteria to be set in determining whether tasks are tailored into, or excluded from, a reliability program.

9.4 Reliability needs

The elements of a reliability program must be selected to meet reliability needs. Identifying and quantifying these needs should be accomplished prior to release of a proposal for the appropriate acquisition phase so that tasks and requirements commensurate with the needs may be included. The tasks and requirements which are included establish the framework for the continuing reliability dialogue between procurement and those who will ultimately be selected to develop the hardware. It is essential to make appropriate analyses and exercise mature judgment in determining reliability needs.

In making this determination, it is necessary to assemble program data concerning mission and performance requirements (preferably at the sub-system level), anticipated environments, and mission reliability and basic reliability requirements. This information is initially gathered in the conceptual phase and refined throughout development. It is the base upon which the reliability needs are determined and adjusted. The initial life profile definition defines, as a minimum, the boundaries of the performance envelope and provides the timeline, both environmental conditions and induced stresses versus time, typical of operations within that envelope. The quantitative requirements, basic reliability and mission reliability, are then determined for the defined life profile.

Using the information on equipment contemplated to provide the required performance, a separate apportionment or allocation of basic reliability and mission reliability can be made to the equipment level. This apportionment is usually based on available reliability data modified to reflect changes in performance requirements, duty cycles, and anticipated environments. If the hardware to be procured is either a subsystem or equipment, the allocations would apply down to the lowest assembly level in terms of Mean-Time-Between-Maintenance-Action (MTBMA), or Mean-Time-Between-Failure, (MTBF) or failure rate. The required modifications are largely a matter of judgment, particularly when a new or considerably modified equipment concept must be synthesized to provide a specified function.

A reliability estimate should be made for each item of equipment independent of, and reasonably soon after, completing the initial apportionment. The equipment estimates should be combined to provide an initial estimate of basic reliability and mission reliability. During the conceptual phases* and validation phases†, design details will probably not be available. Therefore, estimates made during these phases and early in FSED will provide "ball park" numbers, which are nevertheless adequate for initial comparisons with, and for establishing the reasonableness of, the initial apportionment. Reapportionment based on a comparison with details of the estimate may be advisable at this time. The apportionment and the estimate procedures should be repeated until reasonable apportioned values are obtained. The apportionment should be frozen prior to awarding subcontracts that have firm reliability requirements.

Some reliability tasks should be accomplished for an entire system, e.g., development and use of a failure reporting system, periodic estimates of basic reliability and mission reliability. In most cases, needs are self evident while others, which must be selected, may apply only to subsystems. While experience plays a key role in the task selection, it should be supplemented by analysis and investigation.

A useful initial analytical procedure is to compare reliability estimates at the sub-system and equipment level, with the corresponding apportionments. If the estimate is less than the apportionment, the need for improvement is indicated. Where "considerable" improvement is required, the subsystem or equipment should be identified as "reliability critical." This identification

---

* Conceptual phase: The identification and exploration of alternative solutions or solution concepts to satisfy a validated need.

† Validation phase: The period when selected candidate solutions are refined through extensive study and analyses; hardware development, testing and evaluations.

should be done as early as possible in the program so as to impact the equipment through the proper selection of tasks.

Reasons for the disparity between the apportioned and the estimated values of the reliability critical items should be investigated. Discussions of these reasons and tentative ways to attain the apportioned values, (e.g., relaxed performance requirements, either more or less design redundancy, additional environmental protection), should be held with appropriate project personnel. The object of the investigations and discussions is viable recommendations for action to overcome the deficiencies. A significant benefit that can be gained from this process is a consensus on the specific equipment that is considered reliability critical. When systems or equipment performance requirements create a wide and irreconcilable disparity between apportioned and estimated values of required, reliability should be challenged. Elimination of less essential equipment functions can reduce equipment complexity and significantly enhance reliability.

Tasks and requirements can be prioritized and a "rough order of magnitude" estimate made of the time and effort required to complete each task once recommendations for task applications have been determined. This information will be of considerable value in selecting the tasks that can be accomplished within schedule and funding constraints.

9.5 Managing the program

When the technical tasks required to achieve the reliability requirements have been defined, the resources required must be identified and committed to meet objectives efficiently. The task elements should be staffed and time-phased to ensure that reliability objectives are not arbitrarily compromised to meet other program cost or schedule constraints.

The reliability program's success requires that top management be continually informed of program status and unresolved problems that could impact the achievement of program milestones, so that direction and resources can be reoriented as required. In general, the reliability organization should have:

1. A shared responsibility with other disciplines in its engineering department
2. Technical control of reliability disciplines
3. Fiscal control of reliability resources

Management can properly influence the reliability program by placing on the statement of work or contract:

1. Numerical reliability requirements and testing requirements to ensure contractual compliance during development and production
2. The requirement to implement specific reliability tasks during conduct of the program

Working arrangements between reliability and other activities (e.g., maintainability, safety, survivability, vulnerability, testing, quality assurance) should be established to identify mutual interests, maximize benefits of mutually supporting tasks, and minimize effort overlap. Such organizational working relationships can also promote more system-oriented decisions if the work is properly integrated at higher levels.

When all necessary planning for a reliability program has been accomplished, it should be documented as a reliability program plan. A reliability program plan is normally submitted as part of the response to the procuring activity's request for proposals. After mutual agreement has been reached and procurement approval has been granted, the reliability program plan must be made a part of the contract. Since the plan is a contractual tool used to evaluate the reliability program, it should be kept current, subject to procurement approvals.

9.6 General considerations

Both quantitative and qualitative analyses are useful in determining where reliability resources should be applied. For example, modeling, apportionment and estimates of basic reliability and mission reliability (Chapter 4) can scope the improvement which may be required. A Failure Modes, Effects and Criticality Analysis (FMECA—Chapter 7) based on available mission rules and system definition can be used to determine compliance with failure tolerance criteria and to identify single failure points which are critical to either mission success or safety, or both. These kinds of analyses identify improvements which must be made if requirements are to be met.

Reliability analyses are efficient work direction tools, because they can confirm system adequacy or identify the need for design change, providing they are accomplished in conjunction with, or reviewed by, other disciplines. The use of reliability analyses is not limited to the phase traditionally thought of as the design phase. Some of the analyses mentioned above are useful during the early acquisition phases when design criteria, mission requirements, and preliminary designs are being developed. Since the situation is generally fluid during these phases, and firm commitments for full-scale development have not yet been made, a comparison of the reliability benefits of competing configuration concepts may be more readily accepted for use in the decision making process. The ultimate reliability that can be attained by any system or item is limited by the configuration chosen. Therefore, the analyses should be selected to aid configuration definition in light of the existing design criteria and mission requirements. Preliminary reliability estimates and FMECA are generally the most appropriate for this purpose. The depth of the estimates should be sufficient for comparison of the configurations.

The cost of the selected analyses is obviously a function of both the level and breadth requested. For example, an FMECA at the part level for all equipment in a complex system is time consuming, and action taken to reduce reliability risk as a result of such an analysis will probably not be cost effective. However, when the analysis is conducted at a sub-system level, single point failures can be identified and the need for a more detailed analysis or design action can be determined. Similar considerations, which are largely subjective, should be used in tailoring other analyses to fit program needs. The cardinal principles are:

1. For basic reliability, do not analyze below the level at which a failure will cause a demand for maintenance, repair, or logistics support.
2. For mission reliability, do not analyze below the level necessary to identify mission critical failures.

9.7 Summary

Program funding and schedule constraints demand that the limited reliability resources available be used where they are most cost effective. It is also self-evident that major program level requirements and criteria have a more far reaching impact than those developed for lower levels. It is appropriate, therefore, to examine as early as possible the numerical reliability requirements, both basic reliability and mission reliability, mission rules, failure tolerance criteria, etc., so that analyses can be selected to show design compliance or to identify shortcomings. During this examination the numerical requirements and criteria should also be evaluated, and if slight changes to them can improve program cost effectiveness, such information should be presented to program management for appropriate action.

9.8 Exercises

1. Explain the purpose of design reviews.
2. When should formal reviews be conducted?
    a. When all tests have been completed
    b. After failure analysis has been completed
    c. At major program points
    d. Prior to initial design or the Concept phase
3. Explain the function of a failure review board.
4. In which phase of development do most elements of a reliability program plan become "generally applicable?"
    a. CONCEPT
    b. VALID
    c. FSED
    d. PROD
5. List at least six questions which should be asked during the design review.
6. Explain the purpose of the design review team.
7. The design review team may function effectively with two key people.
    a. True
    b. False
8. Explain the "downside" of using a checklist during formal reviews.

9.9 References

[Anonymous]. 1976. *Engineering Design Handbook, Development Guide for Reliability; Part Two: Design for Reliability.* AMCP 706–196. Chambersburg, PA: Letter County Army Depot.

Dhillon, B. S. 1985. *Quality Control, Reliability, and Engineering Design.* New York: Marcel Dekker.

O'Conner, P. D. T. 1993. *Practical Reliability Engineering.* New York: John Wiley & Sons.

US Department of Defense. *MIL-HDBK-217: Reliability Prediction of Electronic Equipment.* Philadelphia: Naval Publications and Forms Center.

US Department of Defense. *MIL-STD-785: Reliability Program for Systems and Equipment Development and Production.* Philadelphia: Naval Publications and Forms Center.

10

Product Safety

A system should be in place to assure that risks are eliminated or controlled within established parameters. Such a system requires that internal procedures be in place for the disposition of product related safety incidents, that include potentially hazardous conditions not yet involved in an incident. MIL-STD-882 may be used as a guide in establishing and maintaining a product safety program that supports the efficient and effective achievement of overall system safety objectives. This chapter describes the use of this military standard.

10.1 Contingency analysis

The first step in any contingency analysis is defining the program. A systematic approach should be used for the product safety program to assure that:

1. Safety is designed into the product in a timely, cost-effective manner
2. Historical safety data, including lessons learned from other products, are considered
3. Minimum risk is sought in accepting and using new technology, materials or new production and operational techniques
4. Retrofit actions required to improve safety is minimized through the timely inclusion of safety features during research and development

5. Changes in design, configuration or requirements are accomplished in a manner that maintains an acceptable level of risk

6. Consideration is given early in the life cycle to both safety and significant safety data documented as "lessons learned"

7. Hazards associated with each system are identified and evaluated then eliminated or reduced to an acceptable level

10.1.1 The product safety program

Military Standard-882, Task 102, describes the System Safety Program Plan in detail and is a recommended reference if development is based on this regulation. Task 102 states that the plan shall describe in detail tasks and activities of safety management and safety engineering required to identify, evaluate, and eliminate or control hazards, or reduce the associated risk to a level acceptable to management throughout the system life cycle. A product safety plan should provide a formal basis of understanding on how the safety program will be executed to meet safety requirements, including general and specific provisions. Sections 10.1.1.1 through 10.1.1.10 are summaries of MIL-STD-882. The System Safety Program Plan (SSPP), in Task 102, will be referred to as the Product Safety Program (PSP).

10.1.1.1 Scope and objectives

The PSP shall describe, as a minimum, four elements of an effective product safety program: a planned approach for task accomplishment, qualified people to accomplish tasks, authority to implement tasks through all levels of management, and appropriate commitment of resources (both personnel and funding) to assure tasks are completed. The PSP shall also define any safety requirements which may be imposed by a contract.

The scope and objectives will describe the interrelationships between system safety and other functional elements of the program and account for all contractually required safety tasks and responsibilities.

10.1.1.2 Organization

The PSP describes the organization of the total program including the organizational and functional relationships, and lines of communication. The organizational relationship between other functional elements having responsibility for safety impacts and safety management all are included in the program plan. The following are probably worth considering for inclusion:

1. Methods are described by which safety personnel may raise issues of concern
2. The organizational unit responsible for executing action needed to eradicate hazards must be identified along with who has authority for the resolution of all identified hazards
3. The qualifications of key safety personnel must be established
4. The process by which management decisions will be made including timely notification of unacceptable risk, necessary action, waivers, deviations, etc.
5. Details of how actions relative to product safety will be effected at the management level possessing resolution authority

10.1.1.3 Milestones

Define product safety program milestones that:

1. Relate to program responsibility and the required inputs and outputs
2. Provide a schedule of tasks including completion dates, reports and reviews
3. Identify subsystem, component, software safety activities as well as integrated system level activities
4. Provide estimates for people-power required to complete each task

10.1.1.4 Requirements and criteria

Establish the risk assessment procedures:

1. Prescribe hazard severity categories, hazard probability levels and system safety precedence
2. Identify any qualitative or quantitative measures to be used, including a description of the acceptable risk levels

3. Describe closed-loop procedures for actions to resolve unacceptable risk

10.1.1.5 Hazard analysis

Describe the analysis techniques and formats to be used in qualitative or quantitative analysis to identify hazards, causes and effects, hazard elimination or risk reduction. The depth to which each technique is used including control of hazards associated with materials must be specified.

10.1.1.6 Safety data

Describe how historical hazard, mishap, and safety lessons learned, data is to be processed. Identify deliverable data and describe procedures for accessibility.

10.1.1.7 Safety verification

Describe verification (test, analysis, inspection, etc.) requirements:
1. Make sure that safety is adequately demonstrated. Identify certification requirements for safety devices, software, etc.
2. Make sure that safety-related verification information gets to the proper authority for review and analysis

10.1.1.8 Audit program

Describe the intended procedures to assure the objectives and requirements of the safety program are being accomplished.

10.1.1.9 Training

Describe the safety training for engineering, technician, operating and maintenance personnel.

10.1.1.10 Interfaces

Describe and identify, in detail, the interface between product safety, product engineering, and all other support disciplines such as: maintainability, quality control, reliability, software development, human factors engineering, medical support (health hazard assessments, and any others).

10.1.2 Safety design requirements

Safety design requirements should be established according to their applicability to the overall design of the product system. Some general system safety design requirements are:

1. Eliminate hazards through design or by material substitution. When elimination is impossible, only those with the least risk should be used.

2. Isolate hazardous substances from other activities or incompatible materials.

3. Locate equipment so that access during operation minimizes personnel exposure to hazards (e.g., hazardous chemicals, high voltage, radiation, cutting edges or sharp points).

4. Minimize risk resulting from excessive environmental conditions (e.g., temperature, pressure, noise or toxicity).

5. Minimize risk created by human error in the operation of the system.

6. Minimize risk from hazards that cannot be eliminated by including interlocks, redundancy, protective clothing, devices or procedures.

7. Protect power sources and critical components by physical separation or shielding.

8. When alternate design approaches cannot eliminate the hazard, place warning devices and caution notes in operation and repair instructions, or provide distinctive markings on hazardous components, materials or facilities to ensure personnel and equipment protection.

10.1.3 Risk assessment

Steps should be taken to eliminate identified hazards or reduce the associated risk to an acceptable level. Decisions regarding the resolve of identified hazards are based on the risk assessment. To aid in achieving the product or system safety objectives, hazards are characterized as to hazard severity categories and hazard probability levels. Since the priority for product or system safety is eliminating hazards by design, a risk assessment procedure considering only hazard severity will generally suffice during the early design phase to minimize the risk. For hazards not eliminated during the early design phase, a risk assessment procedure based upon the hazard probability, hazard severity, as well as risk impact is used to establish priorities for corrective action and resolution of identified hazards.

10.1.4 Hazard severity

Hazard severity categories are defined to provide a qualitative measure of the worst credible mishap resulting from the following: personnel error; environmental conditions; design inadequacies; procedural deficiencies; or system, subsystem or component failure or malfunction as shown in Table 10.1

Table 10.1. Hazard severity categories.

Description	Category	Definition
CATASTROPHIC	I	Death, system loss or severe environmental damage.
CRITICAL	II	Severe injury, severe occupational illness, major system or environmental damage.
MARGINAL	II	Minor injury, minor occupational illness, minor system or environmental damage.
NEGLIGIBLE	V	Less than minor injury, occupational illness, or less than minor system or environmental damage.

NOTE: These hazard severity categories provide guidance to a wide variety of programs. Adaptation to a particular program requires a mutual understanding as to the meaning of the terms used and what constitutes a failure, major or minor system or environmental damage, severe or minor injury and illness. Other criteria may be used provided it meets the overall program objectives.

10.1.5 Hazard probability

The probability that a hazard will be created during the planned life expectancy of the product or system can be described in potential occurrences per unit of time, events, population, items, or activity. Assigning a quantitative hazard probability to a potential design or procedural hazard is generally not possible early in the design process. A qualitative hazard probability may be derived from research, analysis, and evaluation of historical safety data from similar products or systems. An example of a qualitative hazard probability ranking is shown in Table 10.2.

Table 10.2. Hazard probability categories.

Description	Level	Specific Individual Item
FREQUENT	A	Likely to occur frequently
PROBABLE	B	Will occur several times in the life of an item*
OCCASIONAL	C	Likely to occur some time in the life of an item*
REMOTE	D	Unlikely but possible to occur in the life of an item*
IMPROBABLE	E	So unlikely, it can be assumed occurrence may not be experienced*

* Definitions of descriptive words may have to be modified based on complexity and size of the product or system.

10.1.6 Risk impact

The effects and costs of identified risk having the same hazard risk index are assessed for the risk impact. For example, a periodic release of carbon gases may not cause direct physical harm or equipment damage, but can cause extreme damage to the goodwill of the organization.

10.1.7 Management responsibility

The Product Safety Program Manager is responsible for establishing, planning, organizing, implementing and maintaining an effective safety program, as defined below:

1. Establish definitive product safety program requirements (10.1.1.4) for the procurement or development of the system or product. These requirements identify the specific risk levels that are considered acceptable for the system. Acceptable risk levels are defined in terms of a hazard risk index (10.3.1) that is developed through a hazard severity probability matrix (Tables 10.4 or 10.5).

2. Develop a plan that reflects in detail how the total program is to be conducted.

3. Organize key system safety personnel that meet minimum qualifications. Key system safety personnel are usually limited to the person who has authority for the supervisory or technical responsibilities of the system's safety. Some programs require that key system safety personnel possess special qualifications. These special qualifications must be specified in the program safety requirements. A guide for appointing key system safety personnel is provided in Table 10.3.

Table 10.3. Minimum qualifications for key system safety personnel.

Program Complexity	Education	Experience	Certification
High	BS in Engineering, Physical Science or other*	Four years in system safety or related discipline	Desired: CSP** or Professional Engineer
Moderate	Bachelor's Degree plus training in system safety	Two years in system safety or related discipline	Enhancement: CSP or Professional Engineer
Low	High School Diploma plus training in system safety	Four years in system safety	None

* Management may specify other degrees or certification
** CSP—Certified Safety Professional

4. Implement the product safety program in a timely and efficient manner.

5. The program is maintained by monitoring the system safety activities to:
   a. Ensure adequate compliance with the safety requirements
   b. Evaluate new design criteria for inclusion into system standards
   c. Establish system safety groups as required to assist in developing and implementing the program
   d. Ensure that technical and historical safety data is available

Management assuring that an acceptably safe product or system will be developed may be summarized into a three step process:

1. Prevent the initial creation of unnecessary hazards.

2. Tailor product or system safety activities to meet specific program needs[*].

3. Manage residual hazards. This is done by understanding their nature and impact, and assuring they are properly dispositioned. For hazards that are to be "accepted," care should be taken to assure that this acceptance of risk occurs at the proper level of authority. Generally, the greater the risk, the higher the approval level needed for acceptance. The higher level of risks must be justified to the decision makers, not the Safety community.

10.2 Malfunction and multiple failure analysis

The overall goal of any product or system safety program is to design systems that do not contain hazards which can result in an unacceptable level of risk. The nature of most complex systems often makes it impossible or impractical to design them completely hazard-free. As various hazard analyses are performed, hazards will be identified that will require a resolution. The alternatives for eliminating the specific hazards or controlling the associated risks are evaluated so an acceptable method for risk reduction can be agreed upon. A common method for defining the hazards of a product is much like the FMEA process (Chapter 7). With this process applied to product safety, the hazards, effects, severalties and probabilities associated with the system are identified; and present control measures and recommendations for improvement are recorded. Table 10.4 is an example of a multiple hazard analysis worksheet.

10.2.1 Hazard risk assessment models

To determine what actions to take to eliminate or control identified hazards, a system of determining the level of risk involved must be developed. A good hazard risk assessment model will enable decision makers to properly understand the amount of risk involved relative to what it will cost in sched-

---

[*] It is obvious that if step 1 is omitted, a more complex safety effort will be needed to address the greater number and variety of hazards that will populate the design.

ules and dollars to reduce the risk to an acceptable level. To eliminate or otherwise control as many hazards as possible, hazards must be prioritized for corrective actions. A categorization of hazards may be conducted according to risk level criteria. Categorization may be based on severity since not all hazards are of equal magnitude or criticality to personnel safety system success. In some cases, the anticipated consequences of hazardous events may be minimal, while in others, catastrophic. Hazard categorization may also involve the determination of the likelihood of the hazardous event actually occurring. This may be reported in non-numeric (qualitative) terms, such as frequent, occasional, or improbable; or in numeric (quantitative) terms such as once in 10,000 hours, 10^{-4}/hour. Prioritization may be accomplished either subjectively by qualitative analyses resulting in a comparative hazard risk assessment, or through quantification of the probability of occurrence resulting in a numeric priority factor for that hazardous condition. Tables 10.5 and 10.6 show matrices for hazard risk assessment which can be applied to provide qualitative priority factors for assigning corrective action. In the first matrix an identified hazard assigned a hazard risk index of 1A, 1B, 1C, 2A, 2B, or 3A might require immediate corrective action. A hazard risk index of 1D, 2C, 2D, 3B, or 3C would be tracked for possible corrective action. A hazard risk index of 1E, 2E, 3D, or 3E might have a lower priority for corrective action and may not warrant any tracking actions. In the second matrix, risk indices of 1 through 20 are assigned (1A=1, 1B=2, 1C=4, 2A=3, 3A=7, 4A=13, ..., etc., with 1 being the highest risk). This matrix design assigns a different index to each frequency-category pair. This eliminates the situation caused by creating indices as products of numbers assigned to frequency and category which causes common results such as 2 x 6 = 3 x 4 = 4 x 3. This situation could hide information pertinent to prioritization. These are only examples of risk assessment methods and do not fit all programs.

Table 10.4. Hazard analysis worksheet.

System: Caustic Wash Station				Project Engineer: Willie B. Safe	
Sub-system: Caustic Tank				Date: 4-22-93	
Hazard and Number	**Hazard Effect**	**Hazard Severity**	**Hazard Probability**	**Present Control**	**Recommended Control**
#1.—Platform slippery when wet	Personnel could fall into tank	I	E	Surface painted with anti-skid coating	Expanded grating plus anti-skid coating
#2.—Walkway on same level with caustic solution	Caustic solution could splash on personnel	II	B	Emergency shower on platform; protective clothing	Transparent guard attached to handrail around platform
#3.—Tank leaking	Environment concerns	II	D	NONE	Double wall container around tank
#4.—					

Table 10.5. First hazard risk assessment matrix.

	HAZARD CATEGORY			
	(1)	**(2)**	**(3)**	**(4)**
FREQUENCY	Catastrophic	Critical	Marginal	Negligible
(A) Frequent $(x > 10^{-1})$*	1A	2A	3A	4A
(B) Probable $(10^{-1} > x > 10^{-2})$*	1B	2B	3B	4B
(C) Occasional $(10^{-2} > x > 10^{-3})$*	1C	2C	3C	4C
(D) Remote $(10^{-3} > x > 10^{-6})$*	1D	2D	3D	4D
(E) Improbable $(10^{-6} > x)$*	1E	2E	3E	4E

* Example of quantitative criteria:

Hazard Risk Index	**Suggested Criteria**
1A, 1B, 1C, 2A, 2B, 3A	Unacceptable
1D, 2C, 2D, 3B, 3C	Undesirable (management decision required)
1E, 2E, 3D, 3E, 4A, 4B	Acceptable (with management review)
4C, 4D, 4E	Acceptable (without review)

Table 10.6. Second hazard risk assessment matrix.

FREQUENCY	HAZARD CATEGORY			
	Catastrophic	Critical	Marginal	Negligible
(A) Frequent	1	3	7	13
(B) Probable	2	5	9	16
(C) Occasional	4	6	11	18
(D) Remote	8	10	14	19
(E) Improbable	12	15	17	20

* Example of quantitative criteria:

Hazard Risk Index	Suggested Criteria
1–5	Unacceptable
6–9	Undesirable (management decision required)
10–17	Acceptable (with management review)
18–20	Acceptable (without review)

10.2.2 Hazard risk impact analysis

This is a means of further prioritizing hazards that may have the same risk hazard index, as well as other factors such as the effects on system operation and economics. An example is the use of a hazardous material that could contaminate the environment, or cause adverse health effects to the general public as well as the user. This material may deserve higher consideration for resolution than a hardware design that could cause a loss of a system through a mishap. Management should identify any hazard risk impacts to be considered when tailoring the system.

10.2.3 Residual risk

Risk associated with significant hazards for which there are no known control measures, no plans to control them, or incomplete control measures, are referred to as residual risk. Any residual risks should be documented as such, along with reasons for non-resolution.

10.2.4 Action on identified hazards

Catastrophic and critical hazards should be resolved through design changes or incorporation of safety devices. These specific hazards should not rely solely on warnings, cautions or procedures for control of the risk. If this is impossible or impractical, alternatives should be recommended. If management desires other hazards to be handled in this way, it must be considered early in the design stages for appropriate action. Actions should be based on process alternative recommendations that are part of the hazard analysis or hazard tracking techniques.

10.2.5 Software hazard risk analysis

The initial assessment of risk for software, and consequently software controlled or software intensive systems, cannot rely solely on the hazard severity and probability. Determination of the probability of failure of a single software function is difficult at best and cannot be based on historical data. Software is generally application specific, and reliability parameters associated with it cannot be estimated in the same manner as hardware. Therefore, another approach is recommended for the initial software risk assessment that considers the potential hazard severity and the degree of control that software exercises. The degree of control is defined using the following software control categories:

I. Software exercises autonomous control over potentially hazardous hardware systems, subsystems or components without the possibility of intervention to preclude the occurrence of a hazard. Failure of the software or a failure to prevent an event leads directly to a hazard's occurrence.

IIa. Software exercises control over potentially hazardous hardware systems, subsystems, or components allowing time for intervention by independent safety systems to mitigate the hazard. However, these systems by themselves are not considered adequate.

IIb. Software item displays information requiring immediate operator action to mitigate a hazard. Software failures will allow, or fail to prevent, the hazard's occurrence.

IIIa. Software item issues commands over potentially hazardous hardware systems, subsystems or components requiring human action to complete the control function. There are several, redundant, independent safety measures for each hazardous event.

IIIb. Software generates information of a safety critical nature used to make safety critical decisions. There are several, redundant, independent safety measures for each hazardous event.

IV. Software does not control safety critical hardware systems, subsystems or components and does not provide safety critical information.

10.2.6 Software hazard criticality matrix

The Software Hazard Criticality Matrix (Table 10.7) is similar to the Hazard Risk Assessment Matrix (Tables 10.5 and 10.6). This matrix is established using the hazard categories for the rows and the Software Control Categories for the columns. The matrix is completed by assigning Software Hazard Risk Index numbers to each element just as Hazard Risk Index (HRI) numbers are assigned in the Hazard Risk Assessment Matrix. A Software Hazard Risk Index (SHRI) of 1 from the matrix implies that the risk may be unacceptable. A SHRI from 2 to 4 is undesirable or requires acceptance from the managing activity. Unlike the hardware related HRI, a low index number does not mean that a design is unacceptable. Rather, it indicates that greater resources need to be applied to the analysis and testing of the software and its interaction with the system.

Table 10.7. Software hazard criticality matrix.

CONTROL CATEGORY	HAZARD CATEGORY			
	Catastrophic	Critical	Marginal	Negligible
I	1	1	3	5
II	1	2	4	5
III	2	3	5	5
IV	3	4	5	5

* Example of quantitative criteria:

Hazard Risk Index	Suggested Criteria
1	High Risk—Significant analysis and testing resources required
2	Medium Risk—Requirements and design analysis and in-depth testing required
3–4	Moderate Risk—High level analysis and testing acceptable with management review
5	Low Risk—Acceptable

10.3 Exercises

1. A major element for a product safety program is
   a. Identifying hazards
   b. Evaluating hazards
   c. Controlling hazards
   d. Aliminating hazards
   e. All the above are elements of a product safety program

2. Two major elements of a hazard analysis are
   a. Severity and probability
   b. Risk impact and control
   c. Qualitative and quantitative criteria
   d. Criticality and fault tree

3. A contingency analysis should be done to assure that
   a. Changes in design, configuration or requirements are accomplished in a manner that maintains an acceptable level of risk
   b. Consideration is given early in the life cycle to safety and significant safety data documented as "lessons learned"
   c. Hazards associated with each system are identified and evaluated then eliminated or reduced to an acceptable level
   d. All the above should be considered in the contingency analysis

4. One way to minimize the risk from a hazard that cannot be eliminated is
   a. Hazards that cannot be eliminated should always be removed from the design
   b. Initiate restrictions on use of the product
   c. Include protective devices or procedures in the design
   d. Write engineering product safety standards that reclassify the hazard

5. Management is chiefly responsible for the design of
   a. The safety qualification system
   b. The overall product safety program requirements
   c. Hazard identification matrix
   d. Hazard risk assessment models
6. Hazards identified as having the same risk index are assessed for
   a. Their effect on the environment
   b. Their cost
   c. Their overall effects
   d. Their acceptable risk levels
7. The highest number in a hazard severity category normally represents
   a. Something negligible
   b. Something of marginal concern
   c. Something serious
   d. Something catastrophic
8. Hazard probability level "A" assigned to a hazard normally means
   a. The hazard is possible
   b. The hazard is unlikely to occur
   c. The hazard is very likely to occur
   d. The hazard will occur sometime
   e. The hazard will occur several times
9. The main objective of the hazard analysis during design is to
   a. Meet the expectations of safety management
   b. Prevent the initial creation of unnecessary hazards
   c. Assure that adequate warning or protective devices are in place
   d. Demonstrate the ability to design a safe product

10. In the hazard risk assessment matrix below, which category-frequency combinations would be the most undesirable?

	HAZARD CATEGORY			
	(1)	(2)	(3)	(4)
FREQUENCY	Catastrophic	Critical	Marginal	Negligible
(A) Frequent $(x>10^{-1})$*	1A	2A	3A	4A
(B) Probable $(10^{-1}>x>10^{-2})$*	1B	2B	3B	4B
(C) Occasional $(10^{-2}>x>10^{-3})$*	1C	2C	3C	4C
(D) Remote $(10^{-3}>x>10^{-6})$*	1D	2D	3D	4D
(E) Improbable $(10^{-6}>x)$*	1E	2E	3E	4E

    a. 1A, 3B, 1E

    b. 1B, 1C, 4D

    c. 3A, 3C, 2E

    d. 2C, 3A, 1D

11. From the hazard analysis worksheet below, the most likely order of priorities are:

System: Caustic Wash Station			Project Engineer: Willie B. Safe		
Sub-system: Caustic Tank			Date: 4-22-93		
Hazard and Number	Hazard Effect	Hazard Severity	Hazard Probability	Present Control	Recommended Control
#1.—Platform slippery when wet	Personnel could fall into tank	I	E	Surface painted with anti-skid coating	Expanded grating plus anti-skid coating
#2.—Walkway on same level with caustic solution	Caustic solution could splash on personnel	II	B	Emergency shower on platform; protective clothing	Transparent guard attached to handrail around platform
#3.—Tank leaking	Environment concerns	II	D	NONE	Double wall container around tank
#4.—					

    a. 3, 2, 1

    b. 2, 3, 1

    c. 1, 2, 3

    d. 3, 1, 2

12. What is meant by the term "residual risk?"
    a. Risks associated with hazards left inherent in design
    b. The small risks remaining as a result of removing larger risks
    c. Risks associated with hazards for which there are no known controls
    d. All of the above

10.4 References

Hammer, Willie. 1980. *Product Safety Management and Engineering*. Englewood Cliffs, NJ: Prentice-Hall.

Rome Air Development Center (RADC). 1983. *The Evaluation and Practical Applications of Failure Modes and Effects Analysis*. Document #ADA131-358. Springfield, VA: National Technical Information Service.

US Department of Defense. 1977. *MIL-STD-882: System Safety Program Requirements*. Philadelphia: Naval Publications and Forms Center.

US Department of Defense. 1980. *MIL-STD-1629: Procedures for Performing a Failure Mode, Effects and Criticality Analysis*. Philadelphia: Naval Publications and Forms Center.

11

Human Factors In Reliability

Human factors engineering must be included in every design that requires human interaction, to achieve the greatest potential for reliability. To increase the human reliability factor, steps should be taken early in the design phase to minimize the probability of error during human interventions. While error in product design may be the "root cause" of a product failure, error in human factors engineering may be the "root cause" of human failure. Human reliability may also be affected by, design characteristics, operational procedures, environments, communications, and standard operational procedures, all of which are discussed in this chapter.

MIL-STD-1472, "Human Engineering Design Criteria for Military Systems, Equipment and Facilities" and MIL-HDBK-759, "Human Factors Engineering Design for Army Materiel" are both good references for human reliability considerations. Military standards and handbooks are available from the Naval Publications and Forms Center, ATTN: NPODS, 5801 Tabor Avenue, Philadelphia, PA 19120-5099. Two good non-government publications for reference are: (1) Human Engineering Guide to Equipment Design, 1972., available from the Superintendent of Documents, US Government Printing Office, Washington, DC 20402; and, (2) American National Standard for Human Factors Engineering of Visual Display Terminal Workstations, (ANSI/HFS 100), available from the Human Factors Society, Inc., P.O. Box 1369, Santa Monica, CA 90406.

MIL-STD-1472 establishes general human engineering criteria for design and development of military systems, equipment and facilities and is the base from which this chapter is built. Its purpose is to present human engineering design criteria, principles and practices to be applied in the design of systems, equipment and facilities so as to:

1. Achieve required performance by operator, control and maintenance personnel
2. Minimize skill and personnel requirements and training time
3. Achieve required reliability of personnel-equipment combinations
4. Foster design standardization within and among systems

11.1 Human factors in design and design principles

Human factors in the reliability engineering process may be defined as: analyzing the desired performance, configuring the physical and mental tasks, and assessing the likelihood for errors that could effect system reliability. Including human factors in design will increase reliability by improving the intractability of humans and components. The objectives of **human factors engineering**, as described by Huchingson (1981), are to improve comfort and performance and to reduce lost time and training cost. McCormick (1957) defines **human engineering** as the adaptation of human tasks to work environments and the working environment to human attributes such as mental, perceptual, sensory, and physical. Edel (1967), states that this adaptation for human use is applicable to various functions, for example, work method development, equipment design, and consumer products.

MIL-STD-1472 defines **human engineering design criteria** as, "the summation of available knowledge which defines the nature and limits of human capabilities as they relate to the checkout, operation, maintenance or control of systems or equipment, and which may be applied during engineering design to achieve optimum compatibility between equipment and human performance." It is essential for the designer to understand capabilities such as; sight, touch, audio, thermal tolerance and vibration if human factors are being considered. The remainder of this section provides brief outlines of these human capabilities. MIL-STD-1472 discusses many more human capabilities that should be considered.

11.1.1 Sight capabilities

The human eye viewing angle and color perception is limited to the position of the head. The ability to see decreases as the viewing angle increases. For example, when a person looks through the normal line of sight (see Figure 11.1), the viewing angle as well as color perception is optimized. MIL-STD-1472 requires that, for critical functions, indicators be located within (15°) of the operator's normal line of sight without requiring the operator to assume an uncomfortable, awkward or unsafe position.

11.1.2. Touch capabilities

The human capability to interpret visual stimuli by the sense of touch is a natural to be utilized by the designer. For example, control knob shapes can be distinguished by touching, therefore the designer is able to take advantage of this sense to relieve the load on the eyes, thereby reducing eyestrain and fatigue. MIL-STD-1472 utilizes this sense by the use of "coding" where control placement, size, shape and color are addressed.

The use of coding for a particular application is governed by the relative advantages and disadvantages of each type of coding. Where coding is used to differentiate among controls, application of the codes are uniform throughout the system (see Table 11.1 for advantages and disadvantages). Coding is defined in Section 5 of this military regulation as follows:

5.4.1.4.2 **Location-coding.** Controls associated with similar functions should be in the same location relative to the operator from workstation to workstation and from panel to panel.

5.4.1.4.3 **Size-coding.** No more than three different sizes of controls shall be used in coding controls for discrimination by absolute size. Controls used for performing the same function on different items of equipment shall be the same size. When knob diameter is used as the coding parameter, differences between diameters shall not be less than

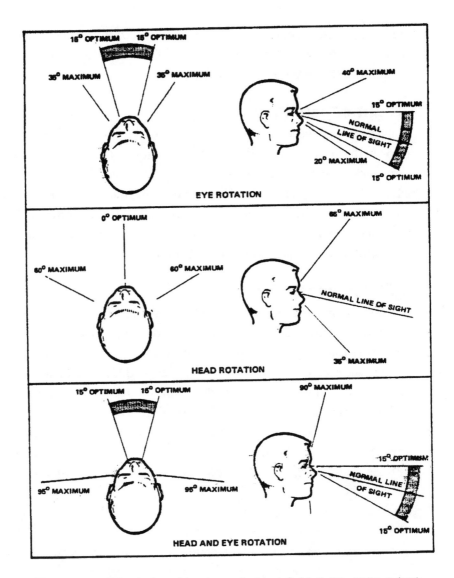

Figure 11.1. Vertical and horizontal visual field (MIL-STD-1472).

13 mm (0.5"). When knob thickness is the coding parameter, differences between thicknesses shall not be less than 10 mm (0.4").

5.4.1.4.4 Shape-coding. Primary use of shape coding for controls is for identification of control knobs or handles by "feel"; however, shapes shall be identifiable both visually and tactually. When shape coding is used:

a. The coded feature shall not interfere with ease of control manipulation.

b. Shapes shall be identifiable by the hand regardless of the position and orientation of the control knob or handle.

c. Shapes shall be tactually identifiable when gloves are worn, where applicable.

d. A sufficient number of identifiable shapes shall be provided to cover the expected number of controls that require tactual identification.

Table 11.1. Advantages and disadvantages of types of coding.

ADVANTAGES	LOCATION	SHAPE	SIZE	MODE OF OPERATION	LABELING	COLOR
Improves visual identification	X	X	X		X	X
Improves non-visual identification (tactual and kinesthetic)	X	X	X	X		
Helps standardization	X	X	X	X	X	X
Aids identification under low levels of illumination and colored lighting	X	X	X	X	(When trans-illuminated)	(When trans-illuminated)
May aid in identifying control position (settings)		X		X	X	
Requires little (if any) training; is not subject to forgetting					X	
DISADVANTAGES						
May require extra space	X	X	X	X	X	
Affects manipulation of the control (ease of use)	X	X	X	X		
Limited in number of available coding categories	X	X	X	X		X
May be less effective if operator wears gloves		X	X	X		
Controls must be viewed (i.e., must be within visual areas and with adequate illumination present)					X	X

Source: MIL-STD-1472

e. Shape coded knobs and handles shall be positively and non-reversibly attached to their shafts to preclude incorrect attachment when replacement is required.

f. Shapes should be associated with, or resemble, control function, and not alternate functions.

An example of coding specifications for the toggle switch control is shown in Figure 11.2.

DIMENSIONS			RESISTANCE	
L Arm Length		D Control Tip		
*	**		Small Switch	Large Switch
Maximum 13 mm (1/2 in.)	38 mm (1-1/2 in.)	3 mm (1/8 in.)	2.8 N (10 oz.)	2.8 N (10 oz.)
Mininmum 50 mm (2 in.)	50 mm (2 in.)	25 mm (1 in.)	4.5 N (16 oz.)	11 N (40 oz.)

DISPLACEMENT BETWEEN POSITIONS	
A	
2 Position	3 Position
Minimum 525 mrad (30°)	525 mrad (30°)
Maximum 1400 mrad (80°)	700 mrad (40°)
Desired —	435 mrad (25°)

SEPARATION			
S			
Single Finger Operation †		Single Finger Sequential Operation	Simultaneous Operation by Different Fingers
Minimum 19 mm (3/4 in.)	25 mm (1 in.)	13 mm (1/2 in.)	16 mm (5/8 in.)
Optimum 50 mm (2 in.)	50 mm (2 in.)	25 mm (1 in.)	19 mm (3/4 in.)

* Use by bare finger   ** Use with heavy handwear   † Using a lever lock toggle switch

Figure 11.2. Toggle switches (adapted from MIL-STD-1472D, p. 96).

Military regulations state that these controls will be coded by "and/either/or" shape, location, labeling, color. For visibility the design shall permit viewing of in-line digital read-out from all operator positions. The dimensions, resistance, and separation (distance between adjacent edges) shall all conform to the criteria in Table 11.2.

Table 11.2. Minimum separator distances for controls.

	TOGGLE SWITCHES	PUSH-BUTTONS	CONTINUOUS ROTARY CONTROLS	ROTARY SELECTOR \SWITCHES	DISCRETE THUMBWHEEL CONTROLS
TOGGLE SWITCHES	SEE FIG 11.2	13 mm (0.5 in.)	19 mm (0.75 in.)	19 mm (0.75 in.)	13 mm (0.5 in.)
PUSH-BUTTONS	13 mm (0.5 in.)	SEE FIG 11.3	13 mm (0.5 in.)	13 mm (0.5 in.)	13 mm (0.5 in.)
CONTINUOUS ROTARY CONTROLS	19 mm (0.75 in.)	13 mm (0.5 in.)	SEE FIG 11.4	25 mm (1.0 in.)	19 mm (0.75 in.)
ROTARY SELECTOR SWITCHES	19 mm (0.75 in.)	13 mm (0.5 in.)	25 mm (1.0 in.)	SEE FIG 11.5	19 mm (0.75 in.)
DISCRETE THUMBWHEEL CONTROLS	13 mm (0.5 in.)	13 mm (0.5 in.)	19 mm (0.75 in.)	19 mm (0.75 in.)	SEE FIG 11.6

Source: MIL-STD-1472

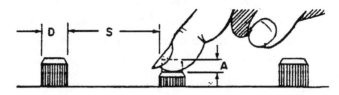

DIMENSIONS		RESISTANCE		
DIAMETER D				
Fingertip	Thumb or Palm	Single Finger	Different Fingers	Thumb or Palm
Minimum	9.5 mm (3/8 in.)	19 mm (3/4 in.)	2.8 N (10 oz.)	1.4 N (5 oz.)	2.8 N (10 oz.)
Maximum	25 mm (1 in.)		11 N (40 oz.)	5.6 N (20 oz.)	23 N (80 oz.)

DISPLACEMENT	
A	
Fingertip	Thumb or Palm
Minimum	2 mm (5/64 in.)	3 mm (1/8 in.)
Maximum	6 mm (1/4 in.)	38 mm (1-1/2 in.)

SEPARATION			
S			
Single Finger	Single Finger Sequential	Different Fingers	Thumb or Palm
Minimum	13 mm (1/2 in.)	6 mm (1/4 in.)	6 mm (1/4 in.)	25 mm (1 in.)
Preferred	50 mm (2 in.)	13 mm (1/2 in.)	13 mm (1/2 in.)	150 mm (6 in.)

Note: Above data for barehand application. For gloved hand operation, minima should be suitably adjusted.

Figure 11.3. Push-buttons (finger or hand operated—adapted from MIL-STD-1472D, p. 91).

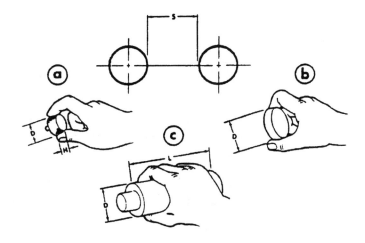

DIMENSIONS				
(a) Fingertip Grasp		(b) Thumb and Finger Encircled	(c) Palm Grasp	
H Height	D Diameter	D Diameter	D Diameter	L Length
Minimum 13 mm (1/2 in.)	10 mm (3/8 in.)	25 mm (1 in.)	38 mm (1-1/2 in.)	75 mm (3 in.)
Maximum 25 mm (1 in.)	100 mm (4 in.)	75 mm (3 in.)	75 mm (3 in.)	—

TORQUE		SEPARATION	
*	**	S One Hand Individually	S Two Hands Simultaneously
Minimum —	—	25 mm (1 in.)	50 mm (2 in.)
Optimum —	—	50 mm (2 in.)	125 mm (5 in.)
Maximum 32 mN-m (4-1/2 in.-oz.)	42 mN-m (6 in.-oz.)	—	—

* To and including 25 mm (1.0 in.) diameter knobs
** Greater than 25 mm (1.0 in.) diameter knobs

Figure 11.4. Knobs (adapted from MIL-STD-1472D, p. 82).

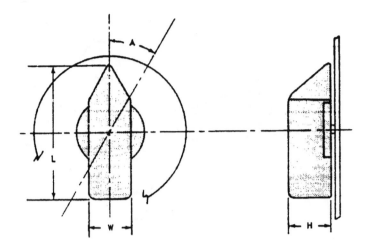

DIMENSIONS			RESISTANCE
L Length	W Width	H Depth	
Minimum	25 mm (1 in.)		16 mm (5.8 in.)	115 mN (1 in.-lb.)
Maximum	100 mm (4 in.)	25 mm (1 in.)	75 mm (3 in.)	680 mN (6 in.-lb.)

DISPLACEMENT		SEPARATION	
A		One-Hand Random	Two-Hand Operation
*	**		
Minimum	262 mrad (15°)	262 mrad (15°)	25 mm (1 in.)	25 mm (1 in.)
Maximum	262 mrad (15°)	262 mrad (15°)	—	—
Preferred	—	—	25 mm (1 in.)	25 mm (1 in.)

* For facilitating performance.
** When special engineering requirements demand large separation or when tactually ("blind") positioned controls are required.

Figure 11.5. Rotary selector switch (adapted from MIL-STD-1472D, p. 76).

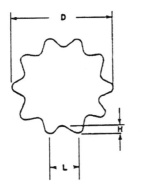
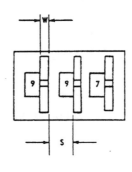

	D DIAMETER	L TROUGH DISTANCE	W WIDTH	H DEPTH	S SEPARATION	RESISTANCE
MINIMUM	30 mm (1-1/8 in.)	11 mm (7/16 in.)	3 mm (1/8 in.)	3 mm (1/8 in.)	10 mm (13/32 in.)	1.7 N (6 oz.)
MAXIMUM	75 mm (3 in.)	19 mm (3/4 in.)		13 mm (1/2 in.)		5.6 N (20 oz.)

Figure 11.6. Discrete thumbwheel control (adapted from MIL-STD-1472D, p. 80).

5.4.1.4.5 Color-coding. Strict rules are applied by military regulations here, where numbers relate to the different contrasts of the colors. (i.e., controls shall be black; 17038, 27038, or 37038; or gray; 26231 or 36231). If color coding is required, only the following colors identified in FED-STD-595 shall be selected for control coding:

a. Red, 11105, 21105, 31105
b. Green, 14187
c. Orange-Yellow, 13538, 23538, 33538
d. White, 17875, 27875, 37875
e. Blue, 15123 shall be used if an additional color is absolutely necessary

5.5 Labeling. Labels, legends, placards, signs or markings, or a combination of these shall be provided whenever it is necessary for personnel to identify, interpret, follow procedures or avoid hazards, except where it is obvious to the observer what an item is and what he or she is to do with it.

5.5.1.2 **Label characteristics.** Label characteristics shall be consistent with such factors as:

a. Accuracy of identification required
b. Time available for recognition or other responses
c. Distance at which the labels must be read
d. Illuminant level and color
e. Criticality of the function label
f. Consistency of label design within and between systems

The orientation, standardization, content, visibility and color are also covered in this section.

11.1.3. Audio capabilities

At some point during the design stage of most equipment the design engineer must decide whether to provide audio communications between the operator and the equipment. Audio signals should be provided when:

1. The information to be processed is short, simple, and transitory, requiring immediate or time-based response
2. The common mode of visual display is restricted by: over-burdening; ambient light variability or limitation; operator mobility; degradation of vision by vibration, high g-forces, hypoxia, or other environmental considerations; or anticipated operator inattention
3. The criticality of transmission response makes supplementary or redundant transmission desirable
4. It is desirable to warn, alert, or cue the operator to subsequent additional response
5. Custom or usage has created anticipation of an audio display
6. Voice communication is necessary or desirable

Audio warning signals should be provided, as necessary, to warn personnel of impending danger, to alert an operator to a critical change in system or equipment status, and to remind the operator of a critical action, or actions, that must be taken. An audio warning system or signal should be provided for the purpose of detecting a condition that the operator's normal observation may have overlooked. If audio is used in conjunction with visual displays, audio warning devices should be supplementary or supportive. The audio signal should be used to alert and direct operator attention to the appropriate visual display. When an audio presentation is required, the optimum type of signal should be presented in accordance with Table 11.2. If visual displays are accepted, then the human sight capacities should be considered.

Table 11.2. Functional evaluation of audio signals.

FUNCTION	TONES	TYPE OF SIGNAL COMPLEX SOUNDS	SPEECH
QUANTITATIVE INDICATION	POOR Maximum of 5 or 6 tones absolutely recognizable.	POOR Interpolation between signals inaccurate.	GOOD Minimum time and error in obtaining exact value in terms comparable with response.
QUALITATIVE INDICATION	POOR TO FAIR Difficult to judge approximate value and direction of deviation from null setting unless presented in close temporal sequence.	POOR Difficult to judge approximate deviation from desired value.	GOOD Information concerning displacement, direction, and rate presented in form compatible with required response.
STATUS INDICATION	GOOD Start and stop timing. Continuous information where rate of change of input is low.	GOOD Especially suitable for irregularly occurring signals (e.g., alarm signals).	POOR Inefficient; more easily masked; problem of repeatability.
TRACKING	FAIR Null position easily monitored; problem of signal-response compatibility.	POOR Required qualitative indications difficult to provide.	GOOD Meaning intrinsic in signal.
GENERAL	Good for automatic communication of limited information. Meaning must be learned. Easily generated.	Some sounds available with common meaning (e.g., fire bell). Easily generated.	Most effective for rapid (but not automatic) communication of complex, multidimensional information. Meaning intrinsic in signal and context when standardized. Minimum of new learning required.

Source: MIL-STD-1472

11.1.4. **Human thermal tolerance capabilities**

Some useful guidelines for human thermal tolerance capacity are found in MIL-STD-1472, starting at Section 5.8:

Heating—Heating shall be provided within mobile personnel enclosures utilized for detail work or occupied during extended periods of time to maintain interior dry bulb temperature above 10°C (50°F). Within permanent and semi-permanent facilities, provisions shall be made to maintain an effective temperature[*] (ET) or corrected effective temperature[†] (CET) not less than 18°C (65°F) (see Figure 11.7), unless dictated otherwise by workload or extremely heavy clothing. Heating systems shall be designed such that hot air discharge is not directed on personnel.

Ventilating—Ventilating shall be assured by introducing fresh air into any personnel enclosure. If the enclosure volume is 4.25 m^3 (150 ft^3) or less per person, a minimum of 0.85 m^3 (30 ft^3) of ventilation air per minute shall be introduced into the enclosure; approximately two-thirds should be outdoor air. For larger enclosures, the air supply per person may be in accordance with the curves in Figure 11.8. Air shall be moved past personnel at a velocity not more than 60 m (200 ft) per minute. Where manuals or loose papers are used, airspeed past these items shall be not more that 30 m (100 ft) per minute − 20 m (65 ft) per minute if possible − to preclude pages in manuals from being turned by the air or papers from being blown off work surfaces. Ventilation or other protective measures shall be provided to keep gases, vapors dust, and fumes within permissible exposure limits . Intakes for ventilation systems shall be located to minimize the introduction of contaminated air from such sources as exhaust pipes.

Air Conditioning—The effective temperature or corrected effective temperature within personnel enclosures utilized for detailed work during

---

[*] An arbitrary index which combines into a single value the effect of temperature, humidity, and air movement on the sensation of warmth or cold felt by the human body. the numerical value is that of the temperature of still, saturated air which would induce an identical sensation.

[†] Refer to Welt Bulb Globe Temperature (WBGT).

extended periods shall be maintained at or below 29.5°C (85°F) (see Figure 11.7). Air conditioning systems shall be designed such that cold-air discharge is not directed on personnel.

Humidity—Approximately 45% relative humidity should be provided at 21°C (70°F). This value should decrease with rising temperatures, but should remain above 15% to prevent irritation and drying of body tissues, e.g., eyes, skin, and respiratory tract (see Figure 11.9).

Thermal Tolerance and Comfort Zones—Temperature and humidity exposure should not exceed the effective temperature limits given in Figure 11.9 when corrected for air velocity (Figure 11.8).

Limited Thermal Tolerance Zones—Where hard physical work is to be required for more than two hours, an environment not exceeding a Wet Dry (WD) or Wet Bulb Globe Temperature* (WBGT) index of 25°C (77°F) shall be provided. Where the wearing of protective clothing systems (which reduce evaporation of sweat from the skin) is required, this index shall be decreased 5°C (10°F) for complete protective uniforms, 40°C (70°F) for intermediate clothing.

11.1.5. Human vibration capabilities

Poor performance of mental and physical tasks may be contributed to vibration. For example, when the whole body is exposed to low-frequency, large-amplitude vibrations over a period of time—such things as headaches, motion sickness, eye strain and fatigue can result—all of which affects performance. The human vibration capabilities must be considered to reduce these vibrations. Guidelines found in MIL-STD-1472 are:

---

* A meteorological measurement which can be used as an index to designate conditions of temperature and humidity at which on-set of heat stress can be expected at a particular energy expenditure level. It is calculated as follows:

$$WBGT = 0.7T_{WRnp} + 0.2T_g + 0.1T_A,,$$

where: T_{WRnp} = non-psychrometric (*np*) wet-bulb (*WB*) temperature,

T_g = temperature at interior center of a 15.2 cm (6 in) black globe, and

T_A = non-psychrometric, but shaded, dry bulb (air) temperature.

In the absence of a radiant heat source (e.g., solar, engine, furnace), a modified Wet-Dry (WD_{85} index should be used where

$$WD_{85} = 0.85T_{WRnp} + 0.15T_A$$

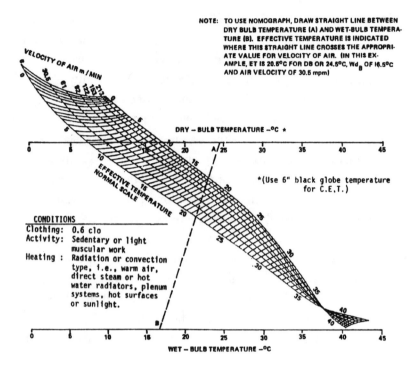

NOTE: TO USE NOMOGRAPH, DRAW STRAIGHT LINE BETWEEN DRY BULB TEMPERATURE (A) AND WET-BULB TEMPERA-TURE (B). EFFECTIVE TEMPERATURE IS INDICATED WHERE THIS STRAIGHT LINE CROSSES THE APPROPRI-ATE VALUE FOR VELOCITY OF AIR. (IN THIS EX-AMPLE, ET IS 20.6°C FOR DB OR 24.5°C, Wd$_B$ OF 16.5°C AND AIR VELOCITY OF 30.5 mpm)

*(Use 6" black globe temperature for C.E.T.)

CONDITIONS
Clothing: 0.6 clo
Activity: Sedentary or light muscular work
Heating : Radiation or convection type, i.e., warm air, direct steam or hot water radiators, plenum systems, hot surfaces or sunlight.

Figure 11.7. Effective temperature (ET) or corrected effective temperature (CET) (MIL-STD-1472D, p. 168).

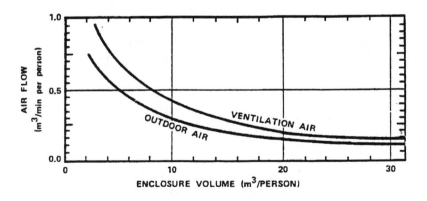

Figure 11.8. Ventilation requirements (MIL-STD-1472D, p. 169).

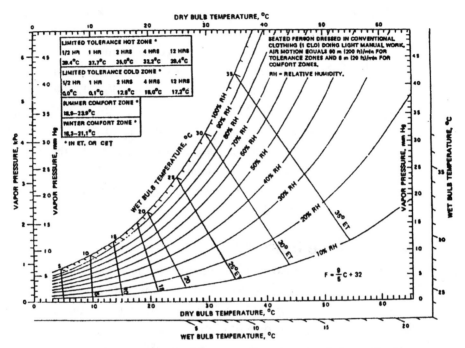

Figure 11.9. Summer and winter comfort zones and thermal tolerance for inhabited compartments (MIL-STD-1472D, p. 170).

Safety Level—In order to protect human health, whole body vibration should not exceed twice the acceleration values shown on Figure 11.10 for the time and frequencies indicated.

Proficiency Level—Where proficiency is required for operational and maintenance tasks, whole body vibration should not exceed the acceleration values shown on Figure 11.10 for the time and frequencies indicated.

Comfort Level—Where comfort is to be maintained, the acceleration values shown on Figure 11.10 should be divided by 3.15.

Motion Sickness—In order to prevent motion sickness, very low frequency vibration should not exceed the limits of Figure 11.11.

Building Vibration—Buildings intended for occupation by humans should be designed to control the transmission of whole body vibration levels that are acceptable to the occupants as specified by ISO 2631.

Equipment Vibration—Where whole body vibrations of the human operator, or parts of the body, are not a factor, equipment oscillations should not impair human performance with respect to control manipulations or the readability of numerals or letters. Equipment vibrations in the shaded area of the upper curve of Figure 11.10 should be avoided.

11.2 Man-machine function allocation

It is often determined that human error is the "root cause" of a failure. Further investigation would determine that this is generally accepted by management as a way to merely place "blame" for an unwanted event. This often leads to an assumption that the individual either has a careless attitude or is incompetent for the desired performance. When management communicates such negative connotations, the victims of such accusations usually become alienated from the improvement process. These assumptions often result in less productivity, a lower overall reliability and sometimes lead to a catastrophe.

The amount of human error is proportional to the human ability to interact with the demands of machine and environment. Thus the combined reliability of both human and machine is increased as the ability to interact is increased. The allocation, or apportionment, of functions between humans and machine is dependent upon the desired output with consideration given to: (1) the environment, (2) the thought process, (3) human-machine communication, (4) specific performance, and (5) desired reliability.

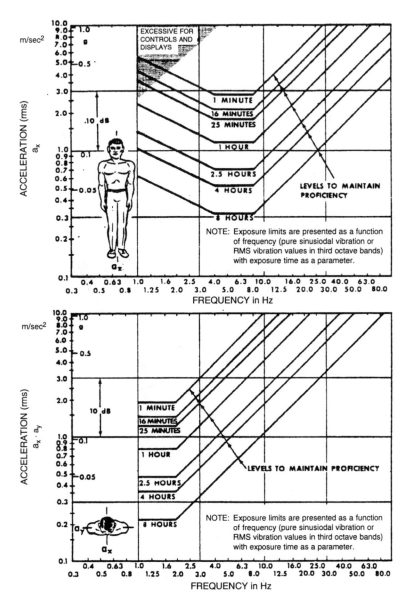

Figure 11.10. Vibration exposure criteria for longitudinal (upper curve) and transverse (lower curve) directions with respect to body axis (MIL-STD-1472D, p. 179).

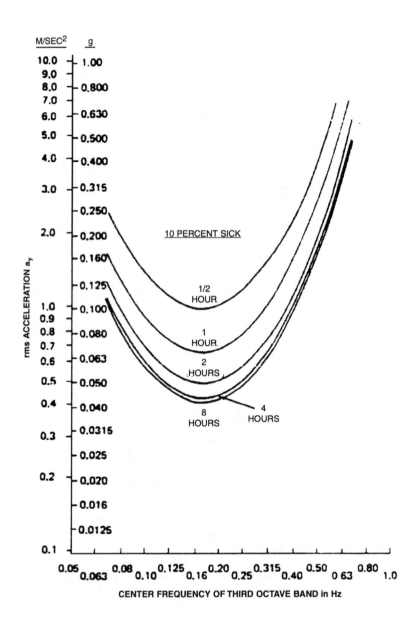

Figure 11.11. The 90% motion sickness protection limits for human exposure to very low frequency vibration (MIL-STD-1472D, p. 181).

A qualitative allocation may be conducted based on Table 11.3. While this table clearly indicates human superiority, it illustrates that the greatest human inefficiencies are the rate of data processing and memory retention (Ireson, 1988).

Table 11.3. Human-machine capabilities.

Human superiority	Machine superiority
Originality (ability to think)	Repetitiveness
Very little reprogramming need for new problems	Quick response to known problems
Recognizing new problems	Recalling data
Detecting new signals	Detecting signals beyond human sensitivity
Performing un-programmed tasks	Functions well under high stress conditions
Interpret data generated from events	Generate large amounts of data
Reasoning inductively (to diagnose general problems	Reasoning deductively (to identify specific problems
Evaluating alternate risks	
Utilizing equipment to and beyond known limits	
Ability to step outside boundaries	

Source: NASA SP-6506, An Introduction to the Assurance of Human Performance in Space Systems, NASA, 1968.

11.2.1 A case study—crash of a Beech King Air

The following is a failure investigation report that was extracted from a paper published by ASME, presented by Smith (1985). It was included to illustrate a very common mistake in data mis-interpretation caused by improper communications between man and machine. The results show the fatal consequences of such interaction.

"On January 25, 1975, a Beech A90 King Air approached Washington National Airport for a landing. During the instrument approach, the King Air struck a radio antenna, the top of which was shrouded by clouds. The National Transportation Safety Board investigation determined that an unauthorized descent to unsafe altitudes was made for undetermined reasons and inferred incompetence in the crew.

"A second investigation by Galipault (1979), independent of government agencies, arose from a lawsuit filed on behalf of the pilots who not only had lost their lives, but had also been branded as unprofessional.

"Minutes before the crash, air traffic control on two occasions issued incorrect atmospheric pressure information. An electromechanical recorder used to transmit data to the approach control room reproduced handwriting of poor quality. The correct value of 29.41 in Hg (99.50 kPa) was transmitted, but the output was interpreted as 30.41 in Hg (102.89 kPa). When transmitted to the pilots, a barometric setting of 30.41 would have led them to believe they were about 930 ft (283 m) higher than was actually the case.

"The approach of the King Air was later duplicated with a similarly equipped plane and experienced pilot. In six flights the pilot was asked to comply with simulated air traffic control instructions. In each case the pilot accepted the incorrect barometric pressure reading and descended to an altitude about 950 ft (290 m) lower than desired. The large change in barometric pressure produced very little apparent motion of the altimeter needles because of the high rate of descent. The descent profiles were nearly identical to that of the fatal flight.

"Transcripts of the exchanges between the pilots and air traffic control reveal that the King Air's low altitude was recognized, yet no altitude advisory or warning was given. The Federal Aviation Administration (FAA) had issued specific procedures and phraseology for the issuance of approach clearances; however, Washington

National was the only facility in the U.S. which had not yet complied with the FAA directive.

"The second investigation by Galipault suggested a bias in the original investigation by federal agencies. The finding of pilot error, subsequently shown to be incorrect, diverted attention from the inaction of air traffic control. Furthermore, because certain speakers could not be identified, the transcript of air traffic control communications was ruled inadmissible as evidence. The transcript clearly shows both knowledge and inaction regarding the altitude of the King Air."

This problem, assumed to be human unreliability, was found to be in the system not in the pilots themselves. The application of the human engineering design criteria found in MIL-STD-1472 (5. DETAILED REQUIREMENTS, paragraph 5.1.1.4) might have prevented this fatal accident. It states that feedback on control response adequacy shall be provided as rapidly as possible. Critical control functions, such as those entered by keyboard, shall provide adequate feedback to the operator to ensure that the data entry is, in fact, errorless and the one that the operator desires to enter. In this case the barometric pressure set by the pilots should have been checked again by ground control and an error message sent immediately to the pilots. Attention to the *general requirements* of MIL-STD-1472, outlined later in 11.3.2, could have aided in the prevention of this catastrophe.

11.3 Human factors in production

Manufacturing deals with the production phase of design. Problems encountered here affects the reliability of the finished product. Workstations should be designed to accommodate the individuals involved in the assembly of the product. The problems become obvious when a person is expected to install a part on a machine above the average head level while standing at floor level, or while installing parts below floor level while standing at floor level. Tasks similar to these may be accomplished by humans, under certain conditions, although these tasks might be nearly impossible to perform.

Some human factors for human interaction in the workstation design are needed for the tasks to be performed proficiently. The following section relates to failures due to poor workstation design.

11.3.1 A case study—steam turbine failure

Following is a portion of a failure investigation report, extracted from a paper published by ASME, (Smith, 1985). It was included to demonstrate the mental limitations of humans when required to interact with machines under "high stress" conditions.

"On New Year's Eve, December 31, 1983, a large single train petrochemical plant in the Gulf Coast area experienced severe operational problems. Several days of unusual subfreezing temperatures were wreaking havoc on the plant, which was not designed for the extreme temperatures. At about 8:00 p.m. operators, operating supervision and management were trying to keep the plant on-stream and were attending to numerous process difficulties when a 22,000 hp (16,400 kW) steam turbine experienced a catastrophic thrust bearing failure. The failure precipitated a two-week plant shutdown. This example considers how the failure was allowed to advance to a catastrophic level. Early detection would have limited the damage and the plant outage to about 12 hours.

"The plant operators enjoyed a reputation for operational excellence; plant availability was over 97% in 1983. The plant turbomachinery was monitored by a computer managed microprocessor based monitoring system. Sensors specifically for monitoring the turbine thrust bearing were two eddy current proximeters for rotor axial position and two thermocouples for thrust bearing temperature.

"Table 11.4 is the computer alarm listing from the early stages of this failure. Procedures would require operators to trip the turbomachinery train at 20:07:00 or 136 seconds after the failure began. However, the equipment operated several additional minutes resulting in massive damage.

"The computer printout, monitor alert and danger lights, monitor level displays, the audible enunciator and an alarm display light on an adjacent process control board all signaled a problem situation and in some cases the severity of the problem. These signals were either not observed or not investigated by the operators. The operators were faced with a myriad of alarms due to the plant upset. As in the Three Mile Island incident, the operators were flooded with more data than they could absorb and respond to.

"The computer print out [Table 11.4] illustrates that human intervention was needed for interpretation. The conversion of data to decision information is quite difficult during a crisis situation. Alarm light emitting diodes located on the individual monitors are small and monitor liquid crystal displays are difficult to read. It was this inability to quickly distinguish between important and unimportant data, along with information overload, that led to the massive secondary damage to the turbine.

"The principal corrective measure for the previously described event was to automate the shutdown of all turbo-machinery when appropriate sensors indicated thrust bearing failure in progress. A sensor voting scheme was incorporated to preclude false trips."

Inappropriate workstation design and the human inability to react appropriately to large amounts of data in a crisis situation may have been closer to the "root cause" of this catastrophic failure. An assumption based on human error would have failed to identify and correct the true cause of this failure. Also, any inappropriate assumptions about human error by management could have led to human performance problems.

The incident just described is a classic example of what is commonly referred to as **high-stress error**. When humans are faced with large amounts of data to process quickly, it sometimes forces the wrong choice or wrong decision. According to a study done by Swain and Guttman (1980), on the potential for error when humans are subjected to high-stress conditions: with 1 minute to react under high stress, there is a 99.9% chance of making the wrong decision; with 5 minutes to react, a 90% chance; with 30 minutes,

10%; and with 2 hours, still a 1% chance of doing the wrong thing. Even 1% is usually unacceptable – especially when human life is at risk.

High-stress error (Latino, 1987) can be avoided or minimized by:

1. Hazard risk analysis to identify potential hazard characteristics
2. Automation in design using computer logic for short time decision making
3. Designing non-confusing displays to ease interaction of humans under stress
4. Drills or rehearsals on how to react when high-stress conditions occur

Table 11 4. Computer printout showing failure progression.

ALARMS	
3 - 13 - 2 GB501T1A1 T + ALRT/20:04:44 31 Dec	Failure onset Temperature alert
ALARMS	
3 - 13 - 2 GB501T1A1 T +DNGR/20:05:46 31 Dec	Temperature danger #2 Thermocouple
ALARMS	
3 - 3 - 2 GB501T1A1 3 - 3 - 2 GB501T1A2 NOT OK/20:06:17 31 Dec TP + ALERT/20:06:17 31 Dec	Axial thrust position alert position 1 and 2
ALARMS	
3 - 5 - 2 GB501T1A1 RV ALRT/20:06:17 31 Dec 3 - 1 - 2 GB501T1Y RV ALRT/20:06:17 31 Dec	Radial vibration alert inboard and outboard turbine
ALARMS	
3 - 3 - 1 GB501T1A1 TP + DNGR/20:06:19 31 Dec 3 - 3 - 2 GB501T1A2	Axial thrust position danger position 1 and 2
ALARMS	
3 - 5 - 2 GB501T1Y RV DNGR/20:06:33 31 Dec	Radial vibration danger
ALARMS	
3 - 1- 2 GB501T1Y RV DNGR/20:06:42 31 Dec	Radial vibration danger
ALARMS	
3 - 13 - 1 GB501T1TT1 T + ALRT/20:07:00 31 Dec T + DNGR/20:07:00 31 Dec	Thrust bearing temperature alert and danger #1 Thermocouple shutdown

Source Smith, Jan B., "Human Reliability Considerations in the Analysis of Mechanical Failures," Presented at the Energy Sources and Technology Conference and Exhibition, February, 1985.

11.3.2 MIL-STD-1472—(4) General requirements

The general requirements of MIL-STD-1472 could have been used in the design phase of the steam turbine support equipment, referred to in 11.3.1., and might have prevented such a catastrophic failure. These requirements are outlined as follows:

The objectives (4.1)—state that "... equipment and facilities shall provide work environments which foster effective procedures, work patterns, and personnel safety and health, and which minimize factors which degrade human performance or increase error. Design shall be such that operator workload, accuracy, time constraint, mental processing and communication requirements do not exceed operator capabilities. Design shall also minimize personnel and training requirements within the limits of time, cost, and performance trade-offs."

Function allocation (4.3)—states that design shall reflect allocation of functions to personnel, equipment and personnel-equipment combinations to achieve the required sensitivity, and precision with the required reliability of system performance. Also the level of skills of personnel required to operate and maintain the system is considered.

Human engineering design (4.4)—reflects human engineering factors that affect human performance such as:

  a. Adequate physical, visual, auditory, and other communication links between personnel, and between personnel and their equipment, under both normal and emergency conditions

  b. Efficient arrangement of operation and maintenance workplaces, equipment, controls, and displays

  c. Provisions for minimizing psycho-physiological stress effects of mission duration and fatigue

  d. Compatibility of the design, location and layout of controls, displays, workspaces, ... Task allocation and control movements shall be compatible with restrictions imposed on human performance

Fail safe design—As defined in the referenced standard, is one in which a failure will not adversely affect the safe operation of the system, equipment, or facility. Paragraph 4.5 (MIL-STD-1472) states that, "... shall be provided in those areas where failure can cause catastrophe through damage to equipment, injury to personnel or inadvertent operation of critical equipment."

Control/display integration (5.1)—requirements are covered in part as follows:

5.1.1.1—The relationships of a control to its associated display and the display to the control shall be immediately apparent and unambiguous to the operator. Controls should be located adjacent to their associated displays and positioned so that neither the control nor the hand normally used for setting the control will obscure the display.

5.1.1.3—The complexity and precision required of control manipulation and display monitoring shall be consistent with the precision required of the system. Control/Display complexity and precision shall not exceed the capability of the operator (in terms of discrimination of display detail) or exceed the operator's manipulative capability under the dynamic conditions and environment (in terms of manual dexterity, coordination or reaction time) in which human performance is expected to occur.

5.1.1.6—If more than one crew member must have simultaneous access to a particular group of controls or displays in order to insure proper functioning of a system or subsystem, the operator assigned to control and monitor a particular function or group of related functions shall have physical and visual access to all controls, displays and communication capability necessary to adequately perform assigned tasks.

11.4 Human factors in field testing

A product's useful life is sometimes determined by field testing and this where all problems, both human and machine, unite to determine the reliability of a product. The following are some interactions to consider during field testing (Ireson, 1988):

1. **Environmental conditions**

    The ability to perform under actual conditions: weather, temperature, vibration, pressures (positive or negative), and the duration, time or speed requirements. Are these requirements appropriate and being addressed with a plan that meets the demands for this interaction?

2. **Application of human thought**

    The ability to make decisions during operational procedures, and the ability to evaluate the consequences of those decisions. The number of decisions may be too great, or difficult, or the sequence of an operation may be too difficult to remember. Artificial intelligence is often built into the system to relieve the probability of human error in both the decision making and sequencing processes. The most simple form of applied artificial intelligence is often referred to as "idiot-proofing" where connectors are designed to prevent swapping during a maintenance operation. Are these requirements appropriate and being addressed with a plan that meets the demands for this interaction?

3. **Communications**

    The ability for the human to communicate with other humans and/or the machine. Are these requirements appropriate and being addressed with a plan that meets the demands for this interaction?

4. **Performance levels**

    The ability for the human to function with the machine in a predetermined manner. Are these requirements appropriate and being addressed with a plan that meets the demands for this interaction?

5. **Human reliability**

    How much does the machine depend on human intervention or interaction. Are these requirements appropriate and being addressed with a plan that meets the demands for this interaction?

11.5 Summary

The objective of this chapter was to address human factors in engineering design as depicted in MIL-STD-1472, and to briefly describe its objectives, purpose, and general requirements. The intent of this chapter was to follow the outlines of the body of knowledge published by ASQC in their CRE certification guide. "Human Factors in Reliability" were thus outlined.

"Human Factors in Design and Design Principles," discussed in the first section, included the human sensory capacities: (1) sight capabilities, (2) touch capabilities, (3) audio and visual capabilities, (4) thermal tolerance capabilities, and (5) vibration capabilities.

"Man-Machine Function Allocation" was in the second section where the human ability to interact with the demands of the machine and its environment are discussed and illustrated by example.

Section 11.3, "Human Factors in Production," discussed workstation design and how it affects human abilities. This seemed to be the appropriate place for the general requirements of MIL-STD-1472D. A case study was included here to help clarify the appropriateness of this section.

Finally, "Human Factors in Field Testing" were discussed where the ability of humans to perform under actual conditions were addressed.

11.6 Exercises

1. The usual consequences of management assuming human error as the "root cause" of a failure is
   a. a repeat of the same failure
   b. disciplinary action for the employee
   c. less productivity
   d. All of the above
   e. a and c

2. Human reliability engineering considerations are most often
   a. difficult to deal with
   b. misjudged by management
   c. neglected during design
   d. all of the above

3. Human engineering design criteria, established by MIL-STD-1472, is best defined as
   a. the qualifications and requirements for the design engineer.
   b. the nature and limits of human capabilities.
   c. criteria furnished to contractors in non-military terms.
   d. criteria established only for military personnel.

4. What is meant by the term "Fail safe design," as defined in MIL-STD-1472?
   a. Designed such that a failure that will not adversely affect the safe operation of the system.
   b. Designed such that failure probability is low if the system is operated safely.
   c. Designed such that the system cannot fail if operated safely.
   d. All of the above.

5. The purpose of MIL-STD-1472 is to present human engineering design criteria so as to
   a. achieve required performance by operator, and maintenance personnel.
   b. minimize skill and personnel requirements and training time.

   c. achieve required reliability of personnel-equipment combinations.

   d. foster design standardization within and among systems.

   e. all of the above.

6. Designing non-confusing displays to ease interaction of humans under stress is a method for reducing
   a. job dissatisfaction
   b. performance problems
   c. the root cause of many problems
   d. high-stress error

7. Rehearsals on how to react when high stress conditions occur are methods of reducing
   a. human mistakes
   b. accidents
   c. high stress error
   d. catastrophic failures
   e. all of the above

8. Human engineering design reflects human engineering factors that affect human performance such as:
   a. Communication links between personnel and their equipment.
   b. Compatibility of the design, location and layout of workspaces.
   c. Psycho physiological stress effects of mission duration.
   d. All of the above.

9. Allocation of functions to personnel and equipment in combinations to achieve the required reliability is defined in MIL-STD-1472 as
   a. human factors allocation
   b. design factors allocation
   c. the function allocation
   d. cross functional allocation

10. Which of the following demonstrates human superiority over machines?
    a. Quick response to known problems
    b. Recalling data
    c. Functioning well under high stress conditions
    d. Interpreting data generated from events

11. Heating shall be provided within mobile personnel enclosures utilized for detail work or occupied during extended periods of time to maintain interior dry bulb temperature above
    a. 50°F
    b. 55°F
    c. 60°F
    d. 65°F

12. Within permanent and semi-permanent facilities, provisions shall be made to maintain an effective temperature (ET) or corrected effective temperature (CET) not less than _____, unless dictated otherwise by workload or extremely heavy clothing.
    a. 50°F
    b. 55°F
    c. 60°F
    d. 65°F

11.7 References

Ireson, G. W., and C. F. Coombs. 1988. *Handbook of Reliability Engineering and Management.* New York: McGraw-Hill.

Latino, Charles J. 1987. Solving human-caused failure problems. *Chemical Engineering Progress* 83(5):42–45.

Martin Marietta Corporation, Baltimore Division. 1968. *NASA SP-6506: An Introduction to the Assurance of Human Performance in Space Systems.* Washington, DC: NASA Scientific and Technical Information Division.

Smith, Jan B. 1985. Human reliability considerations in the analysis of mechanical failures. Paper presented at the Eighth Annual Energy Sources and Technology Conference and Exhibition, February 17–21, 1985, Dallas, TX. Paper 85-Pet-14. New York, NY: ASME, Technical Division.

Swain, A.D., and H. E. Guttman. 1980. *Handbook of Human Reliability Analysis with Emphasis on Nuclear Power Plant Applications.* Albuquerque, NM: US Nuclear Regulatory Commission.

US Department of Defense. 1989. *MIL-STD-1472: Human Engineering Design Criteria for Military Systems, Equipment, and Facilities.* Philadelphia: Naval Publications and Forms Center.

US General Accounting Office. 1981. *FRCD-82-5: Guidelines for Assessing whether Human Factors were Considered in the Weapon Systems Acquisition Process.* Washington, DC: US General Accounting Office.

APPENDIX

A

Area Under the Standard Normal Curve

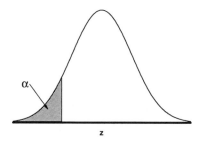

Table A.1. Area under the standard normal curve.

z	0.00	0.01	0.02	0.03	0.04	0.05	0.06	0.07	0.08	0.09
−3.4	0.0003	0.0003	0.0003	0.0003	0.0003	0.0003	0.0003	0.0003	0.0003	0.0002
−3.3	0.0005	0.0005	0.0005	0.0004	0.0004	0.0004	0.0004	0.0004	0.0004	0.0003
−3.2	0.0007	0.0007	0.0006	0.0006	0.0006	0.0006	0.0006	0.0005	0.0005	0.0005
−3.1	0.0010	0.0009	0.0009	0.0009	0.0008	0.0008	0.0008	0.0008	0.0007	0.0007
−3.0	0.0013	0.0013	0.0013	0.0012	0.0012	0.0011	0.0011	0.0011	0.0010	0.0010
−2.9	0.0019	0.0018	0.0018	0.0017	0.0016	0.0016	0.0015	0.0015	0.0014	0.0014
−2.8	0.0026	0.0025	0.0024	0.0023	0.0023	0.0022	0.0021	0.0021	0.0020	0.0019
−2.7	0.0035	0.0034	0.0033	0.0032	0.0031	0.0030	0.0029	0.0028	0.0027	0.0026
−2.6	0.0047	0.0045	0.0044	0.0043	0.0041	0.0040	0.0039	0.0038	0.0037	0.0036
−2.5	0.0062	0.0060	0.0059	0.0057	0.0055	0.0054	0.0052	0.0051	0.0049	0.0048

Continued on next page…

Table A.1—continued...

z	0.00	0.01	0.02	0.03	0.04	0.05	0.06	0.07	0.08	0.09
-2.4	0.0082	0.0080	0.0078	0.0075	0.0073	0.0071	0.0069	0.0068	0.0066	0.0064
-2.3	0.0107	0.0104	0.0102	0.0099	0.0096	0.0094	0.0091	0.0089	0.0087	0.0084
-2.2	0.0139	0.0136	0.0132	0.0129	0.0125	0.0122	0.0119	0.0116	0.0113	0.0110
-2.1	0.0179	0.0174	0.0170	0.0166	0.0162	0.0158	0.0154	0.0150	0.0146	0.0143
-2.0	0.0228	0.0222	0.0217	0.0212	0.0207	0.0202	0.0197	0.0192	0.0188	0.0183
-1.9	0.0287	0.0281	0.0274	0.0268	0.0262	0.0256	0.0250	0.0244	0.0239	0.0233
-1.8	0.0359	0.0351	0.0344	0.0336	0.0329	0.0322	0.0314	0.0307	0.0301	0.0294
-1.7	0.0446	0.0436	0.0427	0.0418	0.0409	0.0401	0.0392	0.0384	0.0375	0.0367
-1.6	0.0548	0.0537	0.0526	0.0516	0.0505	0.0495	0.0485	0.0475	0.0465	0.0455
-1.5	0.0668	0.0655	0.0643	0.0630	0.0618	0.0606	0.0594	0.0582	0.0571	0.0559
-1.4	0.0808	0.0793	0.0778	0.0764	0.0749	0.0735	0.0721	0.0708	0.0694	0.0681
-1.3	0.0968	0.0951	0.0934	0.0918	0.0901	0.0885	0.0869	0.0853	0.0838	0.0823
-1.2	0.1151	0.1131	0.1112	0.1093	0.1075	0.1056	0.1038	0.1020	0.1003	0.0985
-1.1	0.1357	0.1335	0.1314	0.1292	0.1271	0.1251	0.1230	0.1210	0.1190	0.1170
-1.0	0.1587	0.1562	0.1539	0.1515	0.1492	0.1469	0.1446	0.1423	0.1401	0.1379
-0.9	0.1841	0.1814	0.1788	0.1762	0.1736	0.1711	0.1685	0.1660	0.1635	0.1611
-0.8	0.2119	0.2090	0.2061	0.2033	0.2005	0.1977	0.1949	0.1922	0.1894	0.1867
-0.7	0.2420	0.2389	0.2358	0.2327	0.2296	0.2266	0.2236	0.2206	0.2177	0.2148
-0.6	0.2743	0.2709	0.2676	0.2643	0.2611	0.2578	0.2546	0.2514	0.2483	0.2451
-0.5	0.3085	0.3050	0.3015	0.2981	0.2946	0.2912	0.2877	0.2843	0.2810	0.2776
-0.4	0.3446	0.3409	0.3372	0.3336	0.3300	0.3264	0.3228	0.3192	0.3156	0.3121
-0.3	0.3821	0.3783	0.3745	0.3707	0.3669	0.3632	0.3594	0.3557	0.3520	0.3483
-0.2	0.4207	0.4168	0.4129	0.4090	0.4052	0.4013	0.3974	0.3936	0.3897	0.3859
-0.1	0.4602	0.4562	0.4522	0.4483	0.4443	0.4404	0.4364	0.4325	0.4286	0.4247
-0.0	0.5000	0.4960	0.4920	0.4880	0.4840	0.4801	0.4761	0.4721	0.4681	0.4641
0.0	0.5000	0.5040	0.5080	0.5120	0.5160	0.5199	0.5239	0.5279	0.5319	0.5359
0.1	0.5398	0.5438	0.5478	0.5517	0.5557	0.5596	0.5636	0.5675	0.5714	0.5753
0.2	0.5793	0.5832	0.5871	0.5910	0.5948	0.5987	0.6026	0.6064	0.6103	0.6141
0.3	0.6179	0.6217	0.6255	0.6293	0.6331	0.6368	0.6406	0.6443	0.6480	0.6517
0.4	0.6554	0.6591	0.6628	0.6664	0.6700	0.6736	0.6772	0.6808	0.6844	0.6879
0.5	0.6915	0.6950	0.6985	0.7019	0.7054	0.7088	0.7123	0.7157	0.7190	0.7224
0.6	0.7257	0.7291	0.7324	0.7357	0.7389	0.7422	0.7454	0.7486	0.7517	0.7549
0.7	0.7580	0.7611	0.7642	0.7673	0.7704	0.7734	0.7764	0.7794	0.7823	0.7852
0.8	0.7881	0.7910	0.7939	0.7967	0.7995	0.8023	0.8051	0.8078	0.8106	0.8133
0.9	0.8159	0.8186	0.8212	0.8238	0.8264	0.8289	0.8315	0.8340	0.8365	0.8389
1.0	0.8413	0.8438	0.8461	0.8485	0.8508	0.8531	0.8554	0.8577	0.8599	0.8621
1.1	0.8643	0.8665	0.8686	0.8708	0.8729	0.8749	0.8770	0.8790	0.8810	0.8830
1.2	0.8849	0.8869	0.8888	0.8907	0.8925	0.8944	0.8962	0.8980	0.8997	0.9015
1.3	0.9032	0.9049	0.9066	0.9082	0.9099	0.9115	0.9131	0.9147	0.9162	0.9177
1.4	0.9192	0.9207	0.9222	0.9236	0.9251	0.9265	0.9279	0.9292	0.9306	0.9319

Continued on next page...

Table A.1—*continued...*

z	0.00	0.01	0.02	0.03	0.04	0.05	0.06	0.07	0.08	0.09
1.5	0.9332	0.9345	0.9357	0.9370	0.9382	0.9394	0.9406	0.9418	0.9429	0.9441
1.6	0.9452	0.9463	0.9474	0.9484	0.9495	0.9505	0.9515	0.9525	0.9535	0.9545
1.7	0.9554	0.9564	0.9573	0.9582	0.9591	0.9599	0.9608	0.9616	0.9625	0.9633
1.8	0.9641	0.9649	0.9656	0.9664	0.9671	0.9678	0.9686	0.9693	0.9699	0.9706
1.9	0.9713	0.9719	0.9726	0.9732	0.9738	0.9744	0.9750	0.9756	0.9761	0.9767
2.0	0.9772	0.9778	0.9783	0.9788	0.9793	0.9798	0.9803	0.9808	0.9812	0.9817
2.1	0.9821	0.9826	0.9830	0.9834	0.9838	0.9842	0.9846	0.9850	0.9854	0.9857
2.2	0.9861	0.9864	0.9868	0.9871	0.9875	0.9878	0.9881	0.9884	0.9887	0.9890
2.3	0.9893	0.9896	0.9898	0.9901	0.9904	0.9906	0.9909	0.9911	0.9913	0.9916
2.4	0.9918	0.9920	0.9922	0.9925	0.9927	0.9929	0.9931	0.9932	0.9934	0.9936
2.5	0.9938	0.9940	0.9941	0.9943	0.9945	0.9946	0.9948	0.9949	0.9951	0.9952
2.6	0.9953	0.9955	0.9956	0.9957	0.9959	0.9960	0.9961	0.9962	0.9963	0.9964
2.7	0.9965	0.9966	0.9967	0.9968	0.9969	0.9970	0.9971	0.9972	0.9973	0.9974
2.8	0.9974	0.9975	0.9976	0.9977	0.9977	0.9978	0.9979	0.9979	0.9980	0.9981
2.9	0.9981	0.9982	0.9982	0.9983	0.9984	0.9984	0.9985	0.9985	0.9986	0.9986
3.0	0.9987	0.9987	0.9987	0.9988	0.9988	0.9989	0.9989	0.9989	0.9990	0.9990
3.1	0.9990	0.9991	0.9991	0.9991	0.9992	0.9992	0.9992	0.9992	0.9993	0.9993
3.2	0.9993	0.9993	0.9994	0.9994	0.9994	0.9994	0.9994	0.9995	0.9995	0.9995
3.3	0.9995	0.9995	0.9995	0.9996	0.9996	0.9996	0.9996	0.9996	0.9996	0.9997
3.4	0.9997	0.9997	0.9997	0.9997	0.9997	0.9997	0.9997	0.9997	0.9997	0.9998

The Gamma Function

Table B.1. The gamma function

x	$\Gamma(x)$	x	$\Gamma(x)$	x	$\Gamma(x)$	x	$\Gamma(x)$
1.00	1.00000	1.25	0.90640	1.50	0.88623	1.75	0.91906
1.01	0.99433	1.26	0.90440	1.51	0.88659	1.76	0.92137
1.02	0.98884	1.27	0.90250	1.52	0.88704	1.77	0.92376
1.03	0.98355	1.28	0.90072	1.53	0.88757	1.78	0.92623
1.04	0.97844	1.29	0.89904	1.54	0.88818	1.79	0.92877
1.05	0.97350	1.30	0.89747	1.55	0.88887	1.80	0.93138
1.06	0.96874	1.31	0.89600	1.56	0.88964	1.81	0.93408
1.07	0.96415	1.32	0.89464	1.57	0.89049	1.82	0.93685
1.08	0.95973	1.33	0.89338	1.58	0.89142	1.83	0.93969
1.09	0.95546	1.34	0.89222	1.59	0.89243	1.84	0.94261
1.10	0.95135	1.35	0.89115	1.60	0.89352	1.85	0.94561
1.11	0.94740	1.36	0.89018	1.61	0.89468	1.86	0.94869
1.12	0.94359	1.37	0.88931	1.62	0.89592	1.87	0.95184
1.13	0.93993	1.38	0.88854	1.63	0.89724	1.88	0.95507
1.14	0.93642	1.39	0.88785	1.64	0.89864	1.89	0.95838

Continued on next page…

Table B.1—*continued...*

x	$\Gamma(x)$	x	$\Gamma(x)$	x	$\Gamma(x)$	x	$\Gamma(x)$
1.15	0.93304	1.40	0.88726	1.65	0.90012	1.90	0.96177
1.16	0.92980	1.41	0.88676	1.66	0.90167	1.91	0.96523
1.17	0.92670	1.42	0.88636	1.67	0.90330	1.92	0.96877
1.18	0.92373	1.43	0.88604	1.68	0.90500	1.93	0.97240
1.19	0.92089	1.44	0.88581	1.69	0.90678	1.94	0.97610
1.20	0.91817	1.45	0.88566	1.70	0.90864	1.95	0.97988
1.21	0.91558	1.46	0.88560	1.71	0.91057	1.96	0.98374
1.22	0.91311	1.47	0.88563	1.72	0.91258	1.97	0.98768
1.23	0.91075	1.48	0.88575	1.73	0.91467	1.99	0.99581
1.24	0.90852	1.49	0.88595	1.74	0.91683	2.00	1.00000

$$\Gamma(x) = \int_0^\infty e^{-\tau} \tau^{(x-1)} d\tau$$

$$\Gamma(x+1) = x\Gamma(x)$$

Rank Tables

Table C.1. Median ranks.

Order	Sample Size									
	1	2	3	4	5	6	7	8	9	10
1	0.5000	0.2929	0.2063	0.1591	0.1294	0.1091	0.0943	0.0830	0.0741	0.0670
2		0.7071	0.5000	0.3857	0.3138	0.2644	0.2285	0.2011	0.1796	0.1623
3			0.7937	0.6143	0.5000	0.4214	0.3641	0.3205	0.2862	0.2586
4				0.8409	0.6862	0.5786	0.5000	0.4402	0.3931	0.3551
5					0.8706	0.7356	0.6359	0.5598	0.5000	0.4517
6						0.8909	0.7715	0.6795	0.6069	0.5483
7							0.9057	0.7989	0.7138	0.6449
8								0.9170	0.8204	0.7414
9									0.9259	0.8377
10										0.9330

Continued on next page...

Table C.1—*continued...*

Order	Sample Size									
	11	12	13	14	15	16	17	18	19	20
1	0.0611	0.0561	0.0519	0.0483	0.0452	0.0424	0.0400	0.0378	0.0358	0.0341
2	0.1480	0.1360	0.1258	0.1170	0.1094	0.1027	0.0968	0.0915	0.0868	0.0825
3	0.2358	0.2167	0.2004	0.1865	0.1743	0.1637	0.1542	0.1458	0.1383	0.1315
4	0.3238	0.2976	0.2753	0.2561	0.2394	0.2247	0.2118	0.2002	0.1899	0.1805
5	0.4119	0.3785	0.3502	0.3258	0.3045	0.2859	0.2694	0.2547	0.2415	0.2297
6	0.5000	0.4595	0.4251	0.3954	0.3697	0.3471	0.3270	0.3092	0.2932	0.2788
7	0.5881	0.5405	0.5000	0.4651	0.4348	0.4082	0.3847	0.3637	0.3449	0.3280
8	0.6762	0.6215	0.5749	0.5349	0.5000	0.4694	0.4423	0.4182	0.3966	0.3771
9	0.7642	0.7024	0.6498	0.6046	0.5652	0.5306	0.5000	0.4727	0.4483	0.4263
10	0.8520	0.7833	0.7247	0.6742	0.6303	0.5918	0.5577	0.5273	0.5000	0.4754
11	0.9389	0.8640	0.7996	0.7439	0.6955	0.6529	0.6153	0.5818	0.5517	0.5246
12		0.9439	0.8742	0.8135	0.7606	0.7141	0.6730	0.6363	0.6034	0.5737
13			0.9481	0.8830	0.8257	0.7753	0.7306	0.6908	0.6551	0.6229
14				0.9517	0.8906	0.8363	0.7882	0.7453	0.7068	0.6720
15					0.9548	0.8973	0.8458	0.7998	0.7585	0.7212
16						0.9576	0.9032	0.8542	0.8101	0.7703
17							0.9600	0.9085	0.8617	0.8195
18								0.9622	0.9132	0.8685
19									0.9642	0.9175
20										0.9659

Order	Sample Size									
	21	22	23	24	25	26	27	28	29	30
1	0.0325	0.0310	0.0297	0.0285	0.0273	0.0263	0.0253	0.0245	0.0236	0.0228
2	0.0786	0.0751	0.0719	0.0690	0.0662	0.0637	0.0614	0.0592	0.0572	0.0553
3	0.1253	0.1197	0.1146	0.1099	0.1055	0.1015	0.0978	0.0944	0.0911	0.0881
4	0.1721	0.1644	0.1573	0.1509	0.1449	0.1394	0.1343	0.1296	0.1252	0.1210
5	0.2189	0.2091	0.2001	0.1919	0.1843	0.1774	0.1709	0.1648	0.1592	0.1540
6	0.2657	0.2538	0.2430	0.2330	0.2238	0.2153	0.2074	0.2001	0.1933	0.1869
7	0.3126	0.2986	0.2858	0.2741	0.2632	0.2532	0.2440	0.2354	0.2274	0.2199
8	0.3594	0.3433	0.3286	0.3151	0.3027	0.2912	0.2806	0.2707	0.2614	0.2528
9	0.4063	0.3881	0.3715	0.3562	0.3422	0.3292	0.3171	0.3059	0.2955	0.2858
10	0.4531	0.4329	0.4143	0.3973	0.3816	0.3671	0.3537	0.3412	0.3296	0.3187
11	0.5000	0.4776	0.4572	0.4384	0.4211	0.4051	0.3903	0.3765	0.3637	0.3517
12	0.5469	0.5224	0.5000	0.4795	0.4605	0.4431	0.4268	0.4118	0.3977	0.3846
13	0.5937	0.5671	0.5428	0.5205	0.5000	0.4810	0.4634	0.4471	0.4318	0.4176
14	0.6406	0.6119	0.5857	0.5616	0.5395	0.5190	0.5000	0.4824	0.4659	0.4506
15	0.6874	0.6567	0.6285	0.6027	0.5789	0.5569	0.5366	0.5176	0.5000	0.4835

Continued on next page...

Table C.1—*continued...*

Order	Sample Size									
	21	22	23	24	25	26	27	28	29	30
16	0.7343	0.7014	0.6714	0.6438	0.6184	0.5949	0.5732	0.5529	0.5341	0.5165
17	0.7811	0.7462	0.7142	0.6849	0.6578	0.6329	0.6097	0.5882	0.5682	0.5494
18	0.8279	0.7909	0.7570	0.7259	0.6973	0.6708	0.6463	0.6235	0.6023	0.5824
19	0.8747	0.8356	0.7999	0.7670	0.7368	0.7088	0.6829	0.6588	0.6363	0.6154
20	0.9214	0.8803	0.8427	0.8081	0.7762	0.7468	0.7194	0.6941	0.6704	0.6483
21	0.9675	0.9249	0.8854	0.8491	0.8157	0.7847	0.7560	0.7293	0.7045	0.6813
22		0.9690	0.9281	0.8901	0.8551	0.8226	0.7926	0.7646	0.7386	0.7142
23			0.9703	0.9310	0.8945	0.8606	0.8291	0.7999	0.7726	0.7472
24				0.9715	0.9338	0.8985	0.8657	0.8352	0.8067	0.7801
25					0.9727	0.9363	0.9022	0.8704	0.8408	0.8131
26						0.9737	0.9386	0.9056	0.8748	0.8460
27							0.9747	0.9408	0.9089	0.8790
28								0.9755	0.9428	0.9119
29									0.9764	0.9447
30										0.9772

Order	Sample Size									
	31	32	33	34	35	36	37	38	39	40
1	0.0221	0.0214	0.0208	0.0202	0.0196	0.0191	0.0186	0.0181	0.0176	0.0172
2	0.0536	0.0519	0.0503	0.0489	0.0475	0.0462	0.0449	0.0438	0.0427	0.0416
3	0.0853	0.0827	0.0802	0.0779	0.0757	0.0736	0.0716	0.0697	0.0680	0.0663
4	0.1172	0.1136	0.1101	0.1069	0.1039	0.1011	0.0983	0.0958	0.0933	0.0910
5	0.1491	0.1444	0.1401	0.1360	0.1322	0.1285	0.1251	0.1218	0.1187	0.1158
6	0.1809	0.1753	0.1701	0.1651	0.1605	0.1560	0.1519	0.1479	0.1441	0.1406
7	0.2128	0.2063	0.2001	0.1942	0.1887	0.1836	0.1786	0.1740	0.1696	0.1654
8	0.2447	0.2372	0.2301	0.2234	0.2170	0.2111	0.2054	0.2001	0.1950	0.1901
9	0.2766	0.2681	0.2600	0.2525	0.2453	0.2386	0.2322	0.2261	0.2204	0.2149
10	0.3086	0.2990	0.2900	0.2816	0.2736	0.2661	0.2590	0.2522	0.2458	0.2397
11	0.3405	0.3299	0.3200	0.3107	0.3019	0.2936	0.2857	0.2783	0.2712	0.2645
12	0.3724	0.3609	0.3500	0.3398	0.3302	0.3211	0.3125	0.3044	0.2966	0.2893
13	0.4043	0.3918	0.3800	0.3690	0.3585	0.3486	0.3393	0.3305	0.3221	0.3141
14	0.4362	0.4227	0.4100	0.3981	0.3868	0.3762	0.3661	0.3565	0.3475	0.3389
15	0.4681	0.4536	0.4400	0.4272	0.4151	0.4037	0.3929	0.3826	0.3729	0.3637
16	0.5000	0.4845	0.4700	0.4563	0.4434	0.4312	0.4197	0.4087	0.3983	0.3884
17	0.5319	0.5155	0.5000	0.4854	0.4717	0.4587	0.4464	0.4348	0.4237	0.4132
18	0.5638	0.5464	0.5300	0.5146	0.5000	0.4862	0.4732	0.4609	0.4492	0.4380
19	0.5957	0.5773	0.5600	0.5437	0.5283	0.5138	0.5000	0.4870	0.4746	0.4628
20	0.6276	0.6082	0.5900	0.5728	0.5566	0.5413	0.5268	0.5130	0.5000	0.4876

Continued on next page...

Table C.1—*continued...*

Order	Sample Size 31	32	33	34	35	36	37	38	39	40
21	0.6595	0.6391	0.6200	0.6019	0.5849	0.5688	0.5536	0.5391	0.5254	0.5124
22	0.6914	0.6701	0.6500	0.6310	0.6132	0.5963	0.5803	0.5652	0.5508	0.5372
23	0.7234	0.7010	0.6800	0.6602	0.6415	0.6238	0.6071	0.5913	0.5763	0.5620
24	0.7553	0.7319	0.7100	0.6893	0.6698	0.6514	0.6339	0.6174	0.6017	0.5868
25	0.7872	0.7628	0.7400	0.7184	0.6981	0.6789	0.6607	0.6435	0.6271	0.6116
26	0.8191	0.7937	0.7699	0.7475	0.7264	0.7064	0.6875	0.6695	0.6525	0.6363
27	0.8509	0.8247	0.7999	0.7766	0.7547	0.7339	0.7143	0.6956	0.6779	0.6611
28	0.8828	0.8556	0.8299	0.8058	0.7830	0.7614	0.7410	0.7217	0.7034	0.6859
29	0.9147	0.8864	0.8599	0.8349	0.8113	0.7889	0.7678	0.7478	0.7288	0.7107
30	0.9464	0.9173	0.8899	0.8640	0.8395	0.8164	0.7946	0.7739	0.7542	0.7355
31	0.9779	0.9481	0.9198	0.8931	0.8678	0.8440	0.8214	0.7999	0.7796	0.7603
32		0.9786	0.9497	0.9221	0.8961	0.8715	0.8481	0.8260	0.8050	0.7851
33			0.9792	0.9511	0.9243	0.8989	0.8749	0.8521	0.8304	0.8099
34				0.9798	0.9525	0.9264	0.9017	0.8782	0.8559	0.8346
35					0.9804	0.9538	0.9284	0.9042	0.8813	0.8594
36						0.9809	0.9551	0.9303	0.9067	0.8842
37							0.9814	0.9562	0.9320	0.9090
38								0.9819	0.9573	0.9337
39									0.9824	0.9584
40										0.9828

Order	Sample Size 41	42	43	44	45	46	47	48	49	50
1	0.0168	0.0164	0.0160	0.0156	0.0153	0.0150	0.0146	0.0143	0.0140	0.0138
2	0.0406	0.0396	0.0387	0.0379	0.0370	0.0362	0.0355	0.0347	0.0340	0.0333
3	0.0647	0.0632	0.0617	0.0603	0.0590	0.0577	0.0565	0.0553	0.0542	0.0531
4	0.0888	0.0867	0.0847	0.0828	0.0810	0.0792	0.0776	0.0760	0.0744	0.0729
5	0.1130	0.1103	0.1078	0.1054	0.1030	0.1008	0.0987	0.0966	0.0947	0.0928
6	0.1372	0.1339	0.1308	0.1279	0.1251	0.1224	0.1198	0.1173	0.1149	0.1126
7	0.1614	0.1575	0.1539	0.1504	0.1471	0.1439	0.1409	0.1380	0.1352	0.1325
8	0.1855	0.1812	0.1770	0.1730	0.1692	0.1655	0.1620	0.1587	0.1555	0.1524
9	0.2097	0.2048	0.2000	0.1955	0.1912	0.1871	0.1831	0.1794	0.1757	0.1722
10	0.2339	0.2284	0.2231	0.2181	0.2133	0.2087	0.2043	0.2000	0.1960	0.1921
11	0.2581	0.2520	0.2462	0.2406	0.2353	0.2302	0.2254	0.2207	0.2162	0.2119
12	0.2823	0.2756	0.2693	0.2632	0.2574	0.2518	0.2465	0.2414	0.2365	0.2318
13	0.3065	0.2992	0.2923	0.2857	0.2794	0.2734	0.2676	0.2621	0.2568	0.2517
14	0.3307	0.3229	0.3154	0.3083	0.3015	0.2950	0.2888	0.2828	0.2770	0.2715
15	0.3549	0.3465	0.3385	0.3308	0.3235	0.3166	0.3099	0.3035	0.2973	0.2914

Continued on next page...

Table C.1—*continued...*

Order	|	41	42	43	44	45	46	47	48	49	50
						Sample Size					
16	|	0.3790	0.3701	0.3616	0.3534	0.3456	0.3381	0.3310	0.3242	0.3176	0.3113
17		0.4032	0.3937	0.3846	0.3760	0.3677	0.3597	0.3521	0.3448	0.3379	0.3311
18		0.4274	0.4173	0.4077	0.3985	0.3897	0.3813	0.3733	0.3655	0.3581	0.3510
19		0.4516	0.4410	0.4308	0.4211	0.4118	0.4029	0.3944	0.3862	0.3784	0.3709
20		0.4758	0.4646	0.4539	0.4436	0.4338	0.4245	0.4155	0.4069	0.3987	0.3907
21		0.5000	0.4882	0.4769	0.4662	0.4559	0.4460	0.4366	0.4276	0.4189	0.4106
22		0.5242	0.5118	0.5000	0.4887	0.4779	0.4676	0.4577	0.4483	0.4392	0.4305
23		0.5484	0.5354	0.5231	0.5113	0.5000	0.4892	0.4789	0.4690	0.4595	0.4503
24		0.5726	0.5590	0.5461	0.5338	0.5221	0.5108	0.5000	0.4897	0.4797	0.4702
25		0.5968	0.5827	0.5692	0.5564	0.5441	0.5324	0.5211	0.5103	0.5000	0.4901
26		0.6210	0.6063	0.5923	0.5789	0.5662	0.5540	0.5423	0.5310	0.5203	0.5099
27		0.6451	0.6299	0.6154	0.6015	0.5882	0.5755	0.5634	0.5517	0.5405	0.5298
28		0.6693	0.6535	0.6384	0.6240	0.6103	0.5971	0.5845	0.5724	0.5608	0.5497
29		0.6935	0.6771	0.6615	0.6466	0.6323	0.6187	0.6056	0.5931	0.5811	0.5695
30		0.7177	0.7008	0.6846	0.6692	0.6544	0.6403	0.6267	0.6138	0.6013	0.5894
31		0.7419	0.7244	0.7077	0.6917	0.6765	0.6619	0.6479	0.6345	0.6216	0.6093
32		0.7661	0.7480	0.7307	0.7143	0.6985	0.6834	0.6690	0.6552	0.6419	0.6291
33		0.7903	0.7716	0.7538	0.7368	0.7206	0.7050	0.6901	0.6758	0.6621	0.6490
34		0.8145	0.7952	0.7769	0.7594	0.7426	0.7266	0.7112	0.6965	0.6824	0.6689
35		0.8386	0.8188	0.8000	0.7819	0.7647	0.7482	0.7324	0.7172	0.7027	0.6887
36		0.8628	0.8425	0.8230	0.8045	0.7867	0.7698	0.7535	0.7379	0.7230	0.7086
37		0.8870	0.8661	0.8461	0.8270	0.8088	0.7913	0.7746	0.7586	0.7432	0.7285
38		0.9112	0.8897	0.8692	0.8496	0.8308	0.8129	0.7957	0.7793	0.7635	0.7483
39		0.9353	0.9133	0.8922	0.8721	0.8529	0.8345	0.8169	0.8000	0.7838	0.7682
40		0.9594	0.9368	0.9153	0.8946	0.8749	0.8561	0.8380	0.8206	0.8040	0.7881
41		0.9832	0.9604	0.9383	0.9172	0.8970	0.8776	0.8591	0.8413	0.8243	0.8079
42			0.9836	0.9613	0.9397	0.9190	0.8992	0.8802	0.8620	0.8445	0.8278
43				0.9840	0.9621	0.9410	0.9208	0.9013	0.8827	0.8648	0.8476
44					0.9844	0.9630	0.9423	0.9224	0.9034	0.8851	0.8675
45						0.9847	0.9638	0.9240	0.9240	0.9053	0.8874
46							0.9850	0.9645	0.9447	0.9256	0.9072
47								0.9854	0.9653	0.9458	0.9271
48									0.9857	0.9660	0.9469
49										0.9860	0.9667
50											0.9862

Table C.2. 95% ranks.

Order	Sample Size									
	1	2	3	4	5	6	7	8	9	10
1	0.9500	0.7764	0.6316	0.5271	0.4507	0.3930	0.3482	0.3123	0.2831	0.2589
2		0.9747	0.8646	0.7514	0.6574	0.5818	0.5207	0.4707	0.4291	0.3942
3			0.9830	0.9024	0.8107	0.7287	0.6587	0.5997	0.5496	0.5069
4				0.9873	0.9236	0.8468	0.7747	0.7108	0.6551	0.6066
5					0.9898	0.9372	0.8712	0.8071	0.7486	0.6965
6						0.9915	0.9466	0.8889	0.8312	0.7776
7							0.9927	0.9536	0.9023	0.8500
8								0.9936	0.9590	0.9127
9									0.9943	0.9632
10										0.9949

Order	Sample Size									
	11	12	13	14	15	16	17	18	19	20
1	0.2384	0.2209	0.2058	0.1926	0.1810	0.1707	0.1616	0.1533	0.1459	0.1391
2	0.3644	0.3387	0.3163	0.2967	0.2794	0.2640	0.2501	0.2377	0.2264	0.2161
3	0.4701	0.4381	0.4101	0.3854	0.3634	0.3438	0.3262	0.3103	0.2958	0.2826
4	0.5644	0.5273	0.4946	0.4657	0.4398	0.4166	0.3956	0.3767	0.3594	0.3437
5	0.6502	0.6091	0.5726	0.5400	0.5108	0.4844	0.4605	0.4389	0.4191	0.4010
6	0.7288	0.6848	0.6452	0.6096	0.5774	0.5483	0.5219	0.4978	0.4758	0.4556
7	0.8004	0.7547	0.7130	0.6750	0.6404	0.6090	0.5803	0.5540	0.5300	0.5078
8	0.8649	0.8190	0.7760	0.7364	0.7000	0.6666	0.6360	0.6078	0.5819	0.5580
9	0.9212	0.8771	0.8343	0.7939	0.7563	0.7214	0.6892	0.6594	0.6319	0.6064
10	0.9667	0.9281	0.8873	0.8473	0.8091	0.7733	0.7399	0.7088	0.6799	0.6531
11	0.9953	0.9695	0.9340	0.8960	0.8583	0.8222	0.7881	0.7560	0.7261	0.6980
12		0.9957	0.9719	0.9389	0.9033	0.8679	0.8336	0.8010	0.7703	0.7413
13			0.9961	0.9740	0.9432	0.9097	0.8762	0.8437	0.8125	0.7829
14				0.9963	0.9758	0.9469	0.9154	0.8836	0.8525	0.8227
15					0.9966	0.9773	0.9501	0.9203	0.8901	0.8604
16						0.9968	0.9787	0.9530	0.9247	0.8959
17							0.9970	0.9799	0.9555	0.9286
18								0.9972	0.9810	0.9578
19									0.9973	0.9819
20										0.9974

Continued on next page…

Table C.2—*continued...*

Order	|				Sample Size					
	21	**22**	**23**	**24**	**25**	**26**	**27**	**28**	**29**	**30**
1	0.1329	0.1273	0.1221	0.1173	0.1129	0.1088	0.1050	0.1015	0.0981	0.0950
2	0.2067	0.1981	0.1902	0.1829	0.1761	0.1698	0.1640	0.1585	0.1534	0.1486
3	0.2706	0.2595	0.2492	0.2398	0.2310	0.2229	0.2153	0.2082	0.2016	0.1953
4	0.3292	0.3159	0.3036	0.2923	0.2817	0.2719	0.2627	0.2542	0.2461	0.2386
5	0.3844	0.3691	0.3549	0.3418	0.3296	0.3182	0.3076	0.2977	0.2884	0.2796
6	0.4370	0.4198	0.4039	0.3891	0.3754	0.3626	0.3506	0.3394	0.3289	0.3190
7	0.4874	0.4685	0.4510	0.4347	0.4195	0.4054	0.3921	0.3797	0.3680	0.3570
8	0.5359	0.5155	0.4964	0.4787	0.4622	0.4468	0.4323	0.4187	0.4060	0.3939
9	0.5828	0.5609	0.5405	0.5214	0.5036	0.4870	0.4714	0.4567	0.4429	0.4299
10	0.6281	0.6048	0.5832	0.5629	0.5439	0.5262	0.5095	0.4938	0.4790	0.4651
11	0.6719	0.6475	0.6246	0.6032	0.5832	0.5643	0.5466	0.5300	0.5143	0.4994
12	0.7142	0.6887	0.6649	0.6424	0.6214	0.6016	0.5829	0.5654	0.5488	0.5331
13	0.7550	0.7287	0.7039	0.6806	0.6586	0.6379	0.6184	0.6000	0.5825	0.5661
14	0.7943	0.7673	0.7418	0.7176	0.6949	0.6734	0.6530	0.6338	0.6156	0.5984
15	0.8318	0.8044	0.7784	0.7536	0.7301	0.7079	0.6869	0.6669	0.6480	0.6301
16	0.8676	0.8401	0.8137	0.7884	0.7644	0.7416	0.7199	0.6993	0.6797	0.6611
17	0.9012	0.8740	0.8475	0.8220	0.7976	0.7743	0.7521	0.7309	0.7107	0.6915
18	0.9322	0.9059	0.8798	0.8543	0.8297	0.8060	0.7834	0.7617	0.7411	0.7213
19	0.9599	0.9354	0.9102	0.8851	0.8605	0.8367	0.8138	0.7918	0.7707	0.7505
20	0.9828	0.9618	0.9383	0.9141	0.8899	0.8662	0.8432	0.8209	0.7995	0.7789
21	0.9976	0.9836	0.9635	0.9410	0.9177	0.8944	0.8715	0.8491	0.8275	0.8067
22		0.9977	0.9843	0.9650	0.9434	0.9210	0.8985	0.8763	0.8547	0.8337
23			0.9978	0.9850	0.9665	0.9457	0.9241	0.9023	0.8808	0.8598
24				0.9979	0.9856	0.9678	0.9478	0.9269	0.9058	0.8850
25					0.9980	0.9862	0.9690	0.9497	0.9295	0.9091
26						0.9980	0.9867	0.9702	0.9515	0.9319
27							0.9981	0.9872	0.9712	0.9531
28								0.9982	0.9876	0.9722
29									0.9982	0.9880
30										0.9983

Continued on next page...

Table C.2—*continued...*

Order	Sample Size									
	31	32	33	34	35	36	37	38	39	40
1	0.0921	0.0894	0.0868	0.0843	0.0820	0.0798	0.0778	0.0758	0.0739	0.0722
2	0.1441	0.1398	0.1359	0.1321	0.1285	0.1251	0.1219	0.1189	0.1160	0.1132
3	0.1895	0.1839	0.1787	0.1738	0.1692	0.1647	0.1605	0.1566	0.1528	0.1492
4	0.2315	0.2248	0.2185	0.2125	0.2069	0.2015	0.1964	0.1916	0.1870	0.1826
5	0.2714	0.2636	0.2563	0.2493	0.2427	0.2365	0.2305	0.2249	0.2195	0.2144
6	0.3096	0.3008	0.2925	0.2846	0.2772	0.2701	0.2634	0.2570	0.2509	0.2450
7	0.3467	0.3369	0.3276	0.3189	0.3106	0.3027	0.2952	0.2880	0.2812	0.2747
8	0.3826	0.3719	0.3618	0.3522	0.3430	0.3344	0.3262	0.3183	0.3108	0.3037
9	0.4177	0.4061	0.3951	0.3847	0.3748	0.3654	0.3564	0.3479	0.3398	0.3320
10	0.4519	0.4394	0.4276	0.4165	0.4058	0.3957	0.3861	0.3769	0.3682	0.3598
11	0.4854	0.4721	0.4596	0.4476	0.4363	0.4255	0.4152	0.4054	0.3960	0.3871
12	0.5182	0.5042	0.4909	0.4782	0.4661	0.4547	0.4438	0.4333	0.4234	0.4139
13	0.5504	0.5356	0.5216	0.5082	0.4955	0.4834	0.4719	0.4609	0.4503	0.4403
14	0.5820	0.5665	0.5518	0.5378	0.5244	0.5117	0.4995	0.4880	0.4769	0.4663
15	0.6130	0.5968	0.5814	0.5668	0.5528	0.5395	0.5268	0.5147	0.5031	0.4919
16	0.6434	0.6266	0.6106	0.5953	0.5808	0.5669	0.5537	0.5410	0.5289	0.5172
17	0.6733	0.6559	0.6393	0.6234	0.6083	0.5939	0.5801	0.5669	0.5543	0.5422
18	0.7025	0.6846	0.6674	0.6511	0.6354	0.6205	0.6062	0.5925	0.5794	0.5669
19	0.7312	0.7127	0.6951	0.6782	0.6621	0.6467	0.6319	0.6178	0.6042	0.5912
20	0.7592	0.7403	0.7223	0.7049	0.6883	0.6725	0.6572	0.6426	0.6286	0.6152
21	0.7866	0.7674	0.7489	0.7312	0.7142	0.6978	0.6822	0.6672	0.6528	0.6389
22	0.8134	0.7938	0.7750	0.7569	0.7395	0.7228	0.7068	0.6913	0.6765	0.6623
23	0.8394	0.8196	0.8005	0.7821	0.7644	0.7473	0.7309	0.7152	0.7000	0.6854
24	0.8646	0.8447	0.8254	0.8068	0.7888	0.7715	0.7547	0.7386	0.7231	0.7082
25	0.8889	0.8691	0.8497	0.8309	0.8127	0.7951	0.7781	0.7617	0.7459	0.7306
26	0.9122	0.8926	0.8732	0.8544	0.8360	0.8182	0.8010	0.7844	0.7683	0.7527
27	0.9342	0.9150	0.8960	0.8772	0.8588	0.8409	0.8235	0.8066	0.7903	0.7745
28	0.9547	0.9363	0.9177	0.8992	0.8809	0.8629	0.8454	0.8284	0.8119	0.7959
29	0.9731	0.9562	0.9383	0.9202	0.9022	0.8843	0.8668	0.8497	0.8331	0.8169
30	0.9884	0.9740	0.9575	0.9402	0.9226	0.9050	0.8876	0.8705	0.8538	0.8375
31	0.9983	0.9888	0.9748	0.9588	0.9420	0.9248	0.9077	0.8907	0.8740	0.8576
32		0.9984	0.9891	0.9755	0.9600	0.9436	0.9269	0.9102	0.8936	0.8773
33			0.9984	0.9894	0.9762	0.9611	0.9452	0.9289	0.9126	0.8964
34				0.9985	0.9898	0.9769	0.9622	0.9467	0.9308	0.9149
35					0.9985	0.9900	0.9775	0.9632	0.9481	0.9326
36						0.9986	0.9903	0.9781	0.9642	0.9494
37							0.9986	0.9906	0.9787	0.9651
38								0.9987	0.9908	0.9792
39									0.9987	0.9910
40										0.9987

Continued on next page...

Table C.2—*continued...*

Order					Sample Size					
	41	42	43	44	45	46	47	48	49	50
1	0.0705	0.0688	0.0673	0.0658	0.0644	0.0630	0.0618	0.0605	0.0593	0.0582
2	0.1106	0.1080	0.1056	0.1033	0.1011	0.0990	0.0970	0.0951	0.0932	0.0914
3	0.1457	0.1424	0.1393	0.1363	0.1334	0.1306	0.1280	0.1254	0.1230	0.1206
4	0.1784	0.1744	0.1706	0.1669	0.1634	0.1600	0.1568	0.1537	0.1507	0.1478
5	0.2095	0.2048	0.2004	0.1961	0.1920	0.1880	0.1843	0.1806	0.1771	0.1738
6	0.2395	0.2342	0.2291	0.2242	0.2195	0.2151	0.2108	0.2066	0.2027	0.1988
7	0.2685	0.2626	0.2569	0.2515	0.2463	0.2413	0.2365	0.2319	0.2274	0.2232
8	0.2969	0.2904	0.2841	0.2781	0.2724	0.2669	0.2616	0.2565	0.2516	0.2469
9	0.3246	0.3175	0.3107	0.3042	0.2980	0.2920	0.2862	0.2807	0.2754	0.2702
10	0.3518	0.3442	0.3368	0.3298	0.3231	0.3166	0.3104	0.3044	0.2986	0.2931
11	0.3785	0.3703	0.3625	0.3549	0.3477	0.3408	0.3341	0.3277	0.3215	0.3156
12	0.4048	0.3961	0.3877	0.3797	0.3720	0.3646	0.3575	0.3507	0.3441	0.3378
13	0.4307	0.4214	0.4126	0.4041	0.3960	0.3881	0.3806	0.3734	0.3664	0.3597
14	0.4562	0.4464	0.4371	0.4282	0.4196	0.4113	0.4034	0.3957	0.3884	0.3813
15	0.4813	0.4711	0.4613	0.4519	0.4429	0.4342	0.4259	0.4178	0.4101	0.4026
16	0.5061	0.4955	0.4852	0.4754	0.4659	0.4568	0.4481	0.4397	0.4316	0.4237
17	0.5306	0.5195	0.5088	0.4986	0.4887	0.4792	0.4701	0.4613	0.4528	0.4446
18	0.5548	0.5433	0.5322	0.5215	0.5112	0.5013	0.4918	0.4827	0.4738	0.4653
19	0.5787	0.5667	0.5552	0.5441	0.5335	0.5232	0.5133	0.5038	0.4946	0.4858
20	0.6023	0.5899	0.5780	0.5665	0.5555	0.5449	0.5346	0.5248	0.5152	0.5060
21	0.6256	0.6128	0.6005	0.5887	0.5773	0.5663	0.5557	0.5455	0.5356	0.5261
22	0.6486	0.6354	0.6228	0.6106	0.5988	0.5875	0.5766	0.5660	0.5558	0.5460
23	0.6713	0.6578	0.6448	0.6322	0.6201	0.6085	0.5972	0.5863	0.5759	0.5657
24	0.6938	0.6799	0.6665	0.6536	0.6412	0.6292	0.6176	0.6065	0.5957	0.5852
25	0.7159	0.7017	0.6880	0.6748	0.6621	0.6498	0.6379	0.6264	0.6153	0.6046
26	0.7377	0.7232	0.7092	0.6957	0.6827	0.6701	0.6579	0.6461	0.6348	0.6238
27	0.7592	0.7444	0.7302	0.7164	0.7030	0.6902	0.6777	0.6657	0.6540	0.6427
28	0.7804	0.7653	0.7508	0.7368	0.7232	0.7100	0.6973	0.6850	0.6731	0.6615
29	0.8012	0.7859	0.7712	0.7569	0.7431	0.7297	0.7167	0.7041	0.6920	0.6802
30	0.8216	0.8062	0.7912	0.7767	0.7627	0.7491	0.7358	0.7230	0.7106	0.6986
31	0.8417	0.8261	0.8110	0.7963	0.7820	0.7682	0.7548	0.7417	0.7291	0.7169
32	0.8613	0.8456	0.8304	0.8155	0.8011	0.7871	0.7735	0.7602	0.7474	0.7349
33	0.8804	0.8647	0.8494	0.8345	0.8199	0.8057	0.7919	0.7785	0.7655	0.7528
34	0.8990	0.8834	0.8680	0.8530	0.8383	0.8240	0.8101	0.7965	0.7833	0.7705
35	0.9170	0.9015	0.8862	0.8712	0.8564	0.8420	0.8280	0.8143	0.8009	0.7879

Continued on next page...

Table C.2—*continued...*

Order	Sample Size									
	41	42	43	44	45	46	47	48	49	50
36	0.9343	0.9191	0.9039	0.8889	0.8742	0.8597	0.8456	0.8317	0.8183	0.8051
37	0.9507	0.9359	0.9210	0.9062	0.8915	0.8770	0.8628	0.8490	0.8354	0.8221
38	0.9660	0.9519	0.9374	0.9229	0.9083	0.8940	0.8798	0.8658	0.8522	0.8388
39	0.9798	0.9668	0.9530	0.9389	0.9246	0.9104	0.8963	0.8824	0.8687	0.8553
40	0.9913	0.9802	0.9676	0.9541	0.9403	0.9263	0.9124	0.8985	0.8849	0.8714
41	0.9987	0.9915	0.9807	0.9683	0.9552	0.9416	0.9280	0.9143	0.9007	0.8873
42		0.9988	0.9917	0.9812	0.9691	0.9562	0.9429	0.9295	0.9161	0.9028
43			0.9988	0.9919	0.9816	0.9698	0.9571	0.9441	0.9310	0.9178
44				0.9988	0.9920	0.9820	0.9704	0.9580	0.9453	0.9324
45					0.9989	0.9922	0.9824	0.9710	0.9589	0.9464
46						0.9989	0.9924	0.9827	0.9716	0.9598
47							0.9989	0.9925	0.9831	0.9722
48								0.9989	0.9927	0.9834
49									0.9990	0.9928
50										0.9990

Table C.3. 5% ranks.

Order	Sample Size									
	1	2	3	4	5	6	7	8	9	10
1	0.0500	0.0253	0.0170	0.0127	0.0102	0.0085	0.0073	0.0064	0.0057	0.0051
2		0.2236	0.1354	0.0976	0.0764	0.0628	0.0534	0.0464	0.0410	0.0368
3			0.3684	0.2486	0.1893	0.1532	0.1288	0.1111	0.0977	0.0873
4				0.4729	0.3426	0.2713	0.2253	0.1929	0.1688	0.1500
5					0.5493	0.4182	0.3413	0.2892	0.2514	0.2224
6						0.6070	0.4793	0.4003	0.3449	0.3035
7							0.6518	0.5293	0.4504	0.3934
8								0.6877	0.5709	0.4931
9									0.7169	0.6058
10										0.7411

Continued on next page...

Table C.3—*continued...*

Order	Sample Size									
	11	12	13	14	15	16	17	18	19	20
1	0.0047	0.0043	0.0039	0.0037	0.0034	0.0032	0.0030	0.0028	0.0027	0.0026
2	0.0333	0.0305	0.0281	0.0260	0.0242	0.0227	0.0213	0.0201	0.0190	0.0181
3	0.0788	0.0719	0.0660	0.0611	0.0568	0.0531	0.0499	0.0470	0.0445	0.0422
4	0.1351	0.1229	0.1127	0.1040	0.0967	0.0903	0.0846	0.0797	0.0753	0.0714
5	0.1996	0.1810	0.1657	0.1527	0.1417	0.1321	0.1238	0.1164	0.1099	0.1041
6	0.2712	0.2453	0.2240	0.2061	0.1909	0.1778	0.1664	0.1563	0.1475	0.1396
7	0.3498	0.3152	0.2870	0.2636	0.2437	0.2267	0.2119	0.1990	0.1875	0.1773
8	0.4356	0.3909	0.3548	0.3250	0.3000	0.2786	0.2601	0.2440	0.2297	0.2171
9	0.5299	0.4727	0.4274	0.3904	0.3596	0.3334	0.3108	0.2912	0.2739	0.2587
10	0.6356	0.5619	0.5054	0.4600	0.4226	0.3910	0.3640	0.3406	0.3201	0.3020
11	0.7616	0.6613	0.5899	0.5343	0.4892	0.4517	0.4197	0.3922	0.3681	0.3469
12		0.7791	0.6837	0.6146	0.5602	0.5156	0.4781	0.4460	0.4181	0.3936
13			0.7942	0.7033	0.6366	0.5834	0.5395	0.5022	0.4700	0.4420
14				0.8074	0.7206	0.6562	0.6044	0.5611	0.5242	0.4922
15					0.8190	0.7360	0.6738	0.6233	0.5809	0.5444
16						0.8293	0.7499	0.6897	0.6406	0.5990
17							0.8384	0.7623	0.7042	0.6563
18								0.8467	0.7736	0.7174
19									0.8541	0.7839
20										0.8609

Order	Sample Size									
	21	22	23	24	25	26	27	28	29	30
1	0.0024	0.0023	0.0022	0.0021	0.0020	0.0020	0.0019	0.0018	0.0018	0.0017
2	0.0172	0.0164	0.0157	0.0150	0.0144	0.0138	0.0133	0.0128	0.0124	0.0120
3	0.0401	0.0382	0.0365	0.0350	0.0335	0.0322	0.0310	0.0298	0.0288	0.0278
4	0.0678	0.0646	0.0617	0.0590	0.0566	0.0543	0.0522	0.0503	0.0485	0.0469
5	0.0988	0.0941	0.0898	0.0859	0.0823	0.0790	0.0759	0.0731	0.0705	0.0681
6	0.1324	0.1260	0.1202	0.1149	0.1101	0.1056	0.1015	0.0977	0.0942	0.0909
7	0.1682	0.1599	0.1525	0.1457	0.1395	0.1338	0.1285	0.1237	0.1192	0.1150
8	0.2057	0.1956	0.1863	0.1780	0.1703	0.1633	0.1568	0.1509	0.1453	0.1402
9	0.2450	0.2327	0.2216	0.2116	0.2024	0.1940	0.1862	0.1791	0.1725	0.1663
10	0.2858	0.2713	0.2582	0.2464	0.2356	0.2257	0.2166	0.2082	0.2005	0.1933
11	0.3281	0.3113	0.2961	0.2824	0.2699	0.2584	0.2479	0.2383	0.2293	0.2211
12	0.3719	0.3525	0.3351	0.3194	0.3051	0.2921	0.2801	0.2691	0.2589	0.2495
13	0.4172	0.3952	0.3754	0.3576	0.3414	0.3266	0.3131	0.3007	0.2893	0.2787
14	0.4641	0.4391	0.4168	0.3968	0.3786	0.3621	0.3470	0.3331	0.3203	0.3085
15	0.5126	0.4845	0.4595	0.4371	0.4168	0.3984	0.3816	0.3662	0.3520	0.3389

Continued on next page...

Table C.3—*continued...*

Order	Sample Size									
	21	22	23	24	25	26	27	28	29	30
16	0.5630	0.5315	0.5036	0.4786	0.4561	0.4357	0.4171	0.4000	0.3844	0.3699
17	0.6156	0.5802	0.5490	0.5213	0.4964	0.4738	0.4534	0.4346	0.4175	0.4016
18	0.6708	0.6309	0.5961	0.5653	0.5378	0.5130	0.4905	0.4700	0.4512	0.4339
19	0.7294	0.6841	0.6451	0.6109	0.5805	0.5532	0.5286	0.5062	0.4857	0.4669
20	0.7933	0.7405	0.6964	0.6582	0.6246	0.5946	0.5677	0.5433	0.5210	0.5006
21	0.8671	0.8019	0.7508	0.7077	0.6704	0.6374	0.6079	0.5813	0.5571	0.5349
22		0.8727	0.8098	0.7602	0.7183	0.6818	0.6494	0.6203	0.5940	0.5701
23			0.8779	0.8171	0.7690	0.7281	0.6924	0.6606	0.6320	0.6061
24				0.8827	0.8239	0.7771	0.7373	0.7023	0.6711	0.6430
25					0.8871	0.8302	0.7847	0.7458	0.7116	0.6810
26						0.8912	0.8360	0.7918	0.7539	0.7204
27							0.8950	0.8415	0.7984	0.7614
28								0.8985	0.8466	0.8047
29									0.9019	0.8514
30										0.9050

Order	Sample Size									
	31	32	33	34	35	36	37	38	39	40
1	0.0017	0.0016	0.0016	0.0015	0.0015	0.0014	0.0014	0.0013	0.0013	0.0013
2	0.0116	0.0112	0.0109	0.0106	0.0102	0.0100	0.0097	0.0094	0.0092	0.0090
3	0.0269	0.0260	0.0252	0.0245	0.0238	0.0231	0.0225	0.0219	0.0213	0.0208
4	0.0453	0.0438	0.0425	0.0412	0.0400	0.0389	0.0378	0.0368	0.0358	0.0349
5	0.0658	0.0637	0.0617	0.0598	0.0580	0.0564	0.0548	0.0533	0.0519	0.0506
6	0.0878	0.0850	0.0823	0.0798	0.0774	0.0752	0.0731	0.0711	0.0692	0.0674
7	0.1111	0.1074	0.1040	0.1008	0.0978	0.0950	0.0923	0.0898	0.0874	0.0851
8	0.1354	0.1309	0.1268	0.1228	0.1191	0.1157	0.1124	0.1093	0.1064	0.1036
9	0.1606	0.1553	0.1503	0.1456	0.1412	0.1371	0.1332	0.1295	0.1260	0.1227
10	0.1866	0.1804	0.1746	0.1691	0.1640	0.1591	0.1546	0.1503	0.1462	0.1424
11	0.2134	0.2062	0.1995	0.1932	0.1873	0.1818	0.1765	0.1716	0.1669	0.1625
12	0.2408	0.2326	0.2250	0.2179	0.2112	0.2049	0.1990	0.1934	0.1881	0.1831
13	0.2688	0.2597	0.2511	0.2431	0.2356	0.2285	0.2219	0.2156	0.2097	0.2041
14	0.2975	0.2873	0.2777	0.2688	0.2605	0.2527	0.2453	0.2383	0.2317	0.2255
15	0.3267	0.3154	0.3049	0.2951	0.2858	0.2772	0.2691	0.2614	0.2541	0.2473
16	0.3566	0.3441	0.3326	0.3218	0.3117	0.3022	0.2932	0.2848	0.2769	0.2694
17	0.3870	0.3734	0.3607	0.3489	0.3379	0.3275	0.3178	0.3087	0.3000	0.2918
18	0.4180	0.4032	0.3894	0.3766	0.3646	0.3533	0.3428	0.3328	0.3235	0.3146
19	0.4496	0.4335	0.4186	0.4047	0.3917	0.3795	0.3681	0.3574	0.3472	0.3377
20	0.4818	0.4644	0.4482	0.4332	0.4192	0.4061	0.3938	0.3822	0.3714	0.3611

Continued on next page...

Table C.3—*continued...*

Order	\multicolumn{10}{c}{Sample Size}									
	31	32	33	34	35	36	37	38	39	40
21	0.5146	0.4958	0.4784	0.4622	0.4472	0.4331	0.4199	0.4075	0.3958	0.3848
22	0.5481	0.5279	0.5091	0.4918	0.4756	0.4605	0.4463	0.4331	0.4206	0.4088
23	0.5823	0.5606	0.5404	0.5218	0.5045	0.4883	0.4732	0.4590	0.4457	0.4331
24	0.6174	0.5939	0.5724	0.5524	0.5339	0.5166	0.5005	0.4853	0.4711	0.4578
25	0.6533	0.6281	0.6049	0.5835	0.5637	0.5453	0.5281	0.5120	0.4969	0.4828
26	0.6904	0.6631	0.6382	0.6153	0.5942	0.5745	0.5562	0.5391	0.5231	0.5081
27	0.7286	0.6992	0.6724	0.6478	0.6252	0.6043	0.5848	0.5667	0.5497	0.5337
28	0.7685	0.7364	0.7075	0.6811	0.6570	0.6346	0.6139	0.5946	0.5766	0.5597
29	0.8105	0.7752	0.7437	0.7154	0.6894	0.6656	0.6436	0.6231	0.6040	0.5861
30	0.8559	0.8161	0.7815	0.7507	0.7228	0.6973	0.6738	0.6521	0.6318	0.6129
31	0.9079	0.8602	0.8213	0.7875	0.7573	0.7299	0.7048	0.6817	0.6602	0.6402
32		0.9106	0.8641	0.8262	0.7931	0.7635	0.7366	0.7120	0.6892	0.6680
33			0.9132	0.8679	0.8308	0.7985	0.7695	0.7430	0.7188	0.6963
34				0.9157	0.8715	0.8353	0.8036	0.7751	0.7491	0.7253
35					0.9180	0.8749	0.8395	0.8084	0.7805	0.7550
36						0.9202	0.8781	0.8434	0.8130	0.7856
37							0.9222	0.8811	0.8472	0.8174
38								0.9242	0.8840	0.8508
39									0.9261	0.8868
40										0.9278

Order	\multicolumn{10}{c}{Sample Size}									
	41	42	43	44	45	46	47	48	49	50
1	0.0013	0.0012	0.0012	0.0012	0.0011	0.0011	0.0011	0.0011	0.0010	0.0010
2	0.0087	0.0085	0.0083	0.0081	0.0080	0.0078	0.0076	0.0075	0.0073	0.0072
3	0.0202	0.0198	0.0193	0.0188	0.0184	0.0180	0.0176	0.0173	0.0169	0.0166
4	0.0340	0.0332	0.0324	0.0317	0.0309	0.0302	0.0296	0.0290	0.0284	0.0278
5	0.0493	0.0481	0.0470	0.0459	0.0448	0.0438	0.0429	0.0420	0.0411	0.0402
6	0.0657	0.0641	0.0626	0.0611	0.0597	0.0584	0.0571	0.0559	0.0547	0.0536
7	0.0830	0.0809	0.0790	0.0771	0.0754	0.0737	0.0720	0.0705	0.0690	0.0676
8	0.1010	0.0985	0.0961	0.0938	0.0917	0.0896	0.0876	0.0857	0.0839	0.0822
9	0.1196	0.1166	0.1138	0.1111	0.1085	0.1060	0.1037	0.1015	0.0993	0.0972
10	0.1387	0.1353	0.1320	0.1288	0.1258	0.1230	0.1202	0.1176	0.1151	0.1127
11	0.1583	0.1544	0.1506	0.1470	0.1436	0.1403	0.1372	0.1342	0.1313	0.1286
12	0.1784	0.1739	0.1696	0.1655	0.1617	0.1580	0.1544	0.1510	0.1478	0.1447
13	0.1988	0.1938	0.1890	0.1845	0.1801	0.1760	0.1720	0.1683	0.1646	0.1612
14	0.2196	0.2141	0.2088	0.2037	0.1989	0.1943	0.1899	0.1857	0.1817	0.1779
15	0.2408	0.2347	0.2288	0.2233	0.2180	0.2129	0.2081	0.2035	0.1991	0.1949

Continued on next page...

Table C.3—*continued...*

Order	Sample Size									
	41	42	43	44	45	46	47	48	49	50
16	0.2623	0.2556	0.2492	0.2431	0.2373	0.2318	0.2265	0.2215	0.2167	0.2121
17	0.2841	0.2768	0.2698	0.2632	0.2569	0.2509	0.2452	0.2398	0.2345	0.2295
18	0.3062	0.2983	0.2908	0.2836	0.2768	0.2703	0.2642	0.2583	0.2526	0.2472
19	0.3287	0.3201	0.3120	0.3043	0.2970	0.2900	0.2833	0.2770	0.2709	0.2651
20	0.3514	0.3422	0.3335	0.3252	0.3173	0.3098	0.3027	0.2959	0.2894	0.2831
21	0.3744	0.3646	0.3552	0.3464	0.3379	0.3299	0.3223	0.3150	0.3080	0.3014
22	0.3977	0.3872	0.3772	0.3678	0.3588	0.3502	0.3421	0.3343	0.3269	0.3198
23	0.4213	0.4101	0.3995	0.3894	0.3799	0.3708	0.3621	0.3539	0.3460	0.3385
24	0.4452	0.4333	0.4220	0.4113	0.4012	0.3915	0.3824	0.3736	0.3652	0.3573
25	0.4694	0.4567	0.4448	0.4335	0.4227	0.4125	0.4028	0.3935	0.3847	0.3762
26	0.4939	0.4805	0.4678	0.4559	0.4445	0.4337	0.4234	0.4137	0.4043	0.3954
27	0.5187	0.5045	0.4912	0.4785	0.4665	0.4551	0.4443	0.4340	0.4241	0.4148
28	0.5438	0.5289	0.5148	0.5014	0.4888	0.4768	0.4654	0.4545	0.4442	0.4343
29	0.5693	0.5536	0.5387	0.5246	0.5113	0.4987	0.4867	0.4752	0.4644	0.4540
30	0.5952	0.5786	0.5629	0.5481	0.5341	0.5208	0.5082	0.4962	0.4848	0.4739
31	0.6215	0.6039	0.5874	0.5718	0.5571	0.5432	0.5299	0.5173	0.5054	0.4940
32	0.6482	0.6297	0.6123	0.5959	0.5804	0.5658	0.5519	0.5387	0.5262	0.5142
33	0.6754	0.6558	0.6375	0.6203	0.6040	0.5887	0.5741	0.5603	0.5472	0.5347
34	0.7031	0.6825	0.6632	0.6451	0.6280	0.6119	0.5966	0.5822	0.5684	0.5554
35	0.7315	0.7096	0.6893	0.6702	0.6523	0.6354	0.6194	0.6043	0.5899	0.5763
36	0.7605	0.7374	0.7159	0.6958	0.6769	0.6592	0.6425	0.6266	0.6116	0.5974
37	0.7905	0.7658	0.7431	0.7219	0.7020	0.6834	0.6659	0.6493	0.6336	0.6187
38	0.8216	0.7952	0.7709	0.7485	0.7276	0.7080	0.6896	0.6723	0.6559	0.6403
39	0.8543	0.8256	0.7996	0.7758	0.7537	0.7331	0.7138	0.6956	0.6785	0.6622
40	0.8894	0.8576	0.8294	0.8039	0.7805	0.7587	0.7384	0.7193	0.7014	0.6844
41	0.9295	0.8920	0.8607	0.8331	0.8080	0.7849	0.7635	0.7435	0.7246	0.7069
42		0.9312	0.8944	0.8637	0.8366	0.8120	0.7892	0.7681	0.7484	0.7298
43			0.9327	0.8967	0.8666	0.8400	0.8157	0.7934	0.7726	0.7531
44				0.9342	0.8989	0.8694	0.8432	0.8194	0.7973	0.7768
45					0.9356	0.9010	0.8720	0.8463	0.8229	0.8012
46						0.9370	0.9030	0.8746	0.8493	0.8262
47							0.9382	0.9049	0.8770	0.8522
48								0.9395	0.9068	0.8794
49									0.9407	0.9086
50										0.9418

D

Beta Table

Table D.1. Values of reliability.

Sample Size	Successes	Confidence Level					
		0.5	0.75	0.90	0.95	0.99	0.995
1	0	0.293	0.134	0.051	0.025	0.005	0.002
	1	0.707	0.500	0.316	0.224	0.100	0.071
2	0	0.206	0.092	0.034	0.017	0.003	0.002
	1	0.500	0.326	0.196	0.135	0.059	0.041
	2	0.794	0.630	0.464	0.368	0.216	0.171
3	1	0.386	0.243	0.142	0.098	0.042	0.029
	2	0.614	0.456	0.320	0.249	0.141	0.111
	3	0.841	0.707	0.562	0.473	0.316	0.266
4	2	0.500	0.359	0.247	0.189	0.106	0.083
	3	0.686	0.546	0.416	0.343	0.222	0.185
	4	0.871	0.758	0.631	0.549	0.398	0.346
5	3	0.579	0.447	0.794	0.271	0.173	0.144
	4	0.736	0.610	0.333	0.418	0.294	0.254
	5	0.891	0.794	0.681	0.607	0.464	0.414

Continued on next page...

Table D.1—*continued...*

Sample Size	Successes	Confidence Level					
		0.5	0.75	0.90	0.95	0.99	0.995
6	4	0.636	0.514	0.404	0.341	0.236	0.203
	5	0.772	0.659	0.547	0.479	0.357	0.315
	6	0.906	0.820	0.720	0.652	0.518	0.469
7	5	0.679	0.567	0.462	0.400	0.293	0.258
	6	0.799	0.697	0.594	0.529	0.410	0.368
	7	0.917	0.841	0.750	0.688	0.562	0.516
8	6	0.714	0.609	0.510	0.450	0.344	0.307
	7	0.820	0.728	0.632	0.571	0.456	0.415
	8	0.926	0.857	0.774	0.717	0.600	0.555
9	7	0.742	0.645	0.550	0.493	0.388	0.352
	8	0.838	0.753	0.663	0.606	0.496	0.456
	9	0.933	0.871	0.794	0.741	0.631	0.589
10	7	0.676	0.580	0.489	0.436	0.340	0.307
	8	0.764	0.674	0.585	0.530	0.428	0.392
	9	0.852	0.773	0.690	0.636	0.530	0.492
12	9	0.725	0.638	0.556	0.505	0.412	0.379
	10	0.800	0.720	0.640	0.590	0.494	0.459
	11	0.874	0.806	0.732	0.684	0.587	0.551
	12	0.948	0.899	0.838	0.794	0.702	0.665
15	12	0.775	0.702	0.629	0.583	0.497	0.466
	13	0.836	0.769	0.700	0.656	0.570	0.537
	14	0.897	0.840	0.778	0.736	0.651	0.619
	15	0.958	0.917	0.866	0.829	0.750	0.718

Continued on next page...

Table D.1—*continued...*

Sample Size	Successes	Confidence Level					
		0.5	0.75	0.90	0.95	0.99	0.995
20	17	0.828	0.769	0.709	0.671	0.596	0.568
	18	0.875	0.822	0.766	0.729	0.656	0.628
	19	0.921	0.877	0.827	0.793	0.723	0.696
	20	0.968	0.936	0.896	0.867	0.803	0.777
25	22	0.861	0.811	0.761	0.728	0.663	0.638
	23	0.898	0.855	0.808	0.777	0.714	0.690
	24	0.936	0.900	0.858	0.830	0.771	0.747
	25	0.974	0.948	0.915	0.891	0.838	0.816
30	27	0.883	0.841	0.797	0.768	0.711	0.689
	28	0.915	0.877	0.837	0.810	0.755	0.734
	29	0.946	0.916	0.880	0.856	0.804	0.784
	30	0.978	0.956	0.928	0.908	0.862	0.843
35	31	0.871	0.831	0.791	0.764	0.710	0.690
	32	0.898	0.862	0.824	0.798	0.747	0.727
	33	0.926	0.894	0.859	0.835	0.786	0.767
	34	0.954	0.927	0.896	0.875	0.829	0.811
	35	0.981	0.962	0.938	0.920	0.880	0.863
40	36	0.887	0.851	0.814	0.790	0.742	0.724
	37	0.911	0.879	0.844	0.822	0.775	0.757
	38	0.935	0.907	0.875	0.854	0.810	0.793
	39	0.959	0.936	0.908	0.889	0.849	0.832
	40	0.983	0.967	0.945	0.930	0.894	0.879
45	41	0.899	0.867	0.834	0.812	0.768	0.751
	42	0.921	0.892	0.860	0.840	0.798	0.781
	43	0.942	0.917	0.888	0.869	0.830	0.814
	44	0.964	0.942	0.918	0.901	0.864	0.849
	45	0.985	0.970	0.951	0.937	0.905	0.891
50	46	0.909	0.880	0.849	0.829	0.789	0.773
	47	0.928	0.902	0.874	0.855	0.816	0.801
	48	0.948	0.925	0.899	0.882	0.845	0.831
	49	0.967	0.948	0.926	0.910	0.877	0.863
	50	0.985	0.973	0.956	0.943	0.914	0.901

Continued on next page...

Table D.1—*continued...*

Sample Size	Successes	Confidence Level					
		0.5	0.75	0.90	0.95	0.99	0.995
75	71	0.939	0.919	0.898	0.884	0.855	0.843
	72	0.952	0.934	0.914	0.901	0.874	0.863
	73	0.965	0.949	0.932	0.920	0.894	0.884
	74	0.978	0.965	0.950	0.939	0.916	0.906
	75	0.991	0.982	0.970	0.961	0.941	0.933
100	95	0.944	0.928	0.910	0.899	0.875	0.866
	96	0.954	0.939	0.922	0.912	0.889	0.880
	97	0.964	0.950	0.935	0.925	0.904	0.896
	98	0.974	0.962	0.948	0.939	0.919	0.911
	99	0.983	0.974	0.962	0.954	0.936	0.929
	100	0.993	0.986	0.978	0.971	0.955	0.949
150	145	0.962	0.951	0.939	0.932	0.916	0.909
	146	0.969	0.959	0.948	0.940	0.925	0.919
	147	0.976	0.966	0.956	0.950	0.935	0.929
	148	0.982	0.974	0.965	0.959	0.946	0.940
	149	0.989	0.982	0.974	0.969	0.957	0.952
	150	0.996	0.991	0.985	0.980	0.970	0.966
200	195	0.972	0.963	0.954	0.948	0.963	0.931
	196	0.977	0.969	0.961	0.955	0.943	0.939
	197	0.982	0.975	0.967	0.962	0.951	0.946
	198	0.987	0.981	0.974	0.969	0.959	0.955
	199	.0992	0.987	0.981	0.977	0.967	0.964
	200	0.996	0.993	0.989	0.985	0.977	0.974

♦ ♦ ♦
APPENDIX

E

The *F* Distribution

Table E.1. Upper 99.5% points.

$$F_{0.995;\nu 1,\nu 2} = 1/F_{0.005;\nu 2,\nu 1}$$

V2\V1	1	2	3	4	5	6	7	8	9	10
1	0.000062	0.005038	0.0180	0.0319	0.0439	0.0537	0.0616	0.0681	0.0735	0.0780
2	0.000050	0.005025	0.0201	0.0380	0.0546	0.0688	0.0806	0.0906	0.0989	0.1061
3	0.000046	0.005021	0.0211	0.0412	0.0605	0.0774	0.0919	0.1042	0.1147	0.1238
4	0.000044	0.005019	0.0216	0.0432	0.0643	0.0831	0.0995	0.1136	0.1257	0.1362
5	0.000043	0.005018	0.0220	0.0445	0.0669	0.0872	0.1050	0.1205	0.1338	0.1455
6	0.000043	0.005017	0.0223	0.0455	0.0689	0.0903	0.1092	0.1258	0.1402	0.1528
7	0.000042	0.005016	0.0225	0.0462	0.0704	0.0927	0.1125	0.1300	0.1452	0.1587
8	0.000042	0.005016	0.0227	0.0468	0.0716	0.0946	0.1152	0.1334	0.1494	0.1635
9	0.000042	0.005015	0.0228	0.0473	0.0726	0.0962	0.1175	0.1363	0.1529	0.1676
10	0.000041	0.005015	0.0229	0.0477	0.0734	0.0976	0.1193	0.1387	0.1558	0.1710
12	0.000041	0.005015	0.0230	0.0483	0.0747	0.0997	0.1223	0.1426	0.1606	0.1766
15	0.000041	0.005014	0.0232	0.0489	0.0761	0.1019	0.1255	0.1468	0.1658	0.1828
20	0.000040	0.005014	0.0234	0.0496	0.0775	0.1043	0.1290	0.1513	0.1715	0.1896
24	0.000040	0.005014	0.0235	0.0499	0.0782	0.1055	0.1308	0.1538	0.1745	0.1933
30	0.000040	0.005013	0.0235	0.0503	0.0790	0.1069	0.1327	0.1563	0.1778	0.1972
40	0.000040	0.005013	0.0236	0.0506	0.0798	0.1082	0.1347	0.1590	0.1812	0.2014
60	0.000040	0.005013	0.0237	0.0510	0.0806	0.1096	0.1368	0.1619	0.1848	0.2058
120	0.000039	0.005013	0.0238	0.0514	0.0815	0.1111	0.1390	0.1649	0.1887	0.2105
∞	0.000039	0.005013	0.0239	0.0517	0.0823	0.1126	0.1413	0.1680	0.1927	0.2155

Continued on next page…

Table E.1—*continued...*

V2\V1	12	15	20	24	30	40	60	120	∞
1	0.0851	0.0926	0.1006	0.1047	0.1089	0.1133	0.1177	0.1223	0.1269
2	0.1175	0.1299	0.1431	0.1501	0.1574	0.1648	0.1726	0.1805	0.1886
3	0.1384	0.1544	0.1719	0.1812	0.1909	0.2010	0.2115	0.2224	0.2335
4	0.1533	0.1723	0.1933	0.2045	0.2163	0.2286	0.2416	0.2551	0.2690
5	0.1647	0.1861	0.2100	0.2229	0.2365	0.2509	0.2660	0.2818	0.2983
6	0.1737	0.1972	0.2236	0.2380	0.2532	0.2693	0.2864	0.3044	0.3233
7	0.1810	0.2063	0.2349	0.2506	0.2673	0.2850	0.3038	0.3239	0.3449
8	0.1871	0.2139	0.2445	0.2613	0.2793	0.2985	0.3190	0.3410	0.3641
9	0.1922	0.2204	0.2528	0.2706	0.2898	0.3104	0.3324	0.3561	0.3812
10	0.1966	0.2261	0.2599	0.2788	0.2990	0.3208	0.3443	0.3697	0.3967
12	0.2038	0.2353	0.2719	0.2924	0.3146	0.3386	0.3647	0.3931	0.4236
15	0.2118	0.2457	0.2856	0.3081	0.3327	0.3596	0.3890	0.4215	0.4568
20	0.2208	0.2576	0.3014	0.3265	0.3542	0.3848	0.4189	0.4570	0.4995
24	0.2257	0.2641	0.3104	0.3371	0.3667	0.3997	0.4367	0.4787	0.5262
30	0.2309	0.2712	0.3202	0.3487	0.3805	0.4164	0.4572	0.5040	0.5582
40	0.2365	0.2789	0.3310	0.3616	0.3962	0.4356	0.4810	0.5345	0.5982
60	0.2425	0.2873	0.3429	0.3762	0.4141	0.4579	0.5096	0.5725	0.6514
120	0.2491	0.2965	0.3564	0.3927	0.4348	0.4846	0.5452	0.6229	0.7316
∞	0.2561	0.3066	0.3715	0.4117	0.4592	0.5172	0.5916	0.6976	1.0000

Table E.2. Upper 99% points.

$$F_{0.99;v1,v2} = 1/F_{0.01;v2,v1}$$

V2\V1	1	2	3	4	5	6	7	8	9	10
1	0.00025	0.01015	0.0293	0.0472	0.0615	0.0728	0.0817	0.0888	0.0947	0.0996
2	0.00020	0.01010	0.0325	0.0556	0.0753	0.0915	0.1047	0.1156	0.1247	0.1323
3	0.00019	0.01008	0.0339	0.0599	0.0829	0.1023	0.1183	0.1317	0.1430	0.1526
4	0.00018	0.01008	0.0348	0.0626	0.0878	0.1093	0.1274	0.1427	0.1557	0.1668
5	0.00017	0.01007	0.0354	0.0644	0.0912	0.1143	0.1340	0.1508	0.1651	0.1774
6	0.00017	0.01007	0.0358	0.0658	0.0937	0.1181	0.1391	0.1570	0.1724	0.1857
7	0.00017	0.01006	0.0361	0.0668	0.0956	0.1211	0.1430	0.1619	0.1782	0.1923
8	0.00017	0.01006	0.0364	0.0676	0.0972	0.1234	0.1462	0.1659	0.1829	0.1978
9	0.00017	0.01006	0.0366	0.0682	0.0984	0.1254	0.1488	0.1692	0.1869	0.2023
10	0.00017	0.01006	0.0367	0.0687	0.0995	0.1270	0.1511	0.1720	0.1902	0.2062
12	0.00016	0.01006	0.0370	0.0696	0.1011	0.1296	0.1546	0.1765	0.1956	0.2125
15	0.00016	0.01006	0.0372	0.0704	0.1029	0.1323	0.1584	0.1813	0.2015	0.2194
20	0.00016	0.01006	0.0375	0.0713	0.1047	0.1352	0.1625	0.1866	0.2080	0.2270
24	0.00016	0.01005	0.0376	0.0718	0.1056	0.1367	0.1646	0.1894	0.2115	0.2311
30	0.00016	0.01005	0.0377	0.0723	0.1066	0.1383	0.1669	0.1924	0.2151	0.2355
40	0.00016	0.01005	0.0379	0.0728	0.1076	0.1400	0.1692	0.1955	0.2190	0.2401
60	0.00016	0.01005	0.0380	0.0732	0.1087	0.1417	0.1717	0.1987	0.2231	0.2450
120	0.00016	0.01005	0.0381	0.0738	0.1097	0.1435	0.1743	0.2022	0.2274	0.2502
∞	0.00016	0.01005	0.0383	0.0743	0.1108	0.1453	0.1770	0.2058	0.2319	0.2558

V2\V1	12	15	20	24	30	40	60	120	∞
1	0.1072	0.1152	0.1235	0.1278	0.1322	0.1367	0.1413	0.1460	0.1507
2	0.1444	0.1573	0.1710	0.1781	0.1855	0.1931	0.2009	0.2089	0.2170
3	0.1680	0.1846	0.2025	0.2120	0.2217	0.2319	0.2424	0.2532	0.2643
4	0.1848	0.2044	0.2257	0.2371	0.2489	0.2612	0.2740	0.2874	0.3011
5	0.1975	0.2195	0.2437	0.2567	0.2703	0.2846	0.2995	0.3151	0.3312
6	0.2074	0.2316	0.2583	0.2727	0.2879	0.3039	0.3206	0.3383	0.3567
7	0.2155	0.2415	0.2704	0.2860	0.3026	0.3201	0.3386	0.3582	0.3786
8	0.2223	0.2497	0.2806	0.2974	0.3152	0.3341	0.3542	0.3755	0.3979
9	0.2279	0.2568	0.2893	0.3071	0.3261	0.3463	0.3679	0.3908	0.4151
10	0.2328	0.2628	0.2969	0.3156	0.3357	0.3571	0.3800	0.4045	0.4305
12	0.2407	0.2728	0.3095	0.3299	0.3517	0.3753	0.4006	0.4280	0.4573
15	0.2494	0.2839	0.3238	0.3462	0.3703	0.3966	0.4251	0.4563	0.4901
20	0.2592	0.2966	0.3404	0.3652	0.3924	0.4221	0.4550	0.4915	0.5319
24	0.2645	0.3036	0.3497	0.3761	0.4050	0.4371	0.4727	0.5128	0.5578
30	0.2702	0.3111	0.3599	0.3880	0.4191	0.4538	0.4930	0.5376	0.5888
40	0.2763	0.3193	0.3711	0.4012	0.4349	0.4730	0.5165	0.5673	0.6272
60	0.2828	0.3282	0.3835	0.4161	0.4529	0.4952	0.5446	0.6040	0.6779
120	0.2899	0.3379	0.3973	0.4329	0.4738	0.5216	0.5793	0.6523	0.7534
∞	0.2975	0.3485	0.4128	0.4521	0.4981	0.5537	0.6241	0.7232	1.0000

Table E.3. Upper 97.5% points.

$$F_{0.975;v1,v2} = 1/F_{0.025;v2,v1}$$

V2\V1	1	2	3	4	5	6	7	8	9	10
1	0.0015	0.0260	0.0573	0.0818	0.0999	0.1135	0.1239	0.1321	0.1387	0.1442
2	0.0013	0.0256	0.0623	0.0939	0.1186	0.1377	0.1529	0.1650	0.1750	0.1833
3	0.0012	0.0255	0.0648	0.1002	0.1288	0.1515	0.1698	0.1846	0.1969	0.2072
4	0.0011	0.0255	0.0662	0.1041	0.1354	0.1606	0.1811	0.1979	0.2120	0.2238
5	0.0011	0.0254	0.0672	0.1068	0.1399	0.1670	0.1892	0.2076	0.2230	0.2361
6	0.0011	0.0254	0.0679	0.1087	0.1433	0.1718	0.1954	0.2150	0.2315	0.2456
7	0.0011	0.0254	0.0684	0.1102	0.1459	0.1756	0.2002	0.2208	0.2383	0.2532
8	0.0010	0.0254	0.0688	0.1114	0.1480	0.1786	0.2041	0.2256	0.2438	0.2594
9	0.0010	0.0254	0.0691	0.1123	0.1497	0.1810	0.2073	0.2295	0.2484	0.2646
10	0.0010	0.0254	0.0694	0.1131	0.1511	0.1831	0.2100	0.2328	0.2523	0.2690
12	0.0010	0.0254	0.0698	0.1143	0.1533	0.1864	0.2143	0.2381	0.2585	0.2762
15	0.0010	0.0254	0.0702	0.1155	0.1556	0.1898	0.2189	0.2438	0.2653	0.2840
20	0.0010	0.0253	0.0706	0.1168	0.1580	0.1935	0.2239	0.2500	0.2727	0.2925
24	0.0010	0.0253	0.0708	0.1175	0.1593	0.1954	0.2265	0.2533	0.2767	0.2971
30	0.0010	0.0253	0.0710	0.1182	0.1606	0.1974	0.2292	0.2568	0.2809	0.3020
40	0.0010	0.0253	0.0712	0.1189	0.1619	0.1995	0.2321	0.2604	0.2853	0.3072
60	0.0010	0.0253	0.0715	0.1196	0.1633	0.2017	0.2351	0.2642	0.2899	0.3127
120	0.0010	0.0253	0.0717	0.1203	0.1648	0.2039	0.2382	0.2682	0.2948	0.3185
∞	0.0010	0.0253	0.0719	0.1211	0.1662	0.2062	0.2414	0.2724	0.3000	0.3246

V2\V1	12	15	20	24	30	40	60	120	∞
1	0.1526	0.1613	0.1703	0.1749	0.1796	0.1844	0.1892	0.1941	0.1990
2	0.1962	0.2099	0.2242	0.2315	0.2391	0.2469	0.2548	0.2628	0.2710
3	0.2235	0.2408	0.2592	0.2687	0.2786	0.2887	0.2992	0.3099	0.3208
4	0.2426	0.2629	0.2845	0.2959	0.3077	0.3199	0.3325	0.3455	0.3588
5	0.2570	0.2796	0.3040	0.3170	0.3304	0.3444	0.3589	0.3740	0.3894
6	0.2682	0.2929	0.3197	0.3339	0.3488	0.3644	0.3806	0.3976	0.4150
7	0.2773	0.3036	0.3325	0.3480	0.3642	0.3811	0.3989	0.4176	0.4369
8	0.2848	0.3126	0.3433	0.3598	0.3772	0.3954	0.4147	0.4349	0.4560
9	0.2910	0.3202	0.3525	0.3700	0.3884	0.4078	0.4284	0.4501	0.4728
10	0.2964	0.3268	0.3605	0.3788	0.3982	0.4187	0.4405	0.4636	9.4879
12	0.3051	0.3375	0.3737	0.3935	0.4146	0.4370	0.4610	0.4867	0.5139
15	0.3147	0.3494	0.3886	0.4103	0.4334	0.4583	0.4851	0.5141	0.5453
20	0.3254	0.3629	0.4058	0.4297	0.4555	0.4836	0.5143	0.5480	0.5848
24	0.3313	0.3703	0.4154	0.4407	0.4682	0.4983	0.5314	0.5683	0.6092
30	0.3375	0.3783	0.4258	0.4527	0.4822	0.5147	0.5509	0.5917	0.6380
40	0.3441	0.3868	0.4372	0.4660	0.4978	0.5333	0.5734	0.6195	0.6733
60	0.3512	0.3962	0.4498	0.4808	0.5155	0.5547	0.6000	0.6536	0.7194
120	0.3588	0.4063	0.4638	0.4975	0.5358	0.5800	0.6325	0.6980	0.7870
∞	0.3669	0.4173	0.4793	0.5165	0.5594	0.6104	0.6741	0.7621	1.0000

Table E.4. Upper 95% points.

$$F_{0.95;v1,v2} = 1/F_{0.05;v2,v1}$$

V2\V1	1	2	3	4	5	6	7	8	9	10
1	0.0062	0.0540	0.0987	0.1297	0.1513	0.1670	0.1788	0.1881	0.1954	0.2014
2	0.0050	0.0526	0.1047	0.1440	0.1728	0.1944	0.2111	0.2243	0.2349	0.2437
3	0.0046	0.0522	0.1078	0.1517	0.1849	0.2102	0.2301	0.2459	0.2589	0.2697
4	0.0045	0.0520	0.1097	0.1565	0.1926	0.2206	0.2427	0.2606	0.2752	0.2875
5	0.0043	0.0518	0.1109	0.1598	0.1980	0.2279	0.2518	0.2712	0.2872	0.3007
6	0.0043	0.0517	0.1118	0.1623	0.2020	0.2334	0.2587	0.2793	0.2964	0.3108
7	0.0042	0.0517	0.1125	0.1641	0.2051	0.2377	0.2641	0.2857	0.3037	0.3189
8	0.0042	0.0516	0.1131	0.1655	0.2075	0.2411	0.2684	0.2909	0.3096	0.3256
9	0.0042	0.0516	0.1135	0.1667	0.2095	0.2440	0.2720	0.2951	0.3146	0.3311
10	0.0041	0.0516	0.1138	0.1677	0.2112	0.2463	0.2750	0.2988	0.3187	0.3358
12	0.0041	0.0515	0.1144	0.1692	0.2138	0.2500	0.2797	0.3045	0.3254	0.3433
15	0.0041	0.0515	0.1149	0.1707	0.2165	0.2539	0.2848	0.3107	0.3327	0.3515
20	0.0040	0.0514	0.1155	0.1723	0.2194	0.2581	0.2903	0.3174	0.3405	0.3605
24	0.0040	0.0514	0.1158	0.1732	0.2209	0.2603	0.2932	0.3210	0.3448	0.3653
30	0.0040	0.0514	0.1161	0.1740	0.2224	0.2626	0.2962	0.3247	0.3492	0.3704
40	0.0040	0.0514	0.1164	0.1749	0.2240	0.2650	0.2994	0.3286	0.3539	0.3758
60	0.0040	0.0513	0.1167	0.1758	0.2257	0.2674	0.3026	0.3327	0.3588	0.3815
120	0.0039	0.0513	0.1170	0.1767	0.2274	0.2699	0.3060	0.3370	0.3640	0.3876
∞	0.0039	0.0513	0.1173	0.1777	0.2291	0.2725	0.3096	0.3415	0.3694	0.3939

V2\V1	12	15	20	24	30	40	60	120	∞
1	0.2106	0.2201	0.2298	0.2348	0.2398	0.2448	0.2499	0.2551	0.2603
2	0.2574	0.2716	0.2863	0.2939	0.3016	0.3094	0.3174	0.3255	0.3337
3	0.2865	0.3042	0.3227	0.3324	0.3422	0.3523	0.3626	0.3731	0.3838
4	0.3068	0.3273	0.3489	0.3602	0.3718	0.3837	0.3960	0.4086	0.4214
5	0.3220	0.3447	0.3689	0.3816	0.3947	0.4083	0.4222	0.4367	0.4515
6	0.3338	0.3584	0.3848	0.3987	0.4131	0.4281	0.4436	0.4598	0.4763
7	0.3432	0.3695	0.3978	0.4128	0.4284	0.4446	0.4616	0.4792	0.4974
8	0.3511	0.3787	0.4087	0.4246	0.4413	0.4587	0.4769	0.4959	0.5156
9	0.3576	0.3865	0.4179	0.4347	0.4523	0.4708	0.4902	0.5105	0.5317
10	0.3632	0.3931	0.4259	0.4435	0.4620	0.4814	0.5019	0.5234	0.5460
12	0.3722	0.4040	0.4391	0.4580	0.4780	0.4991	0.5215	0.5453	0.5704
15	0.3821	0.4161	0.4539	0.4745	0.4963	0.5196	0.5445	0.5713	0.5997
20	0.3931	0.4296	0.4708	0.4934	0.5177	0.5438	0.5721	0.6029	0.6363
24	0.3991	0.4371	0.4802	0.5041	0.5298	0.5577	0.5882	0.6217	0.6586
30	0.4055	0.4451	0.4904	0.5157	0.5432	0.5733	0.6064	0.6434	0.6848
40	0.4122	0.4537	0.5016	0.5286	0.5581	0.5907	0.6272	0.6688	0.7167
60	0.4194	0.4629	0.5138	0.5428	0.5749	0.6108	0.6518	0.6998	0.7579
120	0.4272	0.4730	0.5273	0.5588	0.5940	0.6343	0.6815	0.7397	0.8176
∞	0.4354	0.4839	0.5423	0.5768	0.6161	0.6624	0.7193	0.7967	1.0000

Table E.5. Upper 90% points.

$$F_{0.9;\nu1,\nu2} = 1 / F_{0.1;\nu2,\nu1}$$

V2\V1	1	2	3	4	5	6	7	8	9	10
1	0.0251	0.1173	0.1806	0.2200	0.2463	0.2648	0.2786	0.2892	0.2976	0.3044
2	0.0202	0.1111	0.1831	0.2312	0.2646	0.2887	0.3070	0.3212	0.3326	0.3419
3	0.0187	0.1091	0.1855	0.2386	0.2763	0.3041	0.3253	0.3420	0.3555	0.3666
4	0.0179	0.1082	0.1872	0.2435	0.2841	0.3144	0.3378	0.3563	0.3714	0.3838
5	0.0175	0.1076	0.1884	0.2469	0.2896	0.3218	0.3468	0.3668	0.3831	0.3966
6	0.0172	0.1072	0.1892	0.2494	0.2937	0.3274	0.3537	0.3748	0.3920	0.4064
7	0.0170	0.1070	0.1899	0.2513	0.2969	0.3317	0.3591	0.3811	0.3992	0.4143
8	0.0168	0.1068	0.1904	0.2528	0.2995	0.3352	0.3634	0.3862	0.4050	0.4207
9	0.0167	0.1066	0.1908	0.2541	0.3015	0.3381	0.3670	0.3904	0.4098	0.4260
10	0.0166	0.1065	0.1912	0.2551	0.3033	0.3405	0.3700	0.3940	0.4139	0.4306
12	0.0165	0.1063	0.1917	0.2567	0.3060	0.3443	0.3748	0.3997	0.4204	0.4378
15	0.0163	0.1061	0.1923	0.2584	0.3088	0.3483	0.3799	0.4058	0.4274	0.4457
20	0.0162	0.1059	0.1929	0.2601	0.3119	0.3526	0.3854	0.4124	0.4351	0.4544
24	0.0161	0.1058	0.1932	0.2610	0.3134	0.3548	0.3883	0.4160	0.4392	0.4590
30	0.0161	0.1057	0.1935	0.2620	0.3151	0.3571	0.3913	0.4196	0.4435	0.4639
40	0.0160	0.1056	0.1938	0.2629	0.3167	0.3596	0.3945	0.4235	0.4480	0.4691
60	0.0159	0.1055	0.1941	0.2639	0.3184	0.3621	0.3977	0.4275	0.4528	0.4746
120	0.0159	0.1055	0.1945	0.2649	0.3202	0.3647	0.4012	0.4317	0.4578	0.4804
∞	0.0158	0.1054	0.1948	0.2659	0.3220	0.3673	0.4047	0.4361	0.4631	0.4864

V2\V1	12	15	20	24	30	40	60	120	∞
1	0.3148	0.3254	0.3362	0.3416	0.3471	0.3527	0.3583	0.3639	0.3695
2	0.3563	0.3710	0.3862	0.3940	0.4018	0.4098	0.4178	0.4260	0.4342
3	0.3838	0.4016	0.4202	0.4297	0.4394	0.4492	0.4593	0.4695	0.4798
4	0.4032	0.4235	0.4447	0.4556	0.4668	0.4783	0.4900	0.5019	0.5140
5	0.4177	0.4399	0.4633	0.4755	0.4880	0.5008	0.5140	0.5275	0.5412
6	0.4290	0.4529	0.4782	0.4914	0.5050	0.5190	0.5334	0.5483	0.5635
7	0.4381	0.4634	0.4903	0.5044	0.5190	0.5340	0.5496	0.5658	0.5823
8	0.4455	0.4720	0.5004	0.5153	0.5308	0.5468	0.5634	0.5807	0.5985
9	0.4518	0.4793	0.5089	0.5246	0.5408	0.5578	0.5754	0.5937	0.6127
10	0.4571	0.4856	0.5163	0.5326	0.5496	0.5673	0.5858	0.6052	0.6253
12	0.4657	0.4958	0.5284	0.5459	0.5641	0.5832	0.6033	0.6245	0.6466
15	0.4751	0.5070	0.5420	0.5608	0.5806	0.6015	0.6237	0.6472	0.6721
20	0.4855	0.5197	0.5575	0.5780	0.5998	0.6230	0.6479	0.6747	0.7036
24	0.4912	0.5266	0.5660	0.5876	0.6106	0.6353	0.6619	0.6910	0.7226
30	0.4971	0.5340	0.5753	0.5980	0.6225	0.6489	0.6777	0.7095	0.7448
40	0.5035	0.5419	0.5854	0.6095	0.6356	0.6642	0.6957	0.7312	0.7716
60	0.5103	0.5504	0.5964	0.6222	0.6504	0.6816	0.7167	0.7574	0.8058
120	0.5175	0.5597	0.6085	0.6364	0.6672	0.7019	0.7421	0.7908	0.8548
∞	0.5252	0.5697	0.6220	0.6522	0.6864	0.7259	0.7739	0.8378	1.0000

APPENDIX

F

Critical Values of the *t*-Distribution

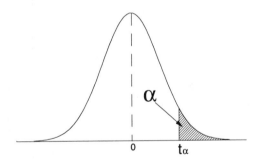

Table F.1. Critical values of the *t*-distribution.

γ	α				
	0.1	0.05	0.025	0.01	0.005
1	3.078	6.314	12.706	31.821	63.657
2	1.886	2.920	4.303	6.965	9.925
3	1.638	2.353	3.182	4.541	5.841
4	1.533	2.132	2.776	3.747	4.604
5	1.476	2.015	2.571	3.365	4.032

Continued on next page…

Table F.1—*continued...*

γ	α				
	0.1	0.05	0.025	0.01	0.005
6	1.440	1.943	2.447	3.143	3.707
7	1.415	1.895	2.365	2.998	3.499
8	1.397	1.860	2.306	2.896	3.355
9	1.383	1.833	2.262	2.821	3.250
10	1.372	1.812	2.228	2.764	3.169
11	1.363	1.796	2.201	2.718	3.106
12	1.356	1.782	2.179	2.681	3.055
13	1.350	1.771	2.160	2.650	3.012
14	1.345	1.761	2.145	2.624	2.977
15	1.341	1.753	2.131	2.602	2.947
16	1.337	1.746	2.120	2.583	2.921
17	1.333	1.740	2.110	2.567	2.898
18	1.330	1.734	2.101	2.552	2.878
19	1.328	1.729	2.093	2.539	2.861
20	1.325	1.725	2.086	2.528	2.845
21	1.323	1.721	2.080	2.518	2.831
22	1.321	1.717	2.074	2.508	2.819
23	1.319	1.714	2.069	2.500	2.807
24	1.318	1.711	2.064	2.492	2.797
25	1.316	1.708	2.060	2.485	2.787
26	1.315	1.706	2.056	2.479	2.779
27	1.314	1.703	2.052	2.473	2.771
28	1.313	1.701	2.048	2.467	2.763
29	1.311	1.699	2.045	2.462	2.756
∞	1.282	1.645	1.960	2.326	2.576

APPENDIX

G

Poisson Probability Sums

Table G.1. Poisson probability sums.

$$\sum_{x=0}^{r} p(x;\mu)$$

r	μ								
	0.1	0.2	0.3	0.4	0.5	0.6	0.7	0.8	0.9
0	0.9048	0.8187	0.7408	0.6703	0.6065	0.5488	0.4966	0.4493	0.4066
1	0.9953	0.9825	0.9631	0.9384	0.9098	0.8781	0.8442	0.8088	0.7725
2	0.9998	0.9989	0.9964	0.9921	0.9856	0.9769	0.9659	0.9526	0.9371
3	1.0000	0.9999	0.9997	0.9992	0.9982	0.9966	0.9942	0.9909	0.9865
4	1.0000	1.0000	1.0000	0.9999	0.9998	0.9996	0.9992	0.9986	0.9977
5	1.0000	1.0000	1.0000	1.0000	1.0000	1.0000	0.9999	0.9998	0.9997
6	1.0000	1.0000	1.0000	1.0000	1.0000	1.0000	1.0000	1.0000	1.0000

Continued on next page…

Table G.1—*continued...*

r	μ								
	1.0	1.5	2.0	2.5	3.0	3.5	4.0	4.5	5.0
0	0.3679	0.2231	0.1353	0.0821	0.0498	0.0302	0.0183	0.0111	0.0067
1	0.7358	0.5578	0.4060	0.2873	0.1991	0.1359	0.0916	0.0611	0.0404
2	0.9197	0.8088	0.6767	0.5438	0.4232	0.3208	0.2381	0.1736	0.1247
3	0.9810	0.9344	0.8571	0.7576	0.6472	0.5366	0.4335	0.3423	0.2650
4	0.9963	0.9814	0.9473	0.8912	0.8153	0.7254	0.6288	0.5321	0.4405
5	0.9994	0.9955	0.9834	0.9580	0.9161	0.8576	0.7851	0.7029	0.6160
6	0.9999	0.9991	0.9955	0.9858	0.9665	0.9347	0.8893	0.8311	0.7622
7	1.0000	0.9998	0.9989	0.9958	0.9881	0.9733	0.9489	0.9134	0.8666
8	1.0000	1.0000	0.9998	0.9989	0.9962	0.9901	0.9786	0.9597	0.9319
9	1.0000	1.0000	1.0000	0.9997	0.9989	0.9967	0.9919	0.9829	0.9682
10	1.0000	1.0000	1.0000	0.9999	0.9997	0.9990	0.9972	0.9933	0.9863
11	1.0000	1.0000	1.0000	1.0000	0.9999	0.9997	0.9991	0.9976	0.9945
12	1.0000	1.0000	1.0000	1.0000	1.0000	0.9999	0.9997	0.9992	0.9980
13	1.0000	1.0000	1.0000	1.0000	1.0000	1.0000	0.9999	0.9997	0.9993
14	1.0000	1.0000	1.0000	1.0000	1.0000	1.0000	1.0000	0.9999	0.9998
15	1.0000	1.0000	1.0000	1.0000	1.0000	1.0000	1.0000	1.0000	0.9999
16	1.0000	1.0000	1.0000	1.0000	1.0000	1.0000	1.0000	1.0000	1.0000

r	μ								
	5.5	6.0	6.5	7.0	7.5	8.0	8.5	9.0	9.5
0	0.0041	0.0025	0.0015	0.0009	0.0006	0.0003	0.0002	0.0001	0.0001
1	0.0266	0.0174	0.0113	0.0073	0.0047	0.0030	0.0019	0.0012	0.0008
2	0.0884	0.0620	0.0430	0.0296	0.0203	0.0138	0.0093	0.0062	0.0042
3	0.2017	0.1512	0.1118	0.0818	0.0591	0.0424	0.0301	0.0212	0.0149
4	0.3575	0.2851	0.2237	0.1730	0.1321	0.0996	0.0744	0.0550	0.0403
5	0.5289	0.4457	0.3690	0.3007	0.2414	0.1912	0.1496	0.1157	0.0885
6	0.6860	0.6063	0.5265	0.4497	0.3782	0.3134	0.2562	0.2068	0.1649
7	0.8095	0.7440	0.6728	0.5987	0.5246	0.4530	0.3856	0.3239	0.2687
8	0.8944	0.8472	0.7916	0.7291	0.6620	0.5925	0.5231	0.4557	0.3918
9	0.9462	0.9161	0.8774	0.8305	0.7764	0.7166	0.6530	0.5874	0.5218
10	0.9747	0.9574	0.9332	0.9015	0.8622	0.8159	0.7634	0.7060	0.6453
11	0.9890	0.9799	0.9661	0.9467	0.9208	0.8881	0.8487	0.8030	0.7520
12	0.9955	0.9912	0.9840	0.9730	0.9573	0.9362	0.9091	0.8758	0.8364
13	0.9983	0.9964	0.9929	0.9872	0.9784	0.9658	0.9486	0.9261	0.8981
14	0.9994	0.9986	0.9970	0.9943	0.9897	0.9827	0.9726	0.9585	0.9400

Continued on next page...

Table G.1—*continued...*

r	μ 5.5	6.0	6.5	7.0	7.5	8.0	8.5	9.0	9.5
15	0.9998	0.9995	0.9988	0.9976	0.9954	0.9918	0.9862	0.9780	0.9665
16	0.9999	0.9998	0.9996	0.9990	0.9980	0.9963	0.9934	0.9889	0.9823
17	1.0000	0.9999	0.9998	0.9996	0.9992	0.9984	0.9970	0.9947	0.9911
18	1.0000	1.0000	0.9999	0.9999	0.9997	0.9993	0.9987	0.9976	0.9957
19	1.0000	1.0000	1.0000	1.0000	0.9999	0.9997	0.9995	0.9989	0.9980
20	1.0000	1.0000	1.0000	1.0000	1.0000	0.9999	0.9998	0.9996	0.9991
21	1.0000	1.0000	1.0000	1.0000	1.0000	1.0000	0.9999	0.9998	0.9996
22	1.0000	1.0000	1.0000	1.0000	1.0000	1.0000	1.0000	0.9999	0.9999
23	1.0000	1.0000	1.0000	1.0000	1.0000	1.0000	1.0000	1.0000	0.9999
24	1.0000	1.0000	1.0000	1.0000	1.0000	1.0000	1.0000	1.0000	1.0000

r	μ 10.0	11.0	12.0	13.0	14.0	15.0	16.0	17.0	18.0
0	0.0000	0.0000	0.0000	0.0000	0.0000	0.0000	0.0000	0.0000	0.0000
1	0.0005	0.0002	0.0001	0.0000	0.0000	0.0000	0.0000	0.0000	0.0000
2	0.0028	0.0012	0.0005	0.0002	0.0001	0.0000	0.0000	0.0000	0.0000
3	0.0103	0.0049	0.0023	0.0011	0.0005	0.0002	0.0001	0.0000	0.0000
4	0.0293	0.0151	0.0076	0.0037	0.0018	0.0009	0.0004	0.0002	0.0001
5	0.0671	0.0375	0.0203	0.0107	0.0055	0.0028	0.0014	0.0007	0.0003
6	0.1301	0.0786	0.0458	0.0259	0.0142	0.0076	0.0040	0.0021	0.0010
7	0.2202	0.1432	0.0895	0.0540	0.0316	0.0180	0.0100	0.0054	0.0029
8	0.3328	0.2320	0.1550	0.0998	0.0621	0.0374	0.0220	0.0126	0.0071
9	0.4579	0.3405	0.2424	0.1658	0.1094	0.0699	0.0433	0.0261	0.0154
10	0.5830	0.4599	0.3472	0.2517	0.1757	0.1185	0.0774	0.0491	0.0304
11	0.6968	0.5793	0.4616	0.3532	0.2600	0.1848	0.1270	0.0847	0.0549
12	0.7916	0.6887	0.5760	0.4631	0.3585	0.2676	0.1931	0.1350	0.0917
13	0.8645	0.7813	0.6815	0.5730	0.4644	0.3632	0.2745	0.2009	0.1426
14	0.9165	0.8540	0.7720	0.6751	0.5704	0.4657	0.3675	0.2808	0.2081
15	0.9513	0.9074	0.8444	0.7636	0.6694	0.5681	0.4667	0.3715	0.2867
16	0.9730	0.9441	0.8987	0.8355	0.7559	0.6641	0.5660	0.4677	0.3751
17	0.9857	0.9678	0.9370	0.8905	0.8272	0.7489	0.6593	0.5640	0.4686
18	0.9928	0.9823	0.9626	0.9302	0.8826	0.8195	0.7423	0.6550	0.5622
19	0.9965	0.9907	0.9787	0.9573	0.9235	0.8752	0.8122	0.7363	0.6509
20	0.9984	0.9953	0.9884	0.9750	0.9521	0.9170	0.8682	0.8055	0.7307
21	0.9993	0.9977	0.9939	0.9859	0.9712	0.9469	0.9108	0.8615	0.7991
22	0.9997	0.9990	0.9970	0.9924	0.9833	0.9673	0.9418	0.9047	0.8551
23	0.9999	0.9995	0.9985	0.9960	0.9907	0.9805	0.9633	0.9367	0.8989
24	1.0000	0.9998	0.9993	0.9980	0.9950	0.9888	0.9777	0.9594	0.9317

Continued on next page...

Table G.1—*continued…*

r	μ 10.0	11.0	12.0	13.0	14.0	15.0	16.0	17.0	18.0
25	1.0000	0.9999	0.9997	0.9990	0.9974	0.9938	0.9869	0.9748	0.9554
26	1.0000	1.0000	0.9999	0.9995	0.9987	0.9967	0.9925	0.9848	0.9718
27	1.0000	1.0000	0.9999	0.9998	0.9994	0.9983	0.9959	0.9912	0.9827
28	1.0000	1.0000	1.0000	0.9999	0.9997	0.9991	0.9978	0.9950	0.9897
29	1.0000	1.0000	1.0000	1.0000	0.9999	0.9996	0.9989	0.9973	0.9941
30	1.0000	1.0000	1.0000	1.0000	0.9999	0.9998	0.9994	0.9986	0.9967
31	1.0000	1.0000	1.0000	1.0000	1.0000	0.9999	0.9997	0.9993	0.9982
32	1.0000	1.0000	1.0000	1.0000	1.0000	1.0000	0.9999	0.9996	0.9990
33	1.0000	1.0000	1.0000	1.0000	1.0000	1.0000	0.9999	0.9998	0.9995
34	1.0000	1.0000	1.0000	1.0000	1.0000	1.0000	1.0000	0.9999	0.9998
35	1.0000	1.0000	1.0000	1.0000	1.0000	1.0000	1.0000	1.0000	0.9999
36	1.0000	1.0000	1.0000	1.0000	1.0000	1.0000	1.0000	1.0000	0.9999
37	1.0000	1.0000	1.0000	1.0000	1.0000	1.0000	1.0000	1.0000	1.0000

Critical Values of the Chi-Square Distribution

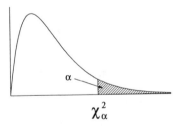

$$\chi^2_\alpha$$

Table H.1. Critical values of the chi-square distribution.

γ	α									
	0.995	0.99	0.98	0.975	0.95	0.90	0.80	0.75	0.70	0.50
	0.00004	0.000	0.001	0.001	0.004	0.016	0.064	0.102	0.148	0.455
2	0.0100	0.020	0.040	0.051	0.103	0.211	0.446	0.575	0.713	1.386
3	0.0717	0.115	0.185	0.216	0.352	0.584	1.005	1.213	1.424	2.366
4	0.207	0.297	0.429	0.484	0.711	1.064	1.649	1.923	2.195	3.357
5	0.412	0.554	0.752	0.831	1.145	1.610	2.343	2.675	3.000	4.351
6	0.676	0.872	1.134	1.237	1.635	2.204	3.070	3.455	3.828	5.348
7	0.989	1.239	1.564	1.690	2.167	2.833	3.822	4.255	4.671	6.346
8	1.344	1.646	2.032	2.180	2.733	3.490	4.594	5.071	5.527	7.344
9	1.735	2.088	2.532	2.700	3.325	4.168	5.380	5.899	6.393	8.343
10	2.156	2.558	3.059	3.247	3.940	4.865	6.179	6.737	7.267	9.342

Continued on next page…

Table H.1—*continued...*

γ	α									
	0.995	0.99	0.98	0.975	0.95	0.90	0.80	0.75	0.70	0.50
11	2.603	3.053	3.609	3.816	4.575	5.578	6.989	7.584	8.148	10.341
12	3.074	3.571	4.178	4.404	5.226	6.304	7.807	8.438	9.034	11.340
13	3.565	4.107	4.765	5.009	5.892	7.042	8.634	9.299	9.926	12.340
14	4.075	4.660	5.368	5.629	6.571	7.790	9.467	10.165	10.821	13.339
15	4.601	5.229	5.985	6.262	7.261	8.547	10.307	11.037	11.721	14.339
16	5.142	5.812	6.614	6.908	7.962	9.312	11.152	11.912	12.624	15.338
17	5.697	6.408	7.255	7.564	8.672	10.085	12.002	12.792	13.531	16.338
18	6.265	7.015	7.906	8.231	9.390	10.865	12.857	13.675	14.440	17.338
19	6.844	7.633	8.567	8.907	10.117	11.651	13.716	14.562	15.352	18.338
20	7.434	8.260	9.237	9.591	10.851	12.443	14.578	15.452	16.266	19.337
21	8.034	8.897	9.915	10.283	11.591	13.240	15.445	16.344	17.182	20.337
22	8.643	9.542	10.600	10.982	12.338	14.041	16.314	17.240	18.101	21.337
23	9.260	10.196	11.293	11.689	13.091	14.848	17.187	18.137	19.021	22.337
24	9.886	10.856	11.992	12.401	13.848	15.659	18.062	19.037	19.943	23.337
25	10.520	11.524	12.697	13.120	14.611	16.473	18.940	19.939	20.867	24.337
26	11.160	12.198	13.409	13.844	15.379	17.292	19.820	20.843	21.792	25.336
27	11.808	12.879	14.125	14.573	16.151	18.114	20.703	21.749	22.719	26.336
28	12.461	13.565	14.847	15.308	16.928	18.939	21.588	22.657	23.647	27.336
29	13.121	14.256	15.574	16.047	17.708	19.768	22.475	23.567	24.577	28.336
30	13.787	14.953	16.306	16.791	18.493	20.599	23.364	24.478	25.508	29.336

γ	α									
	0.30	0.25	0.20	0.10	0.05	0.025	0.02	0.01	0.005	0.001
1	1.074	1.323	1.642	2.706	3.841	5.024	5.412	6.635	7.879	10.828
2	2.408	2.773	3.219	4.605	5.991	7.378	7.824	9.210	10.597	13.816
3	3.665	4.108	4.642	6.251	7.815	9.348	9.837	11.345	12.838	16.266
4	4.878	5.385	5.989	7.779	9.488	11.143	11.668	13.277	14.860	18.467
5	6.064	6.626	7.289	9.236	11.070	12.833	13.388	15.086	16.750	20.515
6	7.231	7.841	8.558	10.645	12.592	14.449	15.033	16.812	18.548	22.458
7	8.383	9.037	9.803	12.017	14.067	16.013	16.622	18.475	20.278	24.322
8	9.524	10.219	11.030	13.362	15.507	17.535	18.168	20.090	21.955	26.124
9	10.656	11.389	12.242	14.684	16.919	19.023	19.679	21.666	23.589	27.877
10	11.781	12.549	13.442	15.987	18.307	20.483	21.161	23.209	25.188	29.588
11	12.899	13.701	14.631	17.275	19.675	21.920	22.618	24.725	26.757	31.264
12	14.011	14.845	15.812	18.549	21.026	23.337	24.054	26.217	28.300	32.909
13	15.119	15.984	16.985	19.812	22.362	24.736	25.472	27.688	29.819	34.528
14	16.222	17.117	18.151	21.064	23.685	26.119	26.873	29.141	31.319	36.123
15	17.322	18.245	19.311	22.307	24.996	27.488	28.259	30.578	32.801	37.697

Continued on next page...

Table H.1—*continued...*

γ	α									
	0.30	**0.25**	**0.20**	**0.10**	**0.05**	**0.025**	**0.02**	**0.01**	**0.005**	**0.001**
16	18.418	19.369	20.465	23.542	26.296	28.845	29.633	32.000	34.267	39.252
17	19.511	20.489	21.615	24.769	27.587	30.191	30.995	33.409	35.718	40.790
18	20.601	21.605	22.760	25.989	28.869	31.526	32.346	34.805	37.156	42.312
19	21.689	22.718	23.900	27.204	30.144	32.852	33.687	36.191	38.582	43.820
20	22.775	23.828	25.038	28.412	31.410	34.170	35.020	37.566	39.997	45.315
21	23.858	24.935	26.171	29.615	32.671	35.479	36.343	38.932	41.401	46.797
22	24.939	26.039	27.301	30.813	33.924	36.781	37.659	40.289	42.796	48.268
23	26.018	27.141	28.429	32.007	35.172	38.076	38.968	41.638	44.181	49.728
24	27.096	28.241	29.553	33.196	36.415	39.364	40.270	42.980	45.559	51.179
25	28.172	29.339	30.675	34.382	37.652	40.646	41.566	44.314	46.928	52.620
26	29.246	30.435	31.795	35.563	38.885	41.923	42.856	45.642	48.290	54.052
27	30.319	31.528	32.912	36.741	40.113	43.195	44.140	46.963	49.645	55.476
28	31.391	32.620	34.027	37.916	41.337	44.461	45.419	48.278	50.993	56.892
29	32.461	33.711	35.139	39.087	42.557	45.722	46.693	49.588	52.336	58.301
30	33.530	34.800	36.250	40.256	43.773	46.979	47.962	50.892	53.672	59.703

Tolerance Interval Factors

Table I.1a. Values of *k* for two-sided limits.

	α = 0.10				α = 0.05				α = 0.01			
n	γ=0.10	γ=0.05	γ=0.01	γ=0.001	γ=0.10	γ=0.05	γ=0.01	γ=0.001	γ=0.10	γ=0.05	γ=0.01	γ=0.001
2	15.978	18.800	24.167	30.227	32.019	37.674	48.430	60.573	160.193	188.491	242.300	303.054
3	5.847	6.919	8.974	11.309	8.380	9.916	12.861	16.208	18.930	22.401	29.055	36.616
4	4.166	4.943	6.440	8.149	5.369	6.370	8.299	10.502	9.398	11.150	14.527	18.383
5	3.494	4.152	5.423	6.879	4.275	5.079	6.634	8.415	6.612	7.855	10.260	13.015
6	3.131	3.723	4.870	6.188	3.712	4.414	5.775	7.337	5.337	6.345	8.301	10.548
7	2.902	3.452	4.521	5.750	3.369	4.007	5.248	6.676	4.613	5.488	7.187	9.142
8	2.743	3.264	4.278	5.446	3.316	3.732	4.891	6.226	4.147	4.936	6.468	8.234
9	2.626	3.125	4.098	5.220	2.967	3.532	4.631	5.899	3.822	4.550	5.966	7.600
10	2.535	3.018	3.959	5.046	2.839	3.379	4.433	5.649	3.582	4.265	5.594	7.129
11	2.463	2.933	3.849	4.906	2.737	3.259	4.277	5.452	3.397	4.045	5.308	6.766
12	2.404	2.863	3.758	4.792	2.655	3.162	4.150	5.291	3.250	3.870	5.079	6.477
13	2.355	2.805	3.682	4.697	2.587	3.081	4.044	5.158	3.130	3.727	4.893	6.240
14	2.314	2.756	3.618	4.615	2.529	3.012	3.955	5.045	3.029	3.608	4.737	6.043
15	2.278	2.713	3.562	4.545	2.480	2.954	3.878	4.949	2.945	3.507	4.605	5.876
16	2.246	2.676	3.514	4.484	2.437	2.903	3.812	4.865	2.872	3.421	4.492	5.732
17	2.219	2.643	3.471	4.430	2.400	2.858	3.754	4.791	2.808	3.345	4.393	5.607
18	2.194	2.614	3.433	4.382	2.366	2.819	3.702	4.725	2.753	3.279	4.307	5.497
19	2.172	2.588	3.399	4.339	2.337	2.784	3.656	4.667	2.703	3.221	4.230	5.399
20	2.152	2.564	3.368	4.300	2.310	2.752	3.615	4.614	2.659	3.168	4.161	5.312

Continued on next page...

Table I.1a—*continued...*

n	α = 0.10				α = 0.05				α = 0.01			
	γ=0.10	γ=0.05	γ=0.01	γ=0.001	γ=0.10	γ=0.05	γ=0.01	γ=0.001	γ=0.10	γ=0.05	γ=0.01	γ=0.001
21	2.135	2.543	3.340	4.264	2.286	2.723	3.577	4.567	2.620	3.121	4.100	5.234
22	2.118	2.524	3.315	4.232	2.264	2.697	3.543	4.523	2.584	3.078	4.044	5.163
23	2.103	2.506	3.292	4.203	2.244	2.673	3.512	4.484	2.551	3.040	3.993	5.098
24	2.089	2.480	3.270	4.176	2.225	2.651	3.483	4.447	2.522	3.004	3.947	5.039
25	2.077	2.474	3.251	4.151	2.208	2.631	3.457	4.413	2.494	2.972	3.904	4.985
30	2.025	2.413	3.170	4.049	2.140	2.549	3.350	4.278	2.385	2.841	3.733	4.768
35	1.988	2.368	3.112	3.974	2.090	2.490	3.272	4.179	2.306	2.748	3.611	4.611
40	1.959	2.334	3.066	3.917	2.052	2.445	3.213	4.104	2.247	2.677	3.518	4.493
45	1.935	2.306	3.030	3.871	2.021	2.408	3.165	4.042	2.200	2.621	3.444	4.399
50	1.916	2.284	3.001	3.833	1.996	2.379	3.126	3.993	2.162	2.576	3.385	4.323

Table I.1b. Values of *k* for one-sided limits.

n	α = 0.10				α = 0.05				α = 0.01			
	γ=0.10	γ=0.05	γ=0.01	γ=0.001	γ=0.10	γ=0.05	γ=0.01	γ=0.001	γ=0.10	γ=0.05	γ=0.01	γ=0.001
3	4.258	5.310	7.340	9.651	6.158	7.655	10.552	13.857	-	-	-	-
4	3.187	3.957	5.437	7.128	4.163	5.145	7.042	9.215	-	-	-	-
5	2.742	3.400	4.666	6.112	3.407	4.202	5.741	7.501	-	-	-	-
6	2.494	3.091	4.242	5.556	3.006	3.707	50.62	6.612	4.408	5.409	7.334	9.540
7	2.333	2.894	3.972	5.201	2.755	3.399	4.641	6.061	3.856	4.730	6.411	8.348
8	2.219	2.755	3.783	4.955	2.582	3.188	4.353	5.686	3.496	4.287	5.811	7.566
9	2.133	2.649	3.641	4.772	2.454	3.031	4.143	5.414	3.242	3.971	5.389	7.014
10	2.065	2.568	3.532	4.629	2.355	2.911	3.981	5.203	3.048	3.739	5.075	6.603
11	2.012	2.503	3.444	4.515	2.275	2.815	3.852	5.036	2.897	3.557	4.828	6.284
12	1.966	2.448	3.371	4.420	2.210	2.736	3.747	4.900	2.773	3.410	4.633	6.032
13	1.928	2.403	3.310	4.341	2.155	2.670	3.659	4.787	2.677	3.290	4.472	5.826
14	1.895	2.363	3.257	4.274	2.108	2.614	3.585	4.690	2.592	3.189	4.336	5.651
15	1.866	2.329	3.212	4.215	2.068	2.566	3.520	4.607	2.521	3.102	4.224	5.507
16	1.842	2.299	3.172	4.146	2.032	2.523	3.463	4.534	2.458	3.028	4.124	5.374
17	1.820	2.272	3.136	4.118	2.001	2.468	3.415	4.471	2.405	2.962	4.038	5.268
18	1.800	2.249	3.106	4.078	1.974	2.453	3.370	4.415	2.357	2.906	3.961	5.167
19	1.781	2.228	3.078	4.041	1.949	2.423	3.331	4.364	2.315	2.855	3.893	5.078
20	1.765	2.208	3.052	4.009	1.926	2.396	3.295	4.319	2.275	2.807	3.832	5.003

Continued on next page...

Table I.1b—*continued...*

n	α = 0.10				α = 0.05				α = 0.01			
	γ=0.10	γ=0.05	γ=0.01	γ=0.001	γ=0.10	γ=0.05	γ=0.01	γ=0.001	γ=0.10	γ=0.05	γ=0.01	γ=0.001
21	1.750	2.190	3.028	3.979	1.905	2.371	3.262	4.276	2.241	2.768	3.776	4.932
22	1.736	2.174	3.007	3.952	1.887	2.350	3.233	4.238	2.208	2.729	3.727	4.866
23	1.724	2.159	2.987	3.927	1.869	2.329	3.206	4.204	2.179	2.693	3.680	4.806
24	1.712	2.145	2.969	3.904	1.853	2.309	3.181	4.171	2.154	2.663	3.638	4.755
25	1.702	2.132	2.952	3.882	1.838	2.292	3.158	4.143	2.129	2.632	3.601	4.706
30	1.657	2.080	2.884	3.794	1.778	2.220	3.064	4.022	2.029	2.516	3.446	4.508
35	1.623	2.041	2.833	3.730	1.732	2.166	2.994	3.934	1.957	2.431	3.334	4.364
40	1.598	2.010	2.793	3.679	1.697	2.126	2.941	3.866	1.902	2.365	3.250	4.255
45	1.577	1.986	2.762	3.638	1.669	2.092	2.897	3.811	1.857	2.313	3.181	4.168
50	1.560	1.965	2.735	3.604	1.646	2.065	2.963	3.766	1.821	2.296	3.124	4.096

Table I.2. Proportion of population covered with (1–α)% confidence and sample size *n*.

n	α = 0.1	α = 0.05	α = 0.01	α = 0.005
2	0.052	0.026	0.006	0.003
4	0.321	0.249	0.141	0.111
6	0.490	0.419	0.295	0.254
10	0.664	0.606	0.496	0.456
20	0.820	0.784	0.712	0.683
40	0.907	0.887	0.846	0.829
60	0.937	0.924	0.895	0.883
80	0.953	0.943	0.920	0.911
100	0.962	0.954	0.936	0.929
150	0.975	0.969	0.957	0.952
200	0.981	0.977	0.968	0.961
500	0.993	0.991	0.987	0.986
1000	0.997	0.996	0.994	0.993

Table I.3. Sample size require to cover $(1-\gamma)\%$ of the population with $(1-\alpha)\%$ confidence.

γ	$\alpha = 0.1$	$\alpha = 0.05$	$\alpha = 0.01$	$\alpha = 0.005$
0.005	777	947	1325	1483
0.01	388	473	662	740
0.05	77	93	130	146
0.01	38	46	64	72
0.15	25	30	42	47
0.20	18	22	31	34
0.25	15	18	24	27
0.30	12	14	20	22
0.40	6	10	14	16
0.50	7	8	11	12

Useful Integrals

$$\int u\,dv = uv - \int v\,du \tag{J.1}$$

$$\int x^n dx = \frac{x^{n+1}}{n+1} \;,\; n \neq -1 \tag{J.2}$$

$$\int \frac{dx}{x} = \ln x \tag{J.3}$$

$$\int e^{ax} dx = \frac{e^{ax}}{a} \tag{J.4}$$

$$\int x e^{ax} dx = \frac{e^{ax}}{a^2}(ax - 1) \tag{J.5}$$

$$\int x^m e^{ax} dx = \begin{cases} \dfrac{x^m e^{ax}}{a} - \dfrac{m}{a}\displaystyle\int x^{m-1} e^{ax} dx \\ \qquad\qquad or \\ e^{ax} \displaystyle\sum_{r=0}^{m}(-1)^r \dfrac{m!\,x^{m-r}}{(m-r)!\,a^{r+1}} \end{cases} \tag{J.6}$$

$$\int \ln x\,dx = x \ln x - x \tag{J.7}$$

$$\int x^n \ln(ax)dx = \frac{x^{n+1}}{n+1}\ln ax - \frac{x^{n+1}}{(n+1)^2} \tag{J.8}$$

$$\int \frac{dx}{x\ln x} = \ln(\ln x) \tag{J.9}$$

$$\frac{d}{dc}\int_p^q f(x,c)dx = \int_p^q \frac{d}{dc}f(x,c)dx + f(q,c)\frac{dq}{dc} - f(p,c)\frac{dp}{dc} \tag{J.10}$$

Government Documents

A small reliability library is available at no cost from the United States government. The following documents can be obtained by calling the DODSSP Special Assistance Desk at 215-697-2667 or 215-697-2179.

LC-78-2 *Storage Reliability Analysis Report* (Vol. 1, *Electrical and Electronic Devices;* Vol. 2, *Electromechanical Devices;* Vol. 3, *Hydraulic and Pneumatic Devices;* Vol. 4, *Ordnance Devices;* Vol. 5, *Optical Devices and Electro-Optical Devices*)

MIL-HDBK-189 *Reliability Growth Management*

MIL-HDBK-217 *Reliability Prediction of Electronic Equipment*

MIL-HDBK-251 *Reliability/Design Thermal Applications*

MIL-HDBK-263 *Electrostatic Discharge Control Handbook for Protection of Electrical and Electronic Parts, Assemblies and Equipment*

MIL-HDBK-338 *Electronic Reliability Design Handbook*

MIL-HDBK-472 *Maintainability Prediction*

MIL-HDBK-781 *Reliability Test Methods, Plans, and Environments for Engineering Development, Qualification, and Production*

MIL-STD-470 *Maintainability Program Requirements for Systems and Equipment*

MIL-STD-690 *Failure Rate Sampling Plans and Procedures*

MIL-STD-721 *Definition of Terms for Reliability and Maintainability*

MIL-STD-756 *Reliability Modeling and Prediction*

MIL-STD-757 *Reliability Evaluation from Demonstration Data*

MIL-STD-781 *Reliability Testing for Engineering Development, Qualification, and Production*

MIL-STD-785 *Reliability Program for Systems and Equipment, Development and Production*

MIL-STD-790 *Reliability Assurance for Electronic Parts*

MIL-STD-810 *Environmental Test Methods and Engineering Guidelines*

MIL-STD-883 *Test Methods and Procedures for Microelectronics*

MIL-STD-965 *Parts Control Program*

MIL-STD-1472 *Human Engineering Design Criteria for Military Systems, Equipment and Facilities*

MIL-STD-1629 *Procedures for Performing a Failure Mode, Effects and Criticality Analysis*

MIL-STD-1635 *Reliability Growth Testing*

MIL-STD-2068 *Reliability Development Tests*

MIL-STD-2074 *Failure Classification for Reliability Testing*

NPRD-2 *Nonelectric Parts Reliability Data*

RADC-TR-75-22 *Nonelectric Reliability Notebook*

Financial Formulas

To find the future value (F), given a present value (P), an interest rate (i), and a period (n)

$$F = P(1+i)^n \tag{L.1}$$

To find the present value, given the future value

$$P = F(1+i)^{-n} \tag{L.2}$$

To find the annuity (A), given a future value

$$A = F\left[\frac{i}{(1+i)^n - 1}\right] \tag{L.3}$$

To find the future value given an annuity

$$F = A\left[\frac{(1+i)^n - 1}{i}\right] \tag{L.4}$$

To find the annuity given a present value

$$A = P \left[\frac{i(1+i)^n}{(1+i)^n - 1} \right]$$
(L.5)

To find the present value given an annuity

$$P = A \left[\frac{(1+i)^n - 1}{i(1+i)^n} \right]$$
(L.6)

APPENDIX

M

For Further Information...

How to obtain military specifications and standards

The Department of Defense Single Stock Point (DODSSP) was created to centralize control and distribution, and provide access to extensive technical information within the collection of Military Specifications and Standards and related documents produced or adopted by the DOD. The DODSSP mission was assumed by the Defense Printing Service in October, 1990.

Although the DODSSP collection is extensive, not all documents specified in Government procurements are provided by the DODSSP (e.g. engineering drawings, some Departmental documents and Non-Governmental/Industry documents). For assistance in locating the correct source for these documents, refer to the appropriate procurement package, or contact the DODSSP Special Assistance Desk at (215) 697-2667/2179.

Private industry has two methods to obtain standardization documents from the DODSSP:

1. Subscription to automatic distribution
2. On an "as-needed" basis via **TeleSpecs**

Ordering document subscriptions

A subscription distribution provides new and revised documents automatically on a "push" basis. This method is recommended if you require a broad scope of documents on a recurring schedule. The subscription service is available to private industry providing automatic distribution of both new and revised unrestricted and unclassified standardization documents. (Note: for non-DOD customers, this service does NOT include Adopted Non-Government standards. These documents must be obtained via the appropriate preparing technical society).

Upon payment of a nominal subscription fee, you will receive one copy each of any new or revised documents for a one year period after the effective subscription date. (Note: documents issued prior to the subscription date must be ordered individually using the TeleSpecs request method described later in this appendix.

Subscriptions will be accepted on a Federal Supply Class basis for a single class, or for as many individual classes that you choose. The annual subscription cost per class is $16.00.

The Catalog Handbook H2-1 lists all Federal Supply Classes according to subject (example: under Group 47, the title of FSC 4710 is "Pipe and Tube"). Copies of this publication can be obtained free of charge from the DODSSP Subscription Services Desk.

Address your request in letter form to:

DODSSP
Subscription Services Desk
700 Robbins Avenue, Bldg. 4D
Philadelphia, PA 19111-5094

List the desired Federal Supply Class(es) or Area Assignment(s). Enclose check or money order (do not send cash) payable to DODSSP, Philadelphia for $16.00 for each Federal Supply Class desired.

For further information about DODSSP subscription services, you can call the Subscription Services Desk at (215) 697-2569. (Note: subscription requests MUST be mailed to the address above; subscriptions will NOT be taken over the phone). If your requirements for Military Specifications and

Standards documents are infrequent or limited in scope, you should submit your requests individually via TeleSpecs.

Ordering individual documents via TeleSpecs

The fastest and most accurate way to obtain documents "as-needed" is through TeleSpecs. This automated system is your direct connection to the Navy Print on Demand System (NPODS). TeleSpecs eliminates mail and handling delays and puts you in total control of the document request process. TeleSpecs requires only a touch-tone phone, and utilizes an easy-to-use automated voice-prompt system.

TeleSpecs is designed to accept document orders in groups of five. If you wish to order more than five different document, please stay on the line, and TeleSpecs will allow you to order additional documents. Keep in mind that a single document order may contain a request for up to five copies of that document **at no cost to you.** TeleSpecs is "open for business" from 7:00 A.M. to 10:00 P.M. (Eastern Standard Time), Monday through Friday, and has twelve telephone lines to serve you at (215) 697-1187 through 1198.

To use TeleSpecs you must first obtain a customer number. If you have placed a document request within the last several years, a customer number has already been assigned to you; it can be found on a previous shipping invoice or a status letter. If you cannot determine your customer number, or wish to obtain one, call the DODSSP Special Assistance Desk. (215)-697-2667/2179.

Here are some helpful hints for ordering documents through TeleSpecs:

- Use the numbers "7" and "9" for the letters "Q" and "Z" not found on touch-tone phones. (For example: to order MIL Q 9858, input MIL 7 9858).
- Eliminate all document identifier special characters such as slashes, dashes, periods, alpha-revisions and suffixes.
- On-line assistance is available at any time during the call by pressing the "#" key.

- Using the document identifier revision level is not necessary, since the system always supplies the current version. (For example: input MIL STD 1840A as MIL STD 1840).

You may reproduce and redistribute unclassified and unrestricted specifications and standards without reference to any element of the Department of Defense since these documents are in the public domain.

Other available reference documents

The Department of Defense Index of Specifications and Standards (DODISS) is a reference publication available to private industry in a variety of formats. The DODISS is comprised of four parts, and contains catalog listings of the following unclassified document types controlled by the DODSSP:

- Military Specifications and Standards
- Federal Specifications and Standards
- Military Handbooks
- Qualified Products Lists (QPLs)
- Data Item Descriptions (DIDs)
- Commercial Item Descriptions (CIDs)
- Air Force-Navy Aeronautical Standards
- Air Force-Navy Aeronautical Design Standards
- Air Force Specifications Bulletins
- Other Departmental documents
- DOD Adopted Non-Government/Industry Documents (issued to DOD only)

DODSSP special assistance

The DODSSP Special Assistance Desk is ready Monday through Friday, 7:30 A.M. to 4:00 P.M. (Eastern Standard Time) to assist you in matters such as:

- Inquiries about our services
- Status of orders previously placed
- Receiving a Customer Number to establish an account

- Researching sources for documents not carried by the DODSSP
- Special requests, such as obtaining a complete set of documents
- Assistance determining document identifiers

The Special Assistance Desk number is (215) 697-2667/2179. (Note: This number should NOT be used to place orders for documents. Document orders MUST be made via TeleSpecs, as described earlier.)

American Society for Quality Control

ASQC helps sets standards for reliability, and administers the Certified Reliability Engineer Examination.

> ASQC
> 611 E. Wisconsin Ave.
> P.O. Box 3005
> Milwaukee, WI 53201-3005
> (800) 248-1946

Reliability journals

- *Annals of Reliability and Maintainability*
- *IEEE Transactions on Reliability*
- *Proceedings of the Annual Reliability and Maintainability Symposium*
- *Quality and Reliability Engineering International*
- *Reliability Review*
- *Technometrics*
- *Applied Statistics*
- *Journal of Quality Technology*

Reliability data sources

- Center for Information and Numerical Data Analysis and Synthesis, (317) 494-6300
- Concrete Technology Information Analysis Center, (601) 634-3269
- Department of Defense Nuclear Information Analysis Center, (805) 963-6400

- Failure Rate Data—Available from *Fleet Missile Systems Analysis and Evaluation Group*, Department of Defense, Corona, CA; (714) 736-4677
- Government and Industry Data Exchange Program, (714) 736-4677
- IEEE Data, (212) 705-7900
- Licensee Event Reports—failure summaries of components from nuclear power plants. Available from the *Nuclear Regulatory Commission*, Washington, DC
- National Electrical Reliability Council—component failure data from power plants. Available from the *National Electrical Reliability Council*, New York, NY
- Non-electric Parts Reliability Data, (315) 330-4151
- Infrared Information Analysis Center, (313) 994-1200
- Metals and Ceramics Information Center, (614) 424-5000
- National Nuclear Data Center, (516) 282-2103
- Plastics Technical Evaluation Center, (201) 724-3189
- Reliability Analysis Center, (315) 330-4151

Glossary

The following definitions were taken from MIL-STD-721.

Accessibility—A measure of the relative ease of admission to the various areas of an item for the purpose of operation or maintenance.

Achieved—Obtained as the result of measurement.

Alignment—Performing the adjustments that are necessary to return an item to specified operation.

Availability—A measure of the degree to which an item is in an operable and committable state at the start of a mission when the mission is called for at an unknown (random) time. (Item state at start of mission includes the combined effects of the readiness-related system R&M parameters, but excludes mission time; see **Dependability**).

Burn-in (Pre-conditioning)—The operation of an item under stress to stabilize its characteristics. Not to be confused with **de-bugging**.

Calibration—A comparison of a measuring device with a known standard. Not to be confused with alignment (see MIL-C-45662).

Chargeable—Within the responsibility of a given organizational entity (applied to terms such as failures, maintenance time etc.).

Checkout—Tests or observations of an item to determine its condition or status.

Corrective Action—A documented design, process, procedure, or materials change implemented and validated to correct the cause of failure or design deficiency.

Criticality—A relative measure of the consequence of a failure mode and its frequency of occurrences.

De-bugging—A process to detect and remedy inadequacies. Not to be confused with terms such as burn-in, fault isolation or screening.

Degradation—A gradual impairment in ability to perform.

Demonstrated—That which has been measured by the use of objective evidence gathered under specified conditions.

Dependability—A measure of the degree to which an item is operable and capable of performing its required function at any (random) time during a specified mission profile, given item availability at the start of the mission. (Item state during a mission includes the combined effects of the mission-related system R & M parameters but excludes non-mission time; see Availability).

Derating—a) Using an item in such a way that applied stresses are below rated values, or b) the lowering of the rating of an item in one stress field.

Direct Maintenance Man-Hours per Maintenance Action (DMMH/MA) —A measure of the maintainability parameter related to item demand for maintenance manpower. The sum of direct maintenance man hours, divided by the total number of maintenance actions (preventative and corrective) during a stated period of time.

Direct Maintenance Man Hours per Maintenance Event (DMMH/ME)— A measure of the maintainability parameter related to item demand for maintenance manpower. The sum of direct maintenance man hours, divided by the total number of maintenance events (preventative and corrective) during a stated period of time.

Disassemble—Opening an item and removing a number of parts or subassemblies to make the item that is to be replaced accessible for removal. This does not include the actual removal of the item to be replaced.

Dormant—The state wherein an item is able to function but is not required to function. Not to be confused with **down-time operable**—the state of being able to perform the intended function. Dormant is the same as "not operating."

Downing event—The event which causes an item to become unavailable to initiate its mission (the transition from up-time to down-time).

Durability—A measure of useful life (a special case of reliability).

Environment—The aggregate of all external and internal conditions (such as temperature, humidity, radiation, magnetic and electric fields, shock vibration , etc.) whether natural or man-made, or self-induced, that influences the form, performance, reliability or survival of an item.

Environmental stress screening (ESS)—A series of tests conducted under environmental stresses to disclose weak parts and workmanship defects for correction.

Failure—The event, or inoperable state, in which any item or part of an item does not , or would not, perform as previously specified.

Failure analysis—Subsequent to a failure, the logical systematic examination of an item, its construction, application, and documentation to identify the failure mode and determine the failure mechanism and its basic course.

Failure catastrophic—A failure that can cause item loss.

Failure critical—A failure, or combination of failures, that prevents an item from performing a specified mission.

Failure dependent—Failure which is caused by the failure of an associated item(s). Not independent.

Failure effect—The consequence(s) a failure mode has on the operation, function, or status of an item. Failure efforts are classified as local effect, next higher level, and end effect.

Failure mode and effects analysis (FMEA)—A procedure by which each potential failure mode in a system is analyzed to determine the results or effects thereof on the system, and to classify each potential failure mode according to its severity.

Failure, independent—Failure which occurs without being caused by the failure of any other item. Not dependent.

Failure, intermittent—Failure for a limited period of time, followed by the item's recovery of its ability to perform within specified limits without any remedial action.

Failure mechanism—The physical, chemical, electrical, thermal or other process which results in failure.

Failure mode—The consequence of the mechanism through which the failure occurs, i.e., short, open, fracture, excessive wear.

Failure, non-chargeable—a) A non-relevant failure, or b) a relevant failure caused by a condition previously specified as not within the responsibility of a given organizational entity (All relevant failures are chargeable to one organizational entity or another).

Failure, non-relevant—a) A failure verified as having been caused by a condition not present in the operational environment, or b) a failure verified as peculiar to an item design that will not enter the operational inventory.

Failure, random—Failure whose occurrence is predictable only in a probabilistic or statistical sense. This applies to all distributions.

Failure rate—The total number of failures within an item population, divided by the total number of life units expended by that population, during a particular measurement interval under stated conditions.

Fault—Immediate cause of failure (e.g., maladjustment, misalignment, defect, etc.).

Fault isolation—the process of determining the location of a fault to the extent necessary to effect repair.

Fault localization—The process of determining the approximate location of a fault.

Inherent R&M value—A measure of reliability or maintainability that includes only the effects of an item design and its application, and assumes an ideal operation and support environment.

Interchange—Removing the item that is to be replaced, and installing the replacement item.

Inventory, active—The group of items assigned to an operational status.

Inventory, inactive—The group of items being held in reserve for possible future assignments to an operational status.

Item—A non-specific term used to denote any product, including systems, materials parts, subassemblies, sets, accessories, etc. (Source: MIL-STD-280).

Life profile—A time-phased description of the events and environments an item experiences from manufacture to final expenditures of removal from the operational inventory, to include one or more mission profiles.

Life units—A measure of use duration applicable to the item (e.g., operating hours, cycles, distance, rounds fired, attempts to operate, etc.).

Maintainability—The measure of the ability of an item to be retained in or restored to specified condition when maintenance is performed by personnel having specified skill levels, using prescribed procedures and resources, at each prescribed level of maintenance and repair.

Maintainability, mission—The measure of the ability of an item to be retained in or restored to specified condition when maintenance is performed during the course of a specified mission profile. (The mission-related system maintainability parameter).

Maintenance—All actions necessary for retaining an item in or restoring it to a specified condition.

Maintenance action—An element of a maintenance event. One or more tasks (i.e. , fault localization, fault isolation, servicing and inspection) necessary to retain an item in or restore it to a specified condition.

Maintenance, corrective—All actions performed as a result of failure, to restore an item to a specified condition. Corrective maintenance can include any or all of the following steps: localization, isolation, disassembly, interchange, reassemble, alignment and checkout.

Maintenance event—One or more maintenance actions required to effect corrective and preventative maintenance due to any type of failure or malfunction, false alarm or scheduled maintenance plan.

Maintenance manning level—The total authorized or assigned personnel, per system at specified levels of maintenance organization.

Maintenance, preventive—All actions performed in an attempt to retain an item in specified condition by providing systematic inspection, detection, and prevention of incipient failures.

Maintenance ratio—A measure of the total maintenance manpower burden required to maintain an item. It is expressed as the cumulative number of man-hours of maintenance expended in direct labor during a given period of the life units divided by the cumulative number of end item life units during the same period.

Maintenance scheduled—Preventive maintenance performed at prescribed points in the item's life.

Maintenance time—An element of down time which excludes modification and delay time.

Maintenance, unscheduled—Corrective maintenance required by item conditions.

Malfunction—The event, or inoperable state, in which any item or part of an item does not, or would not, perform as previously specified. The same as **failure**.

Mean maintenance time—The measure of item maintainability taking into account maintenance policy. The sum of preventive and corrective maintenance times, divided by the sum of scheduled and unscheduled maintenance events, during a stated period of time.

Mean time between demands (MTBD)—A measure of the system reliability parameter related to demand for logistic support. The total number of system life units divided by the total number of item demands on the supply system during a stated period of item, e.g. Shop Replaceable Unit (SRU), Weapon Replaceable Unit (WRU), Line Replacement Unit (LRU), and Shop Replaceable Assembly (SRA).

Mean time between downing events (MTBDE)—A measure of the system reliability parameter related to availability and readiness. The total number of system life units, divided by the total number of events in which the system becomes unavailable to initiate its mission(s), during a stated period of time.

Mean time between failure (MTBF)—A basic measure of reliability for repairable items: The mean number of life units during which all parts of the item perform within their specified limits, during a particular measurement interval under stated conditions.

Mean time between maintenance (MTBM)—A measure of the reliability taking into account maintenance policy. The total number of life units expended by a given time, divided by the total number of maintenance events (scheduled and unscheduled) due to that item.

Mean time between maintenance actions (MTBMA)—A measure of the system reliability parameter related to demand for maintenance manpower. The total number of system life units, divided by the total number of maintenance actions (preventive and corrective) during a stated period of time.

Mean time between removals (MTBR)—A measure of the system reliability parameter related to demand for logistic support. The total number of system life units divided by the total number of items removed from that system during a stated period of time. This term is defined to exclude removals performed to facilitate other maintenance and removals for product improvement.

Mean time to failure (MTTF)—A basic measure of reliability for non-repairable items. The total number of life units of an item divided by the total number of failures within that population, during a particular measurement interval under stated conditions.

Mean time to repair (MTTR)—A basic measure of maintainability. The sum of corrective maintenance times at any specific level of repair, divided by the total number of failures within an item repaired at that level, during a particular interval under stated conditions.

Mean time to restore system (MTTRS)—A measure of the system maintainability parameter related to availability and readiness. The total corrective maintenance time, associated with downing events, divided by the total number of downing events, during a stated period of time (Excludes time for off-system maintenance and repair of detached components).

Mean time to service (MTTS)—A measure of an on-system maintainability characteristic related to servicing that is calculated by dividing the total scheduled crew, operator, driver servicing time by the number of times the item was serviced.

Mission profile—A time-phased description of the events and environments an item experiences from initiation to completion of a specified mission, to include the criteria of mission success or critical failures.

Mission time between critical failures (MTBCF)—A measure of mission reliability. The total amount of mission time, divided by the total number of critical failures during a stated series of missions.

Mission time to restore functions (MTTRF)—A measure of mission maintainability. The total corrective critical failure maintenance time, divided by the total number of critical failures, during the course of a specified mission profile.

Not operating (Dormant)—The state wherein an item is able to function but is not required to function. Not to be confused with **Down time**.

Operable—The state of being able to perform the intended function.

Operational readiness—The ability of a military unit to respond to its operation plan(s) upon receipt of an operations order (A function of assigned strength, item availability, status, or supply, training, etc.).

Operational R&M value—A measure of reliability or maintainability that includes the combined effect of item design, installation, quality, environment, operation, maintenance and repair.

Predicted—That which is expected at some future time, postulated on analysis of past experience and tests.

Reassembly—Assembling the items that were removed during disassembly and closing the reassembled items.

Redundancy—The existence of more than one means for accomplishing a given function. Each means of accomplishing the function need not necessarily be identical.

Redundancy, active—That redundancy wherein all redundant items are operating simultaneously.

Redundancy, standby—That redundancy wherein the alternative means of performing the function is not operating until it is activated upon failure of the primary means of performing the function.

Reliability—a) The duration or probability of failure-free performance under stated conditions, or b) the probability that an item can perform its intended function for a specified interval under stated conditions (For non-redundant items this is equivalent to definition *a*. For redundant items this is equivalent to definition of mission reliability.).

Reliability growth—The improvement in a reliability parameter caused by the successful correction of deficiencies in item design or manufacture.

Reliability mission—The ability of an item to perform its required functions for the duration of a specified "mission profile."

R&M accounting—That set of mathematical tasks which establish and allocate quantitative R&M requirements, and predict and measure quantitative R&M requirements.

R&M engineering—That set of design, development and manufacturing tasks by which reliability and maintainability are achieved.

Repairable item—An item which can be restored to perform all of its required functions by corrective maintenance.

Screening—A process for inspecting items to remove those that are unsatisfactory or those likely to exhibit early failure. Inspection includes visual examination, physical dimension measurement and functional performance measurement under specified environmental conditions.

Servicing—The performance of any act needed to keep an item in operating condition, (i.e. lubricating, fueling, oiling, cleaning, etc.), but not including preventative maintenance of parts or corrective maintenance tasks.

Single point failure—The failure of an item which would result in failure of the system and is not compensated for by redundancy or alternative operational procedure.

Sneak circuit analysis—A procedure conducted to identify latent paths which cause occurrence of unwanted functions or inhibit desired functions assuming all components are functioning properly.

Storage life (Shelf life)—The length of time an item can be stored under specified conditions and still meet specified requirements.

Subsystem—A combination of sets, groups, etc. which performs an operational function within a system and is a major subdivision of the system (Example: Data processing subsystem, guidance subsystem). Source MIL-STD-280.

System, general—A composite of equipment and skills, and techniques capable of performing or supporting an operational role, or both. A complete system includes all equipment, related facilities, material, software, services, and personnel required for its operation and support to the degree that it can be considered self-sufficient in its intended operational environment.

System R&M parameter—A measure of reliability or maintainability in which the units of measurement are directly related to operational readiness, mission success, maintenance manpower cost, or logistic support cost.

Test, acceptance—A test conducted under specified conditions by, or on behalf of, the government, using delivered or deliverable items, in order to determine the item's compliance with specified requirements (Includes acceptance of first production units).

Test measurement and diagnostic equipment (TMDE)—Any system or device used to evaluate the condition of an item to identify or isolate any actual or potential failures.

Test, qualification (Design approval)—A test conducted under specified conditions, by or on behalf of the government, using items representative of the production configuration, in order to determine compliance with item design requirements as a basis for production approval (also known as **Demonstration**).

Testing development (Growth)—A series of tests conducted to disclose deficiencies and to verify that corrective actions will prevent recurrence in the operational inventory. Note that repair of test items does not constitute correction of deficiencies (Also known as **Test-Analyze-And-Fix (TAAF)** testing).

Time—The universal measure of duration. The general word "time" will be modified by an additional term when used in reference to operating time, mission time, test time, etc. In general expressions such as "Mean-Time-Between-Failure (MTBF)," time stands for "life units" which must be more specifically defined whenever the general term refers to a particular item. See Figure G.1 for time relationships.

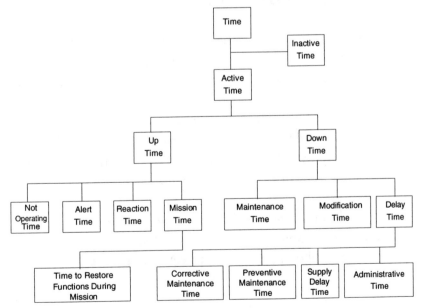

Figure G.1. Time relationships.

Time, active—That time during which an item is in an operational inventory.

Time, administrative—That element of delay time, not included in the supply.

Time, alert—That element of up time during which an item is assumed to be in specified operating condition and is awaiting a command to perform its intended mission.

Time, checkout—That element of maintenance time during which performance of an item is verified to be a specified condition.

Time, delay—That element of down time during which no maintenance is being accomplished on the item because of either supply or administrative delay.

Time, down (Downtime)—That element of active time during which an item is not in condition to perform its required function (Reduces availability and dependability).

Time, inactive—That time during which an item is in reserve.

Time, mission—That element of up time required to perform a stated mission profile.

Time, modification—The time necessary to introduce any specific change(s) to an item to improve its characteristics or to add new ones.

Time, not operating—That element of uptime during which the item is not required to operate.

Time, reaction—That element of uptime needed to initiate a mission, measured from the time command is received.

Time, supply delay—That element of delay time during which a needed replacement item is being obtained.

Time, turn around—That element of maintenance time needed to replenish consumables and check out an item for recommitment.

Time, up (Uptime)—That element of active time during which an item is in condition to perform its required functions.

Uptime ratio—A composite measure of operational availability and dependability that includes the combined effects of item design, installation, quality, environment, operation, maintenance, repair and logistic support. The quotient of uptime divided by uptime plus downtime.

Useful life—The number of life units from manufacture to when the item has an unrepairable failure or unacceptable failure rate.

Utilization rate—The planned or actual number of life units expended, or missions attempted, during a stated interval of calendar time.

Wearout—The process which results in an increase of the failure rate or probability of failure with increasing number of life units.

♦ ♦ ♦

Answers to Selected Exercises

Chapter 1
1. The Present value of the life cycle cost is $36,340 for A and $30,002 for B
2. The Present value of the life cycle cost is $16,882 for Type 1 and $14,791 for Type 2

Chapter 2
1. c
3. d
5. d
7. c
9. a
11. Identifying, Reporting, Verifying, Analyzing, Correcting problems

Chapter 3
2. $R(430) = 0.3085$
5. $E(x) = 8.004$; $V(x) = 11.117$
7. b—the failure rate
9. no defects, 0.0183; 3 or more defects, 0.7619

11. 0.6903

13. 24

15. 1st, 0.84; 2nd, 0.1344; 3rd, 0.0215

17. $E(x) = 80.31; V(x) = 584.5$

19. $E(t) = 940; V(t) = 229,900$

21. $E(y) = 10.9; V(y) = 8.73$

23. $g(A) = \left(\dfrac{1}{A\Pi}\right)\left(\dfrac{1}{\sigma\sqrt{2\Pi}}\right)\left\{\exp\left(-\dfrac{\left[\left(\dfrac{4A}{\Pi}\right)^{0.5} - \mu\right]^2}{2\sigma^2}\right) + \exp\left(-\dfrac{\left[-\left(\dfrac{4A}{\Pi}\right)^{0.5} - \mu\right]^2}{2\sigma^2}\right)\right\}$

25. $R(x) = e^{-\frac{x^2}{2}}; \ h(x) = \dfrac{f(x)}{R(x)} = \dfrac{xe^{-x^2/2}}{e^{-x^2/2}} = x$

27. 0.6703

29. 1192.5

31. 0.9801

33. $\beta = 0.4303, \ \theta = 46,380$

35. $\beta = 0.688, \ \theta = 3708$

37. $\beta = 2.952, \ \theta = 31.47$

39. $\mu = 3.306, \ \sigma = 0.4535$

41. $\mu = 3.255, \ \sigma = 2948$

$2.486 \le \mu \le 3.664$

$0.0651 \le \sigma \le 1.336$

43. $49.16 < \mu < 80.18$

45. $0.698 < p < 0.911$

47. $64.67 - 4.414(14.67)$ and $64.67 + 4.414(14.67) \Rightarrow 0.18$ and 129.16

49. $t = \dfrac{64.67 - 60}{14.61/\sqrt{6}} = 0.7824$

51. $\chi^2 = \dfrac{(n-1)s^2}{\sigma_0^2} = \dfrac{(6-1)213.5}{45} = 23.7$

53. $F = \dfrac{s_1^2}{s_2^2} = \dfrac{111.9}{79.87} = 1.401$

Chapter 4

1. 0.664
3. 0.024
5. 0.556
7. 0.3630
11. 0.004752
21. 18.18
23. 0.055
25. R(130) = 0.0297; MTTF = 54.17
27. 0.1563
29. 0.178
31. R(150) = 0.262
33. 0.8803
35. 0.99925
37. 0.6259

43. $\Lambda = \begin{bmatrix} 0 & 1/40 & 1/60 & 1/75 \\ 0 & 0 & 0 & 0 \\ 0 & 0 & 0 & 0 \\ 0 & 0 & 0 & 0 \end{bmatrix}$

47. $\lambda(\mu)$ = 9.0 failures per CPU hour

$$\frac{d\lambda}{d\mu} = -\frac{\lambda_0}{v_0} = -\frac{10}{300} = -0.033$$

51. β = 1.06, α = 84.7, $\theta_i(1000) = 68.9$
53. λ = 0.000456

Chapter 5

3. $f_o(t) = \frac{1}{\varepsilon} f\left(\frac{t}{\varepsilon}\right) = \frac{1}{150} \exp\left(-\frac{t}{150}\right)$

5. $h_o(t) = \frac{1}{150}$

9. $R_{0(t)=1-\Phi\left(\frac{t-558}{75.6}\right)}$

11. k = 21.76, c = 1633

13. a = 18.5, b = 613.9, c = 0.38

15. 15

19. 42

23. If the true failure rate is 0.05, $E(\lambda) = 31.4$

25. $5394.7 < \theta < 496,940.4$

Chapter 6

3. $M(t) = 1 - \exp\left[-\left(\dfrac{t-10}{\theta}\right)^{\beta}\right] = 1 - \exp\left[-\left(\dfrac{t-10}{130}\right)^{4}\right]$

5. At time zero, the item has not been operated, and thus has not had an opportunity to fail. Availability is a decreasing function of time, that reaches a steady-state as time becomes large.

7. $A(t) = \dfrac{22}{22+50} + \dfrac{50}{22+50}e^{-(22+50)t}$

9. $U(t) = \dfrac{22}{50+22} + \dfrac{22}{(50+22)^{2}t} - \dfrac{22}{(50+22)^{2}t}e^{-(50+22)t}$

11. $A_s = 0.9375$

13. $A_s = 0.9375$

15. Wear-out failures are characterized by an increasing hazard function – failure rate. There is some mechanism that removes useful life during operation, such as two surfaces contacting each other.

17. $T = \infty$

Chapter 7

1. a. Conveyor won't run at all
   b. Conveyor runs less then 90 fpm
   c. Conveyor runs over 110 fpm
   d. Conveyor loaded in excess of 55 tons
   e. Conveyor loaded less than 45 tons

3. a. 1) Broken input shaft; 2) Electrical failure
   b. 1) Loading differential speed/tons; 2) Speed control device
   c. 1) Speed control device; 2) Loading differential speed/tons
   d. 1) Conveyor running to slow for coal size; 2) Wrong size coal dumped into conveyor
   e. 1) Wrong size coal dumped into conveyor; 2) Conveyor running to fast for coal size

5. Install adjustable wiper to prevent coal stacking to high; 38%

7. d

9. b

11. d

13. d

15. c

17. b

Chapter 8

1. To eliminate additional costs for drawings and test data required when using nonstandard parts

3. e

5. a

7. c

9. d

Chapter 9

1. To evaluate progress, consistency of design and test approach

3. Review failure trends and assure that adequate corrective actions are taken in a timely manner during development and production phases of the program.

5. a. Are all functional elements included in the reliability block?
   b. Are all modes of operation considered in the math model?
   c. Are system reliability requirements allocated (subdivided) to useful levels?
   d. Are environmental conditions and part quality representative of the requirements?
   e. Are alternate failure rates (non-MIL) provided along with the rationale for their use?

7. b

Chapter 10

1. e
3. d
5. b
7. a
9. b
11. b

Chapter 11

1. d
3. b
5. e
7. e
9. c
11. a

Index

About the Authors...

Bryan Dodson holds the position of Total Quality Management Coordinator at Alcoa, Warrick Operations in Newburgh, Indiana. He has also worked as an Industrial Engineer for Alcoa. Prior to joining Alcoa. he was an Industrial Engineer at Morton Thiokol in Shreveport, Louisiana.

Mr. Dodson is certified by the American Society for Quality Control as a Reliability Engineer and as a Quality Engineer. He also holds a Professional Engineer's License.

Mr. Dodson holds a Bachelor's degree in Petroleum Engineering, a Master's degree in Industrial Engineering, and a Master of Business Administration. These degrees were all earned at Louisiana Tech University in Ruston, Louisiana.

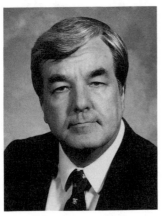

Dennis Nolan is president and principal consultant of Reliability Methods, Inc., located in Evansville, Indiana. His specialty is in training for the continuous improvement process through the application of reliability tools and methods. Prior to the consulting business he held positions with mining and aluminum industries in various maintenance and reliability capacities. Mr. Nolan is a member of ASQC and is an Adjunct Professor at Oakland City University, Oakland City, Indiana. Mr. Nolan has a Bachelor's degree in Industrial Technology and a Master's in Human Resource and Development from Indiana State University, Terre Haute, Indiana.